**THE
URBAN
ADVENTURERS**

THOMAS BOYLE
JAMES MERRITT
Departments of English
and Educational Services
Brooklyn College of the City University of
New York

THE
URBAN
ADVENTURERS

McGRAW-HILL BOOK COMPANY
New York   St. Louis   San Francisco
Düsseldorf   Johannesburg   Kuala Lumpur
London   Mexico   Montreal   New Delhi
Panama   Rio de Janeiro
Singapore   Sydney
Toronto

This book was set in Claro Light by University Graphics, Inc., and printed and bound by George Banta Company, Inc. The designer was Ben Kann; the drawings were done by Edward A. Butler; cover photograph by Judith Mallinson. The editors were David Edwards, Robert Weber, and Susan Gamer. Sally Ellyson supervised production.

Acknowledgments

James Baldwin, "The Black Boy Looks at the White Boy," copyright © 1961 by James Baldwin. From the book *Nobody Knows My Name* by James Baldwin. Reprinted by permission of the publisher, The Dial Press. Originally appeared in *Esquire.*

David Bird, "Three Hundred Protesting Columbia Students Barricade Office of College Dean," from *The New York Times,* April 24, 1968. Copyright © 1970 by The New York Times Company. Reprinted by permission.

Arthur Bryant, excerpt from *Set in a Silver Sea* by Arthur Bryant, copyright © 1966 by Sir Arthur Bryant. Reprinted by permission of Doubleday & Company, Inc.

William S. Burroughs, excerpt from *Naked Lunch,* copyright © 1959 by William Burroughs. Reprinted by permission of Grove Press, Inc.

Stokely Carmichael, "What We Want," reprinted by permission of the Student National Coordinating Committee.

Eldridge Cleaver, "Notes on a Native Son," from *Soul On Ice* by Eldridge Cleaver. Copyright © 1968 by Eldridge Cleaver. Used with permission of McGraw-Hill Book Company.

Frank Conroy, excerpt from *Stop-Time* by Frank Conroy. Copyright © 1965, 1966, 1967 by Frank Conroy. All Rights Reserved. Reprinted by permission of The Viking Press.

Gregory Corso, "Italian Extravaganza," from *Gasoline.* Copyright © 1958 by Gregory Corso. Reprinted by permission of City Lights Books.

Acknowledgments

Herbert A. Deane, "Reflections on Student Radicalism," by Herbert A. Deane, from *Up Against the Ivy Wall, A History of the Columbia Crisis,* by Jerry L. Avorn and Members of the staff of the *Columbia Daily Spectator.* Copyright © 1968 by Members of the Board Associates. Reprinted by permission of Atheneum Publishers.

Ralph Ellison, prologue from *The Invisible Man,* by Ralph Ellison. Copyright 1952 by Ralph Ellison. Reprinted by permission of Random House, Inc.

Sylvan Fox, "One Thousand Police Act to Oust Students from Five Buildings at Columbia; Move in at University's Request," from *The New York Times,* April 30, 1968. Copyright © 1970 by The New York Times Company. Reprinted by permission.

Allen Ginsberg, "A Supermarket in California," from *Howl and Other Poems* by Allen Ginsberg, Copyright © 1956, 1959 by Allen Ginsberg; "First Party at Ken Kesey's with Hell's Angels," from *Planet News* by Allen Ginsberg. Copyright © 1968 by Allen Ginsberg. Reprinted by permission of City Lights Books.

Albert Goldman, "On and On Mick's Orgy Rolls," from *Freakshow: The Rocksoulblues-jazzsickjewblackhumorsexpoppsych Gig and Other Scenes from the Counter-Culture* by Albert Goldman. Copyright © 1969 by Albert Goldman. First appeared in *The New York Times.*

Pete Hamill, "Brooklyn, the Sane Alternative," from *Irrational Ravings* by Pete Hamill. Copyright © 1971 by Pete Hamill. Reprinted by permission of G. P. Putnam's Sons.

Don Heckman, "Pop; No. the Rolling Stones Are Not Fascists," from *The New York Times,* December 28, 1969. Copyright © 1968, 1969 by The New York Times Company. Reprinted by permission.

Aldous Huxley, excerpt from *The Doors of Perception* by Aldous Huxley. Copyright 1954 by Aldous Huxley. Reprinted by permission of Harper & Row, Publishers, Inc.

James S. Kunen, excerpt from *The Strawberry Statement* by James S. Kunen. Copyright © 1968, 1969 by James S. Kunen. Reprinted by permission of Random House, Inc.

J. Anthony Lukas, excerpt from "The Making of a Yippee," as it appeared in *Esquire Magazine,* from *Don't Shoot—We Are Your Children,* by J. Anthony Lukas. Copyright © 1968, 1969, 1971 by J. Anthony Lukas. Reprinted by permission of Random House, Inc.

Steven Marcus, excerpt from *The Other Victorians* by Steven Marcus, copyright © 1964, 1965, 1966 by Steven Marcus. Reprinted by permission of Basic Books, Inc., Publishers, New York.

Acknowledgments

Norman Mailer, excerpt from "The White Negro," from *Advertisements for Myself* by Norman Mailer, copyright © 1959 by Norman Mailer, reprinted by permission of G. P. Putnam's Sons; excerpt from *Miami and the Siege of Chicago* by Norman Mailer, reprinted by permission of The World Publishing Company, copyright © 1968 by Norman Mailer; excerpt from *Cannibals and Christians* by Norman Mailer, reprinted by permission of the author and the author's agents, Scott Meredith Literary Agency, Inc.

Clarence Major, "Vietnam #4" copyright © 1967 by Clarence Major. Used by permission of the author.

Warren Miller, from *The Cool World* by Warren Miller. Copyright ©, 1959 by Warren Miller. By permission of Little, Brown and Co.

Peter Millones, "Fires Break Out in Two Buildings," reprinted from *The New York Times,* May 23, 1968. Copyright © 1968, 1969 by The New York Times Company. Reprinted by permission.

Joseph Mitchell, excerpt from *Joe Gould's Secret* by Joseph Mitchell. Copyright 1942, 1943 by Joseph Mitchell. All rights reserved. Reprinted by permission of The Viking Press. Originally appeared in *The New Yorker.*

Raymond Mungo, "If Mr. Thoreau Calls, Tell Him I've Left the Country," from the book *Total Loss Farm: A Year in the Life,* by Raymond Mungo. Copyright © 1970 by Raymond Mungo. Published by E. P. Dutton & Co., Inc. and reprinted with their permission. This version originally appeared in the *Atlantic Monthly.*

The New York Times, "Columbia Closes Campus after Disorders," from *The New York Times,* April, 1968. Copyright © 1970 by The New York Times Company. Reprinted by permission.

Jack Newfield, "Pre-Fitting the News at the Paper of Record," reprinted from *The Village Voice,* May 9, 1968. Reprinted by permission of The Village Voice. Copyrighted by The Village Voice, Inc., 1968.

Frank O'Hara, "The Day Lady Died," from *Lunch Poems* by Frank O'Hara. Copyright © 1964 by Frank O'Hara. Reprinted by permission of City Lights Books.

Rolling Stone, excerpt from "Let it Bleed," Issue No. 50, January 21, 1970. Copyright © 1970 by Straight Arrow Publishers, Inc. All rights reserved. Reprinted by permission.

Henry Roth, "Prologue," from *Call It Sleep,* by Henry Roth. Copyright 1934 by Henry Roth. Reprinted by arrangement with Cooper Square Publishers, Inc.

Mark Rudd, "Symbols of the Revolution," by Mark Rudd, from *Up Against the Ivy Wall, A*

Acknowledgments

History of the Columbia Crisis, by Jerry L. Avorn and members of the staff of the *Columbia Daily Spectator.* Copyright © 1968 by Members of the Board Associates. Reprinted by permission of Atheneum Publishers.

Gail Sheehy, "Speed Is of the Essence," from *New York* magazine, July 21, 1969. Copyright © 1969 by Gail Sheehy. Reprinted by permission of The Sterling Lord Agency, Inc.

J. L. Simmons and Barry Winograd, "A Note from the Underground," from *Marihuana: Myths and Realities,* ed. J. L. Simmons and Barry Winograd. Reprinted with the permission of Marc-Laird Publishers. Copyright © 1968 by J. L. Simmons and Barry Winograd.

Time, "California: A State of Excitement," reprinted from *Time, The Weekly Newsmagazine,* November 7, 1969. Copyright Time Inc., 1969.

Nancy Willard, "The Graffiti Poet," reprinted from *The Writing on the Wall* with the kind permission of the poet.

Tom Wolfe, "The Girl of the Year," from *The Kandy-Kolored Tangerine-Flake Streamlined Baby,* by Tom Wolfe. Copyright © 1964 by New York Herald Tribune, Inc. Reprinted with the permission of Farrar, Straus & Giroux, Inc.

Contents

Contents

Contents

Contents

Preface

The guiding principle of *The Urban Adventurers* is that immediacy of subject matter and strong rhetorical methods most greatly stimulate discussion and writing — or, verbal communication. Our collective experience during ten years of teaching in college classrooms indicates that nothing turns a class off so quickly — that is, enervates any desire to communicate (in class or on paper) — as an irrelevant essay. This situation is intensified considerably when a student comes from the ghetto areas of our cities, where material poverty is so clearly manifested in students' inability to master the basic verbal skills of Received Standard English and their natural consequent lack of confidence and their disinclination to deal with anything that looks, or is, "heavy."

One objection to our approach is easy to anticipate: "Students are here to learn, not to be indulged." *Exactly.* But the indulgence lies in treating the classroom of a skills course such as freshman composition as a dispensary of special information, a situation in which, unfortunately, the teacher and a coterie of favorites are often the group being indulged, not the class as a whole. Of course, we grant that if the selections offered here were spiritually and intellectually banal as well as easy to acquire — like Joyce Kilmer's "Trees," the staple poem to memorize in half the traditional American classrooms — there would be nothing to gain from this book. However, though we certainly have chosen the following pieces with an eye toward immediacy of interest for the beginning urban student, we also have been at least as much concerned for the contemporary (and historical) importance of the issues dealt with, especially in terms of their function as a guide to the nuances of verbal communication, and for the frequently striking nature of their rhetoric.

Thomas Boyle
James Merritt

**THE
URBAN
ADVENTURERS**

Introduction

This book is structured according to the issues which the selections raise: cities (streets and total), urban history, students, rock music, drugs, ghettoes, and America as an entity. Although by and large the readings favor statements to which the young urban reader can react immediately, even viscerally, they are by no means designed to suggest their relationship to issues raised under the other headings in a process of cross-fertilization (or cross-pollination, if you will). For example, the Black Panther pamphlet, "Where It's At" ("Drugs") is hardly limited by a temporal or "issue" orientation. Its most obvious extracurricular function would be as an example of a new form of Engel's Marxism ("A Sense of Where We Were"), by the oppressed themselves, or, more generally, as an expression of ghetto activism, or to be contrasted with Boyle's Hawaiian drug-culture cavaliers ("America, Amerika"). Any aspect of the rock phenomenon (perhaps the most tenuous of our categories) can be both literally and "vibrationally" related to the fulfillment of Mailer's prophecy in "The White Negro," or seen in terms of Women's Liberation (as it is in the essay on the Grateful Dead), or in myriad relationships to students as essential points in our psychic history. It is of interest to note, for instance, that the "Weatherman" faction of SDS (see Mark Rudd) takes its name from Bob Dylan's "Subterranean Homesick Blues": "You don't need a weatherman to know which way the wind blows." The point is, finally, that as one becomes familiar with the contents, he perceives that the categories are pretty much arbitrary and almost anything in this book is rather closely related to pieces in other sections and can be discussed in those terms.

To us as teachers and students of English, the *manner* of presentation continually asserts its importance. Each piece, we hope, exists not only as a statement on an issue, but as a distinctive assertion of a personal voice. And, in line with the cross-referential nature of the issues described above, these voices can be read, heard, analyzed, supported, or attacked best when considered in conjunction with another voice discussing a related subject. Tom Wolfe's psychedelic exuberance and Allen Ginsberg's wry restraint in dealing with Kesey and the Hells Angels set one another into striking relief, as Ginsberg's supermarket in California gives the reader a quicker insight to Whitman. The pathetic, inarticulate eloquence of the child of the "Cool World" of white writer Warren Miller's novel is conditioned by Cleaver's strutting and heady verbal manifestation of "Soul." The glad-handing euphemism of the Chamber of Commerce brochure is denied by Hamill's hard-boiled historian, while Hamill's sentimentality is questioned by the stoned cynicism of William Burroughs. The gut issues of today are therefore, to push one's own metaphor a bit, suspended in the glittering aspic of style which so pervades the city streets of involved young and old alike: Shake it a bit and it quivers; change the light, the position, and the insight is different; keep at it long enough and you are changed. Point of view, style, voice, call it what you will; change it by one word, one intonation, and the *effect* is changed. Maybe you are.

OUT ON THE STREET

Our first section, "Out on the Street," is deliberately a random sample, formless in that it hopes to approximate the myriad and momentary impressions grasped in the streets of a large city. It features pamphlets, songs, poems, and excerpts, mostly brief, from fictional and factual treatments of the highs and lows, excesses, insights (both well-taken and hard-to-take—take *your* pick), of the continuing story of sidewalk passions.

PART ONE

WOULD YOU
LIKE OUR VERMIN
COLD APTS
FILTHY HALLWAYS
AND JUNKIES?

The Graffiti Poet
NANCY WILLARD

I grew up in the schoolrooms of the Dakotas,
I sat by the wood stove and longed for spring.
My desk leaned like a clavichord, stripped of its hammers,
and on it I carved my name, forever and ever,
so the seed of that place should never forget me.
Outside, in their beehive tombs, I could hear
the dead spinning extravagant honey.
I remembered their names and wanted only
that the living remember mine.

I am the invisible student, dead end
of a crowded class. I write and nobody answers.
On the Brooklyn Bridge, I write a poem:
the rain washed it away.
On the walls of the Pentagon, I made
My sign; a workman blasted me off like dung.
From the halls of Newark to the shores
of Detroit, I engrave my presence with fire
so the lords of those places may never forget me.

Save me. I can hardly speak. So we pass,
not speaking. In bars where your dreams drink,
I scrawl your name, my name, in a heart
that the morning daily erases.
At Dachau, at Belsen I blazoned my cell
with voices and saw my poem sucked
into a single cry:
throw me a fistful of stars.
I died writing, as the walls fell.

I am lonely. More than any monument,
I want you to see me writing: *I love
you* (or someone), *I live* (or you live).
Canny with rancour, with love, I teach you
to spell, to remember your name
and your epitaphs which are always changing.
Listen to me, stranger, keep me alive.
                              I am you.

Photograph by Thomas Boyle.

This handbill was passed out on a New York street corner to anyone who would take it.

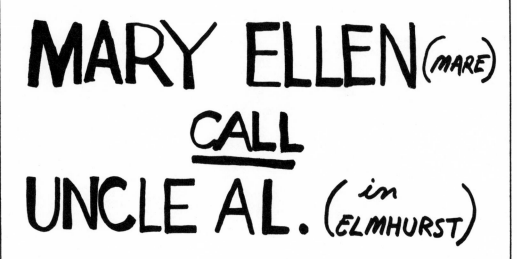

MARY ELLEN (MARE)
<u>CALL</u>
UNCLE AL. (in ELMHURST)

" I'm ON YOUR SIDE — CAN HELP YOU AND ANDY."

MY TELEPHONE IN QUEENS TELEPHONE BOOK — OR CALL MY OFFICE — EXTENSION 3610

She's Leaving Home
JOHN LENNON AND PAUL
McCARTNEY

Wednesday morning at five o'clock as the day begins
Silently closing her bedroom door
Leaving the note that she hoped would say more
She goes downstairs to the kitchen clutching her handkerchief
Quietly turning the backdoor key
Stepping outside she is free.
She (We gave her most of our lives) is leaving (Sacrificed most
   of our lives) home (We gave her everything money could buy)
She's leaving home after living alone
For so many years. Bye, bye.

Father snores as his wife gets into her dressing gown
Picks up the letter that's lying there
Standing alone at the top of the stairs
She breaks down and cries to her husband
Daddy our baby's gone.
How would she treat us so thoughtlessly
How could she do this to me.
She (We never thought of ourselves) is leaving (Never a thought
   for ourselves) home (We struggled all of our lives to get by)
She's leaving home after living alone
For so many years. Bye, bye.

Friday morning at nine o'clock she is far away.
Waiting to keep the appointment she made
Meeting a man from the motor trade
She (What did we do that was wrong) is having (We didn't know
   what was wrong) fun (Fun is the one thing that money can't
   buy)
Something inside that was always denied
For so many years. Bye, bye.
She's leaving home bye bye.

It Should've Been Me
MEMPHIS CURTIS

As I passed by
A real fine hotel
A chick walked up.
She sure looked swell.
I gave the eye
And started to carry on

When a Cadillac cruised up
And SWISH, she was gone.

It should've been me
With that real fine chick
It should've been me
Driving that Cadillac.

A little later on
A theatre I passed.
I spotted another chick
And did she have class.

I was all set
To write her name in my book
When her husband came up and gave me
A real dirty look.

It should've been me
To have been her
Chaperone.

When I got to the corner
I saw a sharp cat
With a $300 suit on
And a $100 hat.
He was standing on the sidewalk
By a Dynaflow
When a voice within said:
"C'mon Daddy, let's go!"

It should've been me
Drivin' that
Dynaflow.

I ate a bowl of chili
And I felt OK,
At least until I passed
This fine cafe.
I saw a guy eating
A great big steak
While a waitress stood by feeding him
Ice cream and cake.

It should've been me
Eating ice cream and cake.

It should've been me
Getting my natural kicks
It should've been me
Getting my natural kicks
Loving those
Crazy chicks.

History of the Gay Liberation Movement

The gay liberation movement came into being during the spring months of 1969. The radicalization that had occurred across the country during the 1960's was also affecting the gay section of the population. The tremendous force for freedom that was felt around the world could also be found among the many gay men and women. They could sympathize most readily with other oppressed peoples, having been oppressed themselves for many centuries. When the Panthers were organizing and calling for liberation, this made many other people start to think of no longer sitting around and hiding the fact that they too were oppressed. The time had come to stand up and confront the old ways and moral standards, in and out of the movement, and wherever gays were openly being ridiculed.

The movement started to come to light in June 1969 when, after much of the usual police harassment of closing bars and arresting people for being in certain neighborhoods, the police raided the Stonewall bar on Christopher Street in New York City. The police thought this would be just another routine matter, but this was not the case. The people in the bar started to push the pigs back and onto the street. The police warned the crowd that was gathering to disperse or be arrested. The people ignored the warning, and more people joined the crowd that had assembled to confront the pigs. They had taken enough shit. The police called in reinforcements to put the crowd back in place, but found out that word had spread throughout the West Village, and many more sisters and brothers came down to help those defending the bar from pig invasion. It was not the Mafia bar as such, which was being defended. Rather, it was the idea of defending just one place, even in a gay ghetto, where people could meet without harassment and intimidation.

What started on the streets that night has emerged into a full-grown movement of many thousands of people. The baptism of the billy clubs resulted in the formation of a new group, The Gay Liberation Front, named after the Vietnamese people's organization for freedom in their country. The fighting that broke out and sent ten pigs to the hospital did not stop that night, but continues to this day.

When the group was formed, it decided to hold a protest demonstration against the pigs' action and the others leading up to it. 500 people marched against the police, and many wanted to march on the precinct house itself; but this was diverted by pressure from the gay establishment, which has existed for years.

The NAACP of the gay movement, Mattachine, is to many gays an opponent of gay liberation and thus an obstacle in the way of change. The relationship of power no longer exists where the gay establishment runs things with a few militants on the outside buzzing them. Today gay radicals are in the forefront of the movement, directing it past the old establishment.

In New York City, GLF picketed *The Village Voice,* a liberal weekly newspaper, for printing derogatory articles about gays while refusing to permit the word "gay" to be used in the bulletin board section of the paper. Both offenses were corrected by this political action. GLF dances are becoming popular among movement straights, as well as the gay brothers and sisters; over 900 people attended the last one. GLF members have joined demonstrations for the Panthers, The Young Lords, anti-war mobilizations, and women's liberation actions. Demonstrations have been held against Time Inc. and ABC Television.

In California, gay liberation groups helped build the various Moratorium events. *The San Francisco Examiner,* a reactionary paper, was picketed for referring to "semi-males", "deviates", and "flexi-wrists". Twelve brothers and sisters were ripped off by the pigs and printers ink was thrown at the demonstrators. Max Rafferty, the super-reactionary State Superintendent of Public Instruction, had a fit when he heard GLF was successfully organizing at San Jose State College. Rafferty was quoted as saying, "I think it's rotten", and the President of San Jose State was denounced for "running a cesspool". The Committee For Homosexual Freedom marched on Delta Airlines for kicking a brother off a plane for wearing a "gay power" button.

The gay liberation movement is less than a year old, and has grown by leaps and bounds nationwide. GLF's and other radical gay organizations exist in most of the major cities and some smaller towns.

Fuck the System

EXCERPTS FROM A YIPPIE (YOUTH
INTERNATIONAL PARTY) PAMPHLET

FREE FURNITURE—By far the best place to get free furniture is on the street. Once a week in every district the sanitation department makes bulk pick-ups. The night before residents put out all kinds of stuff on the street. For the best selection try the West Village on Monday nights and the east Seventies on Tuesday nights. On Wednesday night there are fantastic pick-ups on 35th Street in back of Macy's. Move quickly though, the guards get pissed off easily; the truckers couldn't care less. This street method can furnish your whole pad. Beds, desks, bureaus, lamps, bookcases, chairs, and tables. It's all a matter of transportation. If you don't have access to a car or truck it is almost worth it to rent a station wagon on a weekday and make pick-ups. Alexander's Rent-a-Car is about the cheapest for in-city use. $5.95 and 10¢ a mile for a regular car. A station wagon is slightly more. Call AG 9-2200 for the branch near you.

Also consider demolition and construction sites as a good source for building materials to construct furniture. The large wooden cable spools make great tables. Cinder-blocks, bricks and boards for bookcases. Doors for tables. Nail kegs for stools and chairs.

FREE BUS RIDES—Get on with a large denomination bill just as the bus is leaving.

FREE SUBWAY RIDES—Get a dark green card and flash it quickly as you go through the exit gate. Always test the swing bars in the turnstile before you put in the token. Someone during the day was sure to drop an extra token in and a free turn is just waiting for the first one to take advantage of it. By far the most creative method is the use of German fennigs, Danish ore or Mozambique 10 centavos pieces. These fit most turnstiles except the newest (carry a real token to use in case the freebee doesn't work). These foreign coins come four or five to a penny. Large amounts must be purchased outside New York City.

Most dealers will not sell you large amounts since the Transit Authority has been pressuring them. Try telling dealers you want them to make jewelry. Another interesting coin is the 5 aurar from Iceland. This is the same size as a quarter and will work in most vending machines. They sell for three or four to the penny. There are other coins that also work. Buy a bag of assorted foreign coins from a coin dealer and do a little measuring. You are sure to find some that fit the bill. Speaking of fitting the bill, we have heard that dollar bills can be duplicated on any Xerox machine (fronts done separately from backs and pasted together) and used in vending machines that give change for a dollar. This method has not been field tested.

The best form of free transportation is hitch-hiking. This is so novel in New York that it often works. Crosstown on 8th Street is good.

FREE PHONE CALLS—A number 14 brass washer with a small piece of scotch tape over one side of the hole will work in old style phones (also parking meters, laundromat dryers, soda and other vending machines). The credit card bit works on long distance calls. Code letter for 1968 is J, then a phone number and then a three digit district number. A district number, as well as the phone number, can be made up by using any three numbers from about 051 to 735. Example: J-573-2100-421 or J-637-3400-302. The phone number should end in 00 since most large corporations have numbers that end that way. The people that you call often get weird phone calls from the company but not much else. There are also legitimate credit card numbers available. One recent number belonged to Steve McQueen. A phone bill of $50,000 was racked up in one month. McQueen, of course, was not held responsible.

FREE MONEY—Panhandling nets some people up to Twenty dollars a day. The best places are Third Avenue in the fifties and the Theater District off Times Square. Both best in the evening on weekends.

Uptown guys with dates are the best touch especially if they are just leaving some guilt movie like "Guess Who's Coming to Dinner?" The professional panhandlers don't waste their time on the Lower East Side except on weekends when the tourists come out.

Devise a street theatre act or troupe. It can be anything from a funny dance to a five piece band or a poetry reading. People give a lot more dough and the whole atmosphere sings a little. SMILE! Panhandle at the rectories and nunneries on the side of every Catholic Church. Contrary to rumor the brother and sister freeloaders in black live very well and will always share something with a fellow panhandler.

Also see previous sections on the use of foreign coins.

FREE RENT—There are many abandoned buildings that are still habitable especially if you know someone with electrical skills who, with a minimum of effort can supply you with free electricity. You can be busted for criminal trespassing but many people are getting away with it. If you are already in an apartment, eviction proceedings in New York take about six months even if you don't pay rent.

You can sleep in the parks during the day. Day or night you can sleep on the roofs which are fairly safe and comfortable if you can find a shady spot. The tar gets very hot when the sun comes out. Make friends with someone in the building, then if the cops or landlord or other residents give you a problem you can say you are staying with someone in the building. Stay out of hallways, don't sleep on streets or stoops, or in the parks at night.

FREE POETRY, LECTURES, ETC.—The best advice here is to see the back page of the Village Voice for free events that week. There are a variety of talks given at the Free School, 20 East 14th Street. Call 675-7424 for information. For free brochures about free cultural events in New York go to Cultural Information Center, 148 West 57th Street.

Street-fighting Woman's Blues

"We are the vanguard of fantasies.
Where we live is liberated territory."
Motherfuckers

i left home when i was just turning 17. i was very inexperienced, not because of prudent values, but just that the situation of living with my parents hadn't provided opportunities. before i had left i was politically turned on, i had smoked and tripped, and cut school a lot. and in theory my sexual ideas were very free—but i had never made it—the situation had never come up.

and so i arrive on the lower east side really "ready". . . . people seemed to be living what my politics always aimed for, but what i had never really experienced. then it all began—the first cat i tried to make it with was really freaked out by me—after all, fucking a cute 17 year old virgin is a boost to any man's perverted ego. but it didn't work. . . .

i began spending more time with the motherfuckers. as one guy would get discouraged with me, another would try, every day in and out, some of them i don't even know their names . . . but *that's* sexual liberation: no demands. and *they* came to me when *they* wanted. i had to be available or else i was up-tight. but "don't infringe on my freedom, girl." if i came to one of the guys i dug and wanted to stay with him, it was, "i'll take you when i want, you know it's sort of a drag anyhow, and just 'cause i tried to make it with you don't get hung-up." that's where the sexual revolution is at.

needless to say, all this made me pretty freaked out about my sexuality . . . in fact they actually put me into a position of feeling guilty that they were wasting their precious . . . time and energy and i couldn't satisfy them!

in the midst of all this unsuccessful balling, i got the clap—by that point i felt i had reached the height of absurdity—gonorrhea—not knowing who had given it to me—i went to the v.d. clinic, where i just became more aware of what my position was as a woman, (specifically a hippy-woman: oppressed by my own men, and doubly oppressed by straight men.) . . .

by this point i had run the full gamut with the motherfuckers. i didn't dig the place i lived in being this crash pad that somehow i always had to clean. the cooking, cleaning, and caring for babies was for the "chicks" cause the men in the motherfuckers were the kings of the rough street fighting men.

women have to share their stories and their feelings with each other, so that they know their personal dissatisfaction is not just their own craziness. my story with the motherfuckers seems so far out i'm afraid women will be able to read it and avoid seeing their own situation by saying, "i was lucky—i just don't have those problems. i've really escaped that with *my* hip man." men can once again say, "just another one of those lib-chicks who have had shitty experiences . . . all she needs is a good lay . . . if only she had been with *ME*."

yes, the motherfuckers are an extreme . . . but it is very reflective of a general attitude that runs through movement men. i have been in and out of different scenes since the motherfuckers, most more honest and groovy, but if i really dig the basic elements of how i was living and relating

to men and women it was all fucked-up. at one point i lived with a guy and it was very unique. from the time we met he didn't come on. we related very honestly and freely as two human beings. i always felt my relationship with him was more like with the women i knew and i was like his friend—we had transcended roles and didn't relate to each other as sex objects. . . .

the alternative to the amerikan death culture [is] the hip sub culture . . and yet as a woman you never really drop-out. our lifestyle: rock music, politics, sexual freedom, dope, is male dominated. we are still trapped by our misconceptions of what we are as women and we are still oppressed—yes even by the "sexually free man."

and i still want to live in the kind of culture i thought i was coming to. i don't merely want to be the equal of the male-defined roles of this society by adapting their style and taking over their jobs and positions. that is why it is essential for women to get our shit together and have the freedom to define their own positions in a new world.

Billie Holliday, known to her fans as "Lady Day" and one of the great female blues singers of all time, immortalized "Strange Fruit" in her tortured, soulful rendition.

Strange Fruit
LEWIS ALLEN

Southern trees bear a strange fruit,
Blood on the leaves and blood at the root,
Black body swinging in the Southern breeze,
Strange fruit hanging from the poplar trees.

Pastoral scene of the gallant South
The bulging eyes and the twisted mouth;
Scent of magnolia sweet and fresh,
Oh, oh, burning flesh!

Here is the fruit for crows to pluck,
For the rain to gather, for wind to suck,
For the sun to rot, for a tree to drop.
Here is a strange and bitter crop.

The Day Lady Died
FRANK O'HARA

It is 12:20 in New York a Friday
three days after Bastille day, yes
it is 1959 and I go get a shoeshine
because I will get off the 4:19 in Easthampton
at 7:15 and then go straight to dinner
and I don't know the people who will feed me
I walk up the muggy street beginning to sun
and have a hamburger and a malted and buy
an ugly NEW WORLD WRITING to see what the poets
in Ghana are doing these days
                                        I go on to the bank
and Miss Stillwagon (first name Linda I once heard)
doesn't even look up my balance for once in her life
and in the GOLDEN GRIFFIN I get a little Verlaine
for Patsy with drawings by Bonnard although I do
think of Hesiod, trans. Richmond Lattimore or
Brendan Behan's new play or *Le Balcon* or *Les Nègres*
of Genet, but I don't, I stick with Verlaine
after practically going to sleep with quandariness

and for Mike I just stroll into the PARK LANE
Liquor Store and ask for a bottle of Strega and
then I go back where I came from to 6th Avenue
and the tobacconist in the Ziegfeld Theatre and
casually ask for a carton of Gauloises and a carton
of Picayunes, and a NEW YORK POST with her face on it

and I am sweating a lot by now and thinking of
leaning on the john door in the 5 SPOT
while she whispered a song along the keyboard
to Mal Waldron and everyone and I stopped breathing

Italian Extravaganza
GREGORY CORSO

Mrs. Lombardi's month-old son is dead.
I saw it in Rizzo's funeral parlor,
A small purplish wrinkled head.

They've just finished having high mass for it;
They're coming out now
. . . wow, such a small coffin!
And ten black cadillacs to haul it in.

Desolation Row

They're selling postcards of the hanging
They're painting the passports brown
The beauty parlor's filled with sailors
The circus is in town
Here comes the blind commissioner
They've got him in a trance
One hand's tied to the tight-rope walker
The other is in his pants
And the riot squad they're restless
They need somewhere to go
As lady and I look out tonight
From Desolation row

Cinderella she seems so easy
It takes one to know one she smiles
Then puts her hands in her back pocket
Bette Davis style
Then in comes Romeo he's moaning
You belong to me I believe
Then someone says you're in the wrong
   place my friend
You'd better leave
And the only sound that's left
After the ambulances go
Is Cinderella sweeping up
On Desolation Row.

Now the moon is almost hidden
The stars are beginning to hide
The fortune telling lady
Has even taken all her things inside
All except for Cain and Abel
And the hunchback of Notre Dame
Everybody is making love
Or else expecting rain
And the good samaritan he's dressing
He's getting ready for the show
He's going to the carnival
Tonight on Desolation Row.

Einstein disguised as Robin Hood
With his memories in a trunk
Passed this way an hour ago
With his friend a jealous monk
He looked so immaculately frightful
As he bummed a cigarette
Then he went off sniffing drain pipes
And reciting the alphabet
Now you would not think to look at him
But he was famous long ago

For playing the electric violin
On Desolation Row.

Doctor filth he keeps his word
Inside of a leather cup
But all his sexless patients
They're trying to blow it up
Now his nurse some local loser
She's in charge of the cyanide hold
And she also keeps the cards that read
Have mercy on his soul
They all play on penny whistles
You can hear them blow
If you lean your head out far enough
From Desolation Row.

Across the street they've nailed the curtains
They're getting ready for the feast
The phantom of the opera
A perfect image of a priest
They're spoon feeding Casanova
To get him to feel more assured
Then they'll kill him with self confidence
After poisoning him with words
And the phantom shouting to skinny girls
Get outta here if you don't know
Casanova is just being punished
For going to Desolation Row.

Now at midnight all the agents
And the super human crew
Come out and round up everyone
That knows more than they do
Then they bring them to the factory
Where the heart attack machine
Is strapped across their shoulders
And then the kerosene
Is brought down from the castles
By insurance men who go
Check to see that nobody is escaping
To Desolation Row.

Praise be to Nero's Neptune
The Titanic sails at dawn
Everybody's shouting
Which side are you on?
And Ezra Pound and T. S. Eliot
Are fighting in the captain's tower
While calypso singers laugh at them
And fishermen hold flowers
Between the windows of the sea
Where lovely mermaids flow
And nobody has to think too much
About Desolation Row.

A SENSE
OF WHERE
WE WERE

In "A Sense of Where We Were," we flash
back to acquire a historical perspective on
cities, the problems of writing about them,
their relevance to the present. Each
author presents his metaphors for the
bump and grind of urban existence within
the context of a kind of descriptive
analysis of a situation in the past. Except
for *Set in the Silver Sea* and *The Other
Victorians*, which look back over 250 and
100 years respectively, each piece was a
contemporary product of the time and
place it analyzes; each perhaps, reveals
more about where the heads—singular
and collective—of the author and his
society were at than were ever intended,
especially in regard to those aspects of
city life which are considered in some
depth in later sections.

PART
TWO

Although this description of London in the seventeenth century was written in the twentieth, the city appears as men living a couple of generations after the death of William Shakespeare saw it. Arthur Bryant, from whose *Set in a Silver Sea* this is taken, gives us a sense of how the city looked—but even more interesting, how it sounded and how it smelled.

FROM
Set in a Silver Sea
ARTHUR BRYANT

PEPYS'S LONDON

Even at night the noise of London persisted, the constable and his watch brawling with midnight revellers, the watchman's cry of "Past one of the clock and a cold frosty windy morning," and the sounds which bespoke the agricultural undertakings hidden behind London's urban exterior, like that "damned noise between a sow gelder and a cow and a dog" which woke Pepys up one sultry summer's night. For the country's capital was still rural at heart, and the rich earthy smell of the fruits and beasts of the home counties lay about it.

One did not only hear London, one smelt it. The lack of sanitation, comparatively innocuous in a country village, was appallingly noticeable in the metropolis. Rivers of filth coursed down the centre of the streets, and, at the time of the emptying of slop-pails, the passer-by nearest the wall had cause to be grateful for the over-hanging stories. Around the city stretched a halo of stinking, steaming lay-stalls, haunted by flies and kites, while in its densest quarters the graveyards, piled high above the surrounding ground, repeopled themselves. Even on a spring evening, when the air was full of scents of sap and blossom from the trees that shaded every court and alley garden, the citizen taking the air on the leads of his house was sometimes driven indoors by —in Pepys's graphic phrase—"the stink of shying of a shitten pot." The most cultured, however nice in their tastes, were utterly innocent of public sanitary sense, the

Photograph by Thomas Boyle.

refined Lord Guilford installing a pump to drive the piled ordure from his cellar into the street.

Public conveniences there were none. The polite would step aside to an alehouse, those less so to the street wall. Mrs. Pepys, taken ill at the theatre, unconcernedly went out into Lincoln's Inn Walks and "there in a corner did her business." Even in their homes their possessors did not always employ the houses of office that the richer among them tucked away in cellar or on leads; Pepys himself occasionally made use of the bedroom chimney. Country mothers wrote anxiously to their sons bidding them have a care of the close, crowded air, and members of parliament, when the end of the session released them to their country homes, recalled with horror the smells descending into the House from the small apartments adjoining the Speaker's chamber. Smallpox and fevers, and more periodically bubonic plague, haunted the town, subsequently spreading all over the kingdom. They were the price England had to pay for the wealth which its growing capital made for it.

Other signs of Mammon's presence attended the city. Between it and the sky visitors frequently noted a pall of smoky vapour, arising from the furnaces of the brewers, soap-boilers and dyers, who, unhindered by State or Corporation, carried on their trades in its heart. Evelyn, the most fastidious observer of his day, wrote indignantly of the "horrid smoke which obscures our churches and makes our palaces look old, which fouls our clothes and corrupts the waters." In winter this coal vapour sometimes descended on the streets in a blanket of fog, so that "horses ran against each other, carts against carts, coaches against coaches." Yet in summer the rays of the sun reached the trees and flowers of the city courts without hindrance, and the Thames, for all its unseen load of filth, still sparkled brightly as in the Middle Ages.

For if the London of Charles II was dirty, it was also beautiful. Colour and the pomp of life, moving in gilded majesty, had come back with the king; the streets were full of bright garments. Pepys clothed his footboy in green lined with red and went abroad himself in a summer suit of coloured camelot, with a flowered tabby vest, very rich, and gold lace sleeves. And on May Day, when he drove in Hyde Park in his new coach, the horses' tails were tied with red ribbon, the standards were gilt and all the reins were green.

Until the Great Fire the background of this pageantry was the medieval city which Chaucer had known and in which Shakespeare had worked. The houses were still framed in oak, with walls of lath and plaster, and their overhanging stories were painted and heavily carved. Compared with Paris London spread outwards rather than upwards; the buildings were low and in the better quarters inhabited by only one family apiece, save round the Court and the New Exchange, where furnished rooms and lodgings could be had at easy rates. But in the outer suburbs, in hovels pent together of weather-boards smeared with pitch, the poor were crowded together in indescribable congestion.

Along the southern side of the Strand were the palaces of the nobility. These had gardens running down to the Thames, with private stairs on to the water. Other great mansions, standing in parks and gardens, were scattered round the western outskirts — Bedford, Wallingford, and Burlington Houses and the vast mansion which Lord Chancellor Clarendon built himself after the Restoration in the fields beside Piccadilly and was never suffered to inhabit. More manageable in size were the substantial houses which rich merchants raised and country magnates, in attendance at parliament or Court, rented. Such was Sir Nathaniel Hobart's fine new house in Chancery Lane "near the 'Three Cranes', next door to the 'Hole in the Wall'," with "a very handsome garden with a wash house in it," carrying a rental of fifty-five pounds a year.

Rising above the houses of rich and poor alike were the churches. The sky of the city, as one saw it from the southern bank, was pierced by over a hundred spires and, dominating all, the nave and tower of St. Paul's. The spire of the cathedral had fallen many years before, and the nave had been half ruined by generations of decay and the depredations of the Interregnum. Cromwell's troopers had used it as a stable, and there had been an unsuccessful attempt to sell part of it as building material for a Jewish synagogue. Yet it was still, after St. Peter's in Rome, the greatest church in Europe.

The streets between the crowded buildings were narrow, cobbled with egg-shaped stones, with posts at the sides of the broader thoroughfares to protect pedestrians, and made fantastically crooked by the uneven frontage of the houses. Above them painted signs, projecting on creaking iron branches, proclaimed to an illiterate age the address of their occupants — the "Three Pigeons" in Great Queen's Street, the "Crooked Billet" "over against Hill, the Quaker cook's, upon the Mall Bank, Westminster." Behind the streets were courtyards and lanes, sometimes giving access on to a hundred others, sometimes ending in nothing, like that "blind alley, on the backside of Mr. Trice's house, just at the close of the evening," where Dryden's wild gallant was wont to make his rendezvous. Here, too, were gardens with fruit and flowers, and here the innumerable stables which the coaches and horses of the capital required. "Now for the stables," wrote a London friend to Buckinghamshire Sir Ralph Verney, "I have my choice of two. One is in Magpie Yard. There is a pond on the yard to wash the horses in and very good water. It will hold four horses, and the hay loft will hold four loads of hay. There is bins for oats. They say they are very honest and civil people; Judge Atkins's coach has stood there this fourteen years. Now there is another at the 'Red Harp' in Fetter Lane; 'tis one turning more beyond the 'Magpie', but it has the same conveniency. The 'Magpie' is sixteen pounds a year if they lodge a man; the other I can have for fourteen pounds."

On winter nights the principal streets were lit until ten or eleven by lanterns placed at regular intervals, and, more spasmodically, by the uncertain efforts of householders who were expected between the feasts of All Saints and Candlemas to expose a light to the street — a civic obligation often compounded for or evaded. More useful were the link-boys who waited at every corner with torch and lantern to light travellers home. These poor urchins—recruited from the ragged company of homeless strays who lodged in doorways and disused penthouses—assailed the passer-by with cries of "Do you want light?" Grander citizens, like Pepys, who went out to supper with the wench carrying a lanthorn before him, provided their own street lighting.

At intervals London was lit by a brighter illumination. The houses were built "as if formed to make one general bonfire", and whenever a careless householder supplied a spark and the wind was in the right quarter, they obliged. The parish authorities with leather buckets, hatchets and iron crows for removing thatch, the enthusiastic Lord Craven and his amateur fire-fighters, and the fire-engines of the early insurance companies—who, however, confined their efforts to the houses of their own clients—did something to keep this perpetually recurring nuisance within bounds. But in September 1666, with a summer gale blowing from the east after long drought, they met their match. In four days a third of the city perished, including the cathedral, the Guildhall, and eighty-four churches.

For nearly a generation after the Fire a man could stand in Cheapside and gaze through bare ruins at the boats on the river and the wooded Surrey slopes beyond. In that dismal desert of calcined stone and ashes, where more than thirteen thousand houses had been burnt, there were nothing but islands of scaffolding rising from the rubble lines of familiar streets, dotted with wretched huts and cabins of board and canvas and the gaunt skeletons of burnt churches. Over all towered the open roof and glassless windows of old St. Paul's, its beautiful portico rent in pieces. This devastated area, into which the Londoner passed as he came out of the populous streets of Tower Hill or left the prosperous western faubourgs at Temple Bar, was the key to the political feelings of a generation which, twenty-two years later, swept away, in a frenzy of Protestant hysteria, the last English sovereign who dared to avow the Catholic faith. It was a reminder of all that an ultra-Protestant England had suffered

since the restoration of the Stuarts—Plague, Fire and the shameful sound of Dutch guns on the Medway. It spelt a legend of nightmarish fears, of popes and red cardinals, priests and foreign dragoons threatening stake, massacre and wooden shoes to the free people of England. And even when a new city of warm coloured brick and pleasant, ordered streets had risen out of the ruins, the legend persisted. On the wall of the house in Pudding Lane on the site where the Fire began, the Lord Mayor of the most bigoted city in the world inscribed the words:

Here by the permission of Heaven Hell broke loose upon this Protestant City from the malicious hearts of barbarous papists.

Popery was the bugbear with which seventeenth century English children were brought up by their mothers and nurses: a terror they never outgrew. They had learnt their religion from the crude woodcuts of Protestants burning at the stake in Foxe's *Book of Martyrs* and their history from tales of the Massacre of St. Bartholomew, the Gunpowder Plot and the Irish Rebellion of '41. The Great Fire seemed to them but one more page in that bloodstained mythology, a prelude to some gruesome Popish plot of assassination, midnight massacre and foreign invasion.

Yet this great calamity, far from holding up London's growth, stimulated it. The new brick houses that arose in the devasted areas were so much more handsome and commodious than the old that property owners whose houses had not been burnt became anxious to rebuild. Moreover, many, who had gardens round their houses in the old London, recouped themselves for their losses by building houses and shops where formerly had been grass and trees. Mr. Swithin's spacious garden by the Royal Exchange reappeared as Swithin's Alley, with twenty-four houses upon it, and what had been the stable yard of the "King's Arms" in Coleman Street became Copthall Court. This example of building on open spaces was followed in the unburnt portions of the town, and one by one the great houses of the nobility disappeared, to be replaced by squares and terraces bearing the names of their former owners. Of the palaces along the Strand only three remained by the end of the century— Somerset House, the Savoy (itself divided into apartments), and Northumberland House—while the names Essex, Norfolk, Salisbury, Worcester, Exeter, Hungerford and York passed into a new chapter of London's topographical nomenclature. And since, while the town was rebuilding, the dispossessed shopkeepers opened their booths on Moorfields and other public open spaces outside the city, these latter also tended to disappear and grow into streets and squares. For where London had once encroached it never receded.

London, 1794
WILLIAM BLAKE

I wander thro' each charter'd street,
Near where the charter'd Thames does flow,
And mark in every face I meet
Marks of weakness, marks of woe.

In every cry of every Man,
In every Infant's cry of fear,
In every voice, in every ban,
The mind-forg'd manacles I hear.

How the Chimney-sweeper's cry
Every black'ning Church appalls;
And the hapless Soldier's sigh
Runs in blood down Palace walls.

But most thro' midnight streets I hear
How the youthful Harlot's curse
Blasts the new born Infant's tear,
And blights with plagues the Marriage hearse.

This selection from a novel by Benjamin Disraeli (who was more famous as a politician and Prime Minister of England than as a novelist) is, presumably, fiction. Disraeli did research into the conditions of the poor in the newly industrialized cities of England, however, and "Devilsdust," the child-hero of this piece, is not an entirely fictional character.

FROM
Sybil
BENJAMIN DISRAELI

DEVILSDUST

About a fortnight after his mother had introduced him into this world, she returned to her factory, and put her infant out to nurse; that is to say, paid threepence a week to an old woman, who takes charge of these new-born babes for the day and gives them back at night to their mothers as they hurriedly return from the scene of their labour to the dungeon or the den, which is still, by courtesy, called a 'home.' The expense is not great: laudanum and treacle administered in the shape of some popular elixir, affords these innocents a brief taste of the sweets of existence, and, keeping them quiet, prepares them for the silence of their impending grave. Infanticide is practised as extensively and as legally in England as it is on the banks of the Ganges; a circumstance which apparently has not yet engaged the attention of the Society of the Propagation of the Gospel in Foreign Parts. . . . But there are infants that will defy even starvation and poison, unnatural mothers and demon nurses. Such was the nameless one of whom we speak. We cannot say he thrived; but he would not die. So, at two years of age, his mother being lost sight of, and the weekly payment having ceased, he was sent out in the street to 'play' in order to be run over. Even this expedient failed. The youngest and the feeblest of the band of victims, Juggernaut spared him to Moloch. All his companions were disposed of. Three months 'play' in the streets got rid of this tender company, shoeless, half-naked, and uncombed, whose age varied from two to five years. Some were crushed, some were lost, some caught cold and fevers, crept back to their garret or their cellars, were dosed with Godfrey's cordial,* and died in peace. The nameless one would not disappear. He always got out of the way of the carts and horses and never lost his own. They gave him no food; he foraged for himself, and shared with the dogs, the garbage of the streets. But still he lived; stunted and pale, he defied even the fatal fever which was the only inhabitant of the cellar that never quitted it. And slumbering at night on a bed of mouldering straw, his only protection against the plashy surface of his den, with a dung-heap at his head, and a cesspool at his feet, he still clung to the only roof which shielded him from the tempest.

At length, when the nameless one had completed his fifth year, the pest which never quitted the nest of cellars of which he was a citizen, raged in the quarter with such intensity, that the extinction of its swarming population was menaced. The haunt of this child was peculiarly visited. All the children gradually sickened except himself; and one night when he returned home he found the old woman herself dead, and surrounded only by corpses. The child before this had slept on the same bed of straw with a corpse, but then there were also breathing beings for his companions. A night passed only with corpses seemed to him in itself a kind of death. He stole out of the cellar, quitted the quarter of the

* A popular children's "medicine" which was full of laudanum.

pestilence, and after much wandering lay down near the door of a factory. Fortune had guided him. Soon after the break of day, he was awakened by the sound of the factory bell, and found assembled a crowd of men, women, and children. The door opened, they entered, the child accompanied them. The roll was called; his unauthorised appearance noticed; he was questioned; his acuteness excited attention. A child was wanting in the Wadding Hole, a place for the manufacture of waste and damaged cotton, the refuse of the mill which is here worked up into counterpanes and coverlets. The nameless one was preferred to the vacant post, received even a salary, more than that, a name; for as he had none, he was christened on the spot DEVILSDUST.

This description of the lives of English workers dates from 1846, the same year as Disraeli's *Sybil.* Friedrich Engels, a German visiting London, shows us that Disraeli's "fiction" approximates the truth. Engels is most famous as the man who completed Karl Marx's anticapitalist treatise, *Das Kapital.*

The Condition of the Working Class in England in 1844
FRIEDRICH ENGELS

A town such as London, where a man may wander for hours together without reaching the beginning of the end, without meeting the slightest hint which could lead to the inference that there is open country within reach, is a strange thing. This colossal centralisation, this heaping together of two and a half millions of human beings at one point, has multiplied the power of this two and a half millions a hundredfold; has raised London to the commercial capital of the world, created the giant docks and assembled the thousand vessels that continually cover the Thames. I know nothing more imposing than the view which the Thames offers during the ascent from the sea to London Bridge. The masses of buildings, the wharves on both sides, especially from Woodwich upwards, the countless ships along both shores crowding ever closer and closer together, until at last only a narrow passage remains in the middle of the river, a passage through which hundreds of steamers shoot by one another; all this is so vast, so impressive, that a man cannot collect himself, but is lost in the marvel of England's greatness before he sets foot upon English soil.

But the sacrifices which all this has cost become apparent later. After roaming the streets of the capital a day or two, making headway with difficulty through the human turmoil and the endless lines of vehicles, after visiting the slums of the metropolis, one realises for the first time that these Londoners have been forced to sacrifice the best qualities of their human nature, to bring to pass all the marvels of civilisation which crowd their city; that a hundred powers which slumbered within them have remained inactive, have been suppressed in order that a few might be developed more fully and multiply through union with those of others. The very turmoil of the streets has something repulsive, something against which human nature rebels. The hundreds of thousands of all classes and ranks crowding past each other, are they not all human beings with the same qualities and powers, and with the same interest in being happy? And have they not in the end to seek happiness in the same way, by the same means? And still they crowd by one another as though they had nothing in common, nothing to do with one another, and their only agreement is the tacit one that each keep to his own side of the pavement so as not to delay the opposing streams of the crowd, while it occurs to no man to honour another with so much as a glance. The brutal indifference, the unfeeling isolation of each in his private interest becomes the more repellant and offensive, the more these individuals are crowded together within a limited space. And however much one may be aware that this isolation of the individual, this narrow self-seeking is the fundamental principle of our society everywhere, it is nowhere so shamelessly barefaced, so self-conscious as here in the crowding of the great city. The dissolution of mankind into monads of which each one

has a separate principle, into the world of atoms, is here carried out to its utmost extreme.

Hence it comes, too, that the social war, the war of each against all, is here openly declared. Just as in Stirner's recent book, people regard each other only as useful objects; each exploits the other, and the end of it all is that the stronger treads the weaker under foot and that the powerful few, the capitalists, seize everything for themselves, while to the weak many, the poor, scarcely a bare existence remains. . . .

Since capital, the direct or indirect control of the means of subsistence and production, is the weapon with which this social warfare is carried on, it is clear that all the disadvantages of such a state must fall upon the poor. For him no man has the slightest concern. Cast into the whirlpool, he must struggle through as well as he can. If he is so happy as to find work, *i.e.,* if the bourgeoisie does him the favour to enrich itself by means of him, wages await him which scarcely suffice to keep body and soul together; if he can get no work he may steal, if he is not afraid of the police, or starve, in which case the police will take care that he does so in a quiet and inoffensive manner. During my residence in England, at least twenty or thirty persons have died of simple starvation under the most revolting circumstances, and a jury has rarely been found possessed of the courage to speak the plain truth in the matter. Let the testimony of the witnesses be never so clear and unequivocal, the bourgeoisie, from which the jury is selected, always finds some backdoor through which to escape the frightful verdict, death from starvation. The bourgeoisie dare not speak the truth in these cases, for it would speak its own condemnation. But indirectly, far more than directly, many have died of starvation where long continued want of proper nourishment has called forth fatal illness, when it has produced such debility that causes which might otherwise have remained inoperative, brought on severe illness and death. The English workingmen call this "social murder," and accuse our whole society of perpetrating this crime perpetually. Are they wrong? . . .

Let us investigate some of the slums. . . . London comes first, and in London the famous rookery of St. Giles which is now, at last, about to be penetrated by a couple of broad streets. St. Giles is in the midst of the most populous part of the town, surrounded by broad, splendid avenues in which the gay world of London idles about, in the immediate neighbourhood of Oxford Street, Regent Street, of Trafalgar Square and the Strand. It is a disorderly collection of tall, three or four-storied houses, with narrow, crooked, filthy streets, in which there is quite as much life as in the great thoroughfares of the town, except that here people of the working class only are to be seen. A vegetable market is held in the street, baskets with vegetables and fruits, naturally all bad and hardly fit to use, obstruct the sidewalk still further, and from these, as well as from the fish-dealers' stalls, arises a horrible smell. The houses are occupied from cellar to garret, filthy within and without, and their appearance is such that no human being could possibly wish to live in them. But all this is nothing in comparison with the dwellings in the narrow courts and alleys between the streets, entered by covered passages between the houses, in which the filth and tottering ruin surpass all description. Scarcely, a whole windowpane can be found, the walls are crumbling, doorposts and window frames loose and broken, doors of old boards nailed together, or altogether wanting in this thieves' quarter, where no doors are needed, there being nothing to steal. Heaps of garbage and ashes lie in all directions, and the foul liquids emptied before the doors gather in stinking pools. Here live the poorest of the poor, the worst paid workers with thieves and the victims of prostitution indiscriminately huddled together, the majority Irish, or of Irish extraction, and those who have not yet sunk in the whirlpool of moral ruin which surrounds them, sinking daily deeper, losing daily more and more of their power to resist the demoralising influence of want, filth, and evil surroundings. . . .

The most extensive working-people's district lies east of the Tower in Whitechapel and Bethnal Green, where the greatest masses of London working people live. Let us hear Mr. G. Alston, preacher of St. Philip's, Bethnal Green, on the condition of his parish. He says:

It contains 1,400 houses, inhabited by 2,795 families, or about 12,000 persons. The space upon which this large population dwells is less than 400 yards (1,200 feet) square, and in this overcrowding it is nothing unusual to find a man, his wife, four or five children, and sometimes both grandparents, all in one single room, where they eat, sleep, and work. I believe that before the Bishop of London called attention to this most poverty-stricken parish, people at the West End knew as little of it as of the savages of Australia or the South Sea Isles. And if we make ourselves acquainted with these unfortunates, through personal observation, if we watch them at their scanty meal and see them bowed by illness and want of work, we shall find such a mass of helplessness and misery, that a nation like ours must blush that these things can be possible. I was rector near Huddersfield during the three years in which the mills were at their worst, but I have never seen such complete helplessness of the poor as since then in Bethnal Green. Not one father of a family in ten in the whole neighbourhood has other clothing than his working suit, and that is as bad and tattered as possible; many, indeed, have no other covering for the night than these rags, and no bed save a sack of straw and shavings.

The foregoing description furnishes an idea of the aspect of the interior of the dwellings. But let us follow the English officials, who occasionally stray thither, into one or two of these workingmen's homes.

On the occasion of an inquest held Nov. 14th, 1843 by Mr. Carter, coroner for Surrey, upon the body of Ann Galway, aged 45 years, the newspapers related the following particulars concerning the deceased. She had lived at No. 3 White Lion Court, Bermondsey Street, London, with her husband and a nineteen-year-old son in a little room, in which neither a bedstead nor any other furniture was to be seen. She lay dead beside her son upon a heap of feathers which were scattered over her almost naked body, there being neither sheet nor coverlet. The feathers stuck so fast over the whole body that the physician could not examine the corpse until it was cleansed, and then found it starved and scarred from the bites of vermin. Part of the floor of the room was torn up, and the hole used by the family as a privy.

On Monday, Jan. 15th, 1844, two boys were brought before the police magistrate because, being in a starving condition, they had stolen and immediately devoured a half-cooked calf's foot from a shop. The magistrate felt called upon to investigate the case further, and received the following details from the policeman. The mother of the two boys was the widow of an ex-soldier, afterwards policeman, and had had a very hard time, since the death of her husband, to provide for her nine children. She lived at No. 2 Pool's Place, Quaker Court, Spitalfields, in the utmost poverty. When the policeman came to her, he found her with six of her children literally huddled together in a little back room, with no furniture but two old rush-bottomed chairs with the seats gone, a small table with two legs broken, a broken cup, and a small dish. On the hearth was scarcely a spark of fire, and in one corner lay as many old rags as would fill a woman's apron, which served the whole family as a bed. For bed clothing they had only their scanty day clothing. The poor woman told him that she had been forced to sell her bedstead the year before to buy food. Her bedding she had pawned with the victualler for food. In short, everything had gone for food. The magistrate ordered the woman a considerable provision from the poor-box.

In February 1844, Theresa Bishop, a widow 60 years old, was recommended, with her sick daughter, aged 26, to the compassion of the police magistrate in Marlborough Street. She lived at No. 5 Brown Street, Grosvenor Square, in a small back room no larger than a closet, in which there was not one single piece of furniture. In one corner lay some rags upon which

both slept; a chest served as table and chair. The mother earned a little by charring. The owner of the house said that they had lived in this way since May 1843, had gradually sold or pawned everything that they had, and had still never paid any rent. The magistrate assigned them £1 from the poor-box. . . .

. . . . In London fifty thousand human beings get up every morning, not knowing where they are to lay their heads at night. The luckiest of this multitude, those who succeed in keeping a penny or two until evening, enter a lodging-house, such as abound in every great city, where they find a bed. But what a bed! These houses are filled with beds from cellar to garret, four, five, six beds in a room; as many as can be crowded in. Into every bed four, five, or six human beings are piled, as many as can be packed in, sick and well, young and old, drunk and sober, men and women, just as they come, indiscriminately. Then come strife, blows, wounds, or, if these bed-fellows agree, so much the worse; thefts are arranged and things done which our language, grown more humane than our deeds, refuses to record. And those who cannot pay for such a refuge? They sleep where they find a place, in passages, arcades, in corners where the police and the owners leave them undisturbed. A few individuals find their way to the refuges which are managed, here and there, by private charity, others sleep on the benches in the parks close under the windows of Queen Victoria. Let us hear the London *Times* (Oct. 12, 1843):

It appears from the report of the proceedings at Marlborough Street Police Court in our columns of yesterday, that there is an average number of 50 human beings of all ages, who huddle together in the parks every night, having no other shelter than what is supplied by the trees and a few hollows of the embankment. Of these, the majority are young girls who have been seduced from the country by the soldiers and turned loose on the world in all the destitution of friendless penury, and all the recklessness of early vice.

This is truly horrible! Poor there must be everywhere. Indigence will find its way and set up its hideous state in the heart of a great and luxurious city. Amid the thousand narrow lanes and bystreets of a populous metropolis there must always, we fear, be much suffering — much that offends the eye — much that lurks unseen.

But that within the precincts of wealth, gaiety and fashion, nigh the real grandeur of St. James, close on the palatial splendor of Bayswater, on the confines of the old and new aristocratic quarters, in a district where the cautious refinement of modern design has refrained from creating one single tenement for poverty; which seems, as it were, dedicated to the exclusive enjoyment of wealth, that there want and famine and disease and vice should stalk in all their kindred horrors, consuming body by body, soul by soul!

It is indeed a monstrous state of things! Enjoyment the most absolute that bodily ease, intellectual excitement or the most innocent pleasures of sense can supply to man's craving, brought in close contact with the most unmitigated misery! Wealth, from its bright saloons, laughing — an insolently heedless laugh — at the unknown wounds of want! Pleasure cruelly but unconsciously mocking the pain that moans below! All contrary things mocking one another — all contrary, save the vice which tempts and the vice which is tempted!

But let all men remember this — that within the most courtly precincts of the richest city of God's earth, there may be found, night after night, winter after winter, women — young in years — old in sin and suffering — outcasts from society — ROTTING FROM FAMINE, FILTH AND DISEASE. Let them remember this, and learn not to theorise but to act. God knows, there is much room for action nowadays.

Women are second-class citizens. It is worth remembering that within *this* century they were thought to lack intelligence enough to vote. When they got the vote, some things began to improve, but the fact remains that they are still, in the eyes of many, "the lesser man" (as Tennyson said). The following excerpt from a book about the Victorian underground shows clearly how women were thought to be not only inferior, but also lacking in the emotions and passions of men.

FROM

The Other Victorians
STEVEN MARCUS

What of woman in this world of torment and fear? . . . They appear in a section devoted to "Marriage,"* and at first sight seem to offer an escape from the nightmare of sexuality. "It is a delusion under which many a previously incontinent man suffers," writes Acton, "to suppose that in newly married life he will be required to treat his wife as he used to treat his mistresses. It is not so in the case of any modest English woman. He need not fear that his wife will require the excitement, or in any respect imitate the ways of a courtezan." This passage contains a cluster of interesting assumptions. It assumes, in the first place, and as a matter of public knowledge, that large numbers of Victorian middle-class men will have had mistresses — who were courtesans. It further assumes that the Victorian wife will not have sexual desires, and as a corollary adds that courtesans or mistresses are in themselves extremely sexual; both of the assumptions seem at least open to question. (It may be useful to note that modern "marriage manuals" reverse the formulation offered by Acton.) The operative word in the passage is of course "fear"; it further underscores the fantasy-conception of sexuality in Acton's work. But it also indicates to what extent this conception is both analogous to and the counterpart by opposition of the fantasies of pornography. In pornography, all women — including wives — are excited and behave like courtesans all the time. Since women are not like this, there is a natural temptation to conjecture that the

---

* The author refers to William Acton's book *The Function and Disorders of the Reproductive Organs, in Childhood, Youth, Adult Age, and Advanced Life Considered in Their Physiological, Social, and Moral Relations.* It was published in 1857 and was remarkably scientific for its age — an age when sex was not mentioned by polite people.

persistence of the pornographic fantasy is somehow connected with this fact. It is indeed connected, but it cannot be accounted for by such a single, simple functional explanation.

But marriage alone is not enough of a safeguard—for either man or woman? Pregnancy and childbearing seem to be the only reliable means of stifling sexual desire.

If the married female conceives every second year, during the nine months that follow conception she experiences no great sexual excitement. The consequence is that sexual desire in the male is somewhat diminished, and the act of coition takes place but rarely. And, again, while women are suckling there is usually such a call on the vital force made by the organs secreting milk that sexual desire is almost annihilated. Now, as all that we have read and heard tends to prove that a reciprocity of desire is, to a great extent, necessary to excite the male, we must not be surprised if we learn that excesses in fertile married life are comparatively rare, and that sensual feelings in the man become gradually sobered down.

This is a representative passage of Acton's thinking. In the first sentence one can observe how belief or received opinion is offered in the form of observation, an unadorned instance of "ideology"—that is, of thought which is socially determined yet unconscious of its determination. The second sentence is a good example of the mode of reasoning one can expect to find in writings of this sort. The "consequence" is a consequence of nothing; or rather it is the consequence of fantasy or wish fulfillment, and the logic of the passage is the logic of intellectual daydream. It may be paraphrased in the statement that the best way of reducing or extinguishing sexual desire is to keep your wife pregnant. On the other hand, to the extent that this passage represents a genuine belief we cannot discount its source in attitudes or behavior or its reciprocal effect on them. Finally, if one compares the tone and content of such a passage—and of this book in general—with analogous ones in

Acton's book on prostitution, it becomes clear that the earlier work is in point of humanity and generosity of feeling superior. And this leads one to suggest that we are confronted here by a disparity which is characteristic of the Victorian period—that during this time the development of social attitudes, of attitudes toward society and social problems, had outstripped the development of personal attitudes, of attitudes toward personal problems or conflicts, and of inwardness in general. Taken as a whole, the Victorian novel—as opposed to Romantic poetry on the one hand and the modern novel on the other—may be regarded as demonstrating a similar inequality.

Some pages further on, Acton recurs to women for the second and last time. He has, he says, "taken pains to obtain and compare abundant evidence on this subject," and goes on to epitomize his findings for the reader.

I should say that the majority of women (happily for them) are not very much troubled with sexual feeling of any kind. What men are habitually, women are only exceptionally. It is too true, I admit, as the divorce courts show, that there are some few women who have sexual desires so strong that they surpass those of men. . . . I admit, of course, the existence of sexual excitement terminating even in nymphomania, a form of insanity which those accustomed to visit lunatic asylums must be fully conversant with; but, with these sad exceptions, there can be no doubt that sexual feeling in the female is in the majority of cases in abeyance . . . and even if roused (which in many instances it never can be) is very moderate compared with that of the male. Many men, and particularly young men, form their ideas of women's feelings from what they notice early in life among loose or, at least, low and vulgar women. . . . Any susceptible boy is easily led to believe, whether he is altogether overcome by the syren or not, that she, and therefore all women, must have at least as strong passions as himself. Such women however give a very false idea of the condition of female sexual feeling in general. Association with the loose women of London streets, in casinos, and other immoral haunts (who, if they have not sexual feeling, counterfeit it so well that the novice does not suspect but that it is genuine), all seem to corroborate such an impression, and . . . it is from these erroneous notions that so many young men think that the marital duties they will have to undertake are beyond their exhausted strength, and from this reason dread and avoid marriage. . . . The best mothers, wives, and managers of households, know little or nothing of sexual indulgences. Love of home, children, and domestic duties, are the only passions they feel.

As a general rule, a modest woman seldom desires any sexual gratification for herself. She submits to her husband, but only to please him; and, but for the desire of maternity, would far rather be relieved from his attentions. No nervous or feeble young man need, therefore, be deterred from marriage by any exaggerated notion of the duties required from him. The married woman has no wish to be treated on the footing of a mistress.

We need not pause to discuss the degree of truth or falsehood in these assertions. What is of more immediate concern is that these assertions indicate a system of beliefs. These beliefs are in the first place associated with class: the "majority of women" evidently fails to include "low and vulgar women"—this final ascription might possibly include all working-class females. These beliefs express yet again the notion that sex is a curse and a torture, and that the only hope of salvation for man lies in marriage to a woman who has no sexual desires and who will therefore make no sexual demands on her husband. At this point, we can observe how sexual responsibility is being projected onto the role of woman; she is being required to save man from himself; and conversely if she is by some accident endowed with a strongly responsive nature, she will become the agent of her husband's ruin. In either event, she is being regarded as essentially a function of masculine needs, whatever the direction in which those needs may run. . . .

FROM
The Domestic Manners of the Americans
FRANCES TROLLOPE

CINCINNATI*

We reached Cincinnati on the 10th of February. It is finely situated on the south side of a hill that rises gently from the water's edge: yet it is by no means a city of striking appearance—it wants domes, towers, and steeples; but its landing-place is noble, extending for more than a quarter of a mile. It is well paved, and surrounded by neat, though not handsome, buildings. I have seen fifteen steam-boats lying there at once, and still half the wharf was unoccupied.

On arriving we repaired to the Washington Hotel, and thought ourselves fortunate when we were told that we were just in time for dinner at the table d'hote; but when the dining-room door was opened, we retreated with a feeling of dismay at seeing between sixty and seventy men already at table. We took our dinner in another room with the females of the family, and then went forth to seek a house for our permanent accommodation.

We went to the office of an advertising agent, who professed to keep a register of all such information, and described the dwelling we wanted. He made no difficulty, but told us his boy should be our guide through the city, and show us what we sought; we accordingly set out with him, and he led us up one street and down another, but evidently without any determinate object; I therefore stopped, and asked him where-about the houses were which we were going to see.

"I am looking for bills" was his reply.

I thought we could have looked for bills as well without him, and I told him so; upon which he assumed an air of great activity, and began knocking regularly at every door we passed, inquiring if the house was to be let. It was impossible to endure this long,

* See "The Making of a Yippie," in Part 3, for a look at modern Cincinnati.

and our guide was dismissed, though I was afterwards obliged to pay him a dollar for his services.

We had the good fortune, however, to find a dwelling before long, and we returned to our hotel, having determined upon taking possession of it as soon as it could be got ready. Not wishing to take our evening meal either with the threescore and ten gentlemen of the dining-room, nor yet with the half-dozen ladies of the bar-room, I ordered tea in my own chamber. A good-humoured Irish woman came forward with a sort of patronising manner, took my hand, and said: "Och, my honey, ye'll be from the old country. I'll see you will have your tay all to yourselves, honey." With this assurance we retired to my room, which was a handsome one as to its size and bed-furniture; but it had no carpet, and was darkened by blinds of paper such as rooms are hung with, which require to be rolled up, and then fastened with strings very awkwardly attached to the window-frames, whenever light or air was wished for. I afterwards met with these same uncomfortable blinds in every part of America.

Our Irish friend soon reappeared, and brought us tea, together with the never-failing accompaniments of American tea-drinking, hung beef, "chipped up" raw, and sundry sweetmeats of brown-sugar hue and flavour. We took our tea, and were enjoying our family talk, relative to our future arrangements, when a loud sharp knocking was heard at our door. My "come in" was answered by the appearance of a portly personage, who proclaimed himself our landlord.

"Are any of you ill?" he began.

"No, thank you, sir; we are all quite well" was my reply.

"Then, madam, I must tell you, that I cannot accommodate you on these terms; we have no family tea-drinkings here, and you must live either with me and my wife, or not at all in my house."

This was said with an air of authority that almost precluded reply, but I ventured a sort of apologetic hint, that we were strangers, and unaccustomed to the manners of the country.

"Our manners are very good manners, and we don't wish any changes from

England," rejoined our sturdy landlord, with an aspect that assuredly did not indicate any very affectionate partiality to the country he named.

I thought of mine host of the Washington afterwards, when reading Scott's *Anne of Geierstein;* he, in truth, strongly resembled the innkeeper therein immortalised, who made his guests eat, drink, and sleep, just where, when, and how he pleased. I made no further remonstrance, but determined to hasten my removal. This we achieved the next day to our great satisfaction.

We were soon settled in our new dwelling, which looked neat and comfortable enough; but we speedily found that it was devoid of nearly all the accommodation that Europeans conceive necessary to decency and comfort. No pump, no cistern, no drain of any kind, no dustman's cart, or any other visible means of getting rid of the rubbish, which vanishes with such celerity in London, that one has no time to think of its existence; but which accumulated so rapidly at Cincinnati, that I sent for my landlord to know in what manner refuse of all kinds was to be disposed of.

"Your Help will just have to fix them all into the middle of the street; but you must mind, old woman, that it is the middle. I expect you don't know as we have got a law what forbids throwing such things at the sides of the streets; they must just all be cast right into the middle, and the pigs soon takes them off."

In truth the pigs are constantly seen doing Herculean service in this way through every quarter of the city: and though it is not very agreeable to live surrounded by herds of these unsavoury animals, it is well they are so numerous, and so active in their capacity of scavengers; for without them the streets would soon be choked up with all sorts of substances, in every stage of decomposition.

We had heard so much of Cincinnati, its beauty, wealth, and unequalled prosperity, that when we left Memphis, to go thither, we almost felt the delight of Rousseau's novice, *"un voyage à faire, et Paris au bout!"** — As soon, therefore, as our little

* "A journey to make, and Paris the end!"

domestic arrangements were completed, we set forth to view this "wonder of the West", this "prophet's gourd of magic growth"—this "infant Hercules"; and surely no travellers ever paraded a city under circumstances more favourable to their finding it fair to the sight. Three dreary months had elapsed since we had left the glories of London behind us; for nearly the whole of that time we had beheld no other architecture than what our ship and steam-boats had furnished; and, excepting at New Orleans, had seen hardly a trace of human habitations. The sight of bricks and mortar was really refreshing, and a house of three stories looked spendid. Of this splendour we saw repeated specimens, and moreover a brick church, which, from its two little peaked spires, is called the two-horned church. But, alas! the flatness of reality after the imagination has been busy! I hardly know what I expected to find in this city, fresh risen from the bosom of the wilderness, but certainly it was not a little town, about the size of Salisbury, without even an attempt at beauty in any of its edifices, and with only just enough of the air of a city to make it noisy and bustling. The population is greater than the appearance of the town would lead one to expect. This is partly owing to the number of free negroes who herd together in an obscure part of the city, called little Africa; and partly to the density of the population round the paper-mills and other manufactories. I believe the number of inhabitants exceeds twenty thousand.

We arrived in Cincinnati in February, 1828, and I speak of the town as it was then; several small churches have been built since, whose towers agreeably relieve its uninteresting mass of buildings. At that time I think Main Street, which is the principal avenue (and runs through the whole town, answering to the High Street of our old cities) was the only one entirely paved. The *trottoir** is of brick, tolerably well laid, but it is inundated by every shower, as Cincinnati has no drains whatever. What makes this omission the more remarkable is, that the situation of of the place is calculated both to facilitate

* Sidewalk.

their construction and to render them necessary. Cincinnati is built on the side of a hill that begins to rise at the river's edge; and were it furnished with drains of the simplest arrangement, the heavy showers of the climate would keep them constantly clean: as it is, these showers wash the higher streets, only to deposit their filth on the first level spot; and this happens to be in the street second in importance to Main Street, running at right-angles to it, and containing most of the large warehouses of the town. This deposit is a dreadful nuisance, and must be productive of miasma during the hot weather.

The town is built, as I believe most American towns are, in squares, as they call them; but these squares are the reverse of ours, being solid instead of hollow. Each consists, or is intended to consist, when the plan of the city is completed, of a block of buildings fronting north, east, west, and south; each house communicating with an alley, furnishing a back entrance. This plan would not be a bad one, were the town properly drained; but as it is, these alleys are horrible abominations, and must, I conceive, become worse with every passing year.

To the north Cincinnati is bounded by a range of forest-covered hills, sufficiently steep and rugged to prevent their being built upon, or easily cultivated, but not sufficiently high to command from their summits a view of any considerable extent. Deep and narrow water-courses, dry in summer, but bringing down heavy streams in winter, divide these hills into many separate heights, and this furnishes the only variety the landscape offers for many miles round the town. The lovely Ohio is a beautiful feature wherever it is visible; but the only part of the city that has the advantage of its beauty, is the street nearest to its bank. The hills of Kentucky, which rise at about the same distance from the river, on the opposite side, form the southern boundary to the basin in which Cincinnati is built.

On first arriving, I thought the many tree-covered hills around very beautiful; but long before my departure, I felt so weary of the confined view, that Salisbury Plain would have been an agreeable variety. I doubt if any inhabitant of Cincinnati ever mounted these hills so often as myself and my children; but it was rather for the enjoyment of a freer air, than for any beauty of prospect, that we took our daily climb. These hills afford neither shrubs nor flowers, but furnish the finest specimens of millepore* in the world; and the water-courses are full of fossil productions.

The forest-trees are neither large nor well grown, and so close as to be nearly knotted together at top: even the wild vine here loses its beauty; for its graceful festoons bear leaves only when they reach the higher branches of the tree that supports them, both air and light being too scantily found below to admit of their doing more than climbing with a bare stem till they reach a better atmosphere. The herb we call penny-royal was the only one I found in abundance, and that only on the brows, where the ground has been partially cleared; vegetation is impossible elsewhere, and it is this circumstance which makes the "eternal forests" of America so detestable. Near New Orleans the undergrowth of palmetto and pawpaw is highly beautiful; but in Tennessee, Indiana, and Ohio, I never found the slightest beauty in the forest-scenery. Fallen trees in every possible stage of decay, and congeries of leaves that have been rotting since the flood, cover the ground and infect the air. The beautiful variety of foliage afforded by evergreens never occurs; and in Tennessee, and that part of Ohio that surrounds Cincinnati, even the sterile beauty of rocks is wanting. On crossing the water to Kentucky the scene is greatly improved; beech and chestnut, of magnificent growth, border the beautiful river; the ground has been well cleared, and the herbage is excellent: the pawpaw grows abundantly, and is a splendid shrub, though it bears neither fruit nor flowers so far north. The noble tulip-tree flourishes here, and blooms profusely.

The river Licking flows into the Ohio nearly opposite Cincinnati; it is a pretty winding stream, and two or three miles from its mouth has a brisk rapid dancing

* Millepore are stoney, reef-building corals. Mrs. Trollope was an enthusiastic amateur archeologist.

among white stones, which, in the absence of better rocks, we found very picturesque.

This astounding piece was written by Hinton Rowan Helper, who was appointed by President Lincoln to serve as consul in Rio de Janeiro, Brazil. It was published in 1868.

The Negroes in Negroland
HINTON ROWAN HELPER

There are now in the United States of America thirty millions of white people, who are (or ought to be) bound together by the ties of a kindred origin, by the affinities of a sameness of noble purpose, by the links of a common nationality, and by the cords of an inseparable destiny. We have here also, unfortunately for us all, four millions of black people, whose ancestors, like themselves, were never known (except in very rare instances, which form the exceptions to a general rule) to aspire to any other condition than that of base and beastlike slavery. These black people are, by nature, of an exceedingly low and groveling disposition. They have no trait of character that is lovely or admirable. They are not high-minded, enterprising, nor prudent. In no age, in no part of the world, have they, of themselves, ever projected or advanced any public or private interest, nor given expression to any thought or sentiment that could worthily elicit the praise, or even the favorable mention, of the better portion of mankind. Seeing, then, that the negro does, indeed, belong to a lower and inferior order of beings, why, in the name of Heaven, why should we forever degrade and disgrace both ourselves and our posterity by entering, of our own volition, into more intimate relations with him? May God, in his restraining mercy, forbid that we should ever do this most foul and wicked thing!

Acting under the influence of that vile spirit of deception and chicanery which is always familiar with every false pretense, the members of a Radical Congress, the editors of a venal press, and other peddlers of perverted knowledge, are now loudly proclaiming that nowhere in our country, henceforth, must there be any distinction, any discrimination, on account of color; thereby covertly inculcating the gross error of inferring or supposing that color is the only difference—and that a very trivial difference—between the whites and the blacks! Now, once and for all, in conscientious deference to truth, let it be distinctly made known and acknowledged, that, in addition to the black and baneful color of the negro, there are numerous other defects, physical, mental, and moral, which clearly mark him, when compared with the white man, as a very different and inferior creature. While, therefore, with an involuntary repugnance which we cannot control, and with a wholesome antipathy which it would be both unnatural and unavailing in us to attempt to destroy, we behold the crime-stained blackness of the negro, let us, also, at the same time, take cognizance of

His low and compressed Forehead;
His hard, thick Skull;
His small, backward-thrown Brain;
His short, crisp Hair;
His flat Nose;
His thick Lips;
His projecting, snout-like mouth;
His strange, Eunuch-toned Voice;
The scantiness of Beard on his Face;
The Toughness and Unsensitiveness of his Skin;
The Thinness and Shrunkenness of his Thighs;
His curved Knees;
His calfless Legs;
His low, short Ankles;
His long, flat Heels;
His glut-shaped Feet;
The general Angularity and Oddity of his Frame;
The Malodorous Exhalations from his Person;
His Puerility of Mind;
His Inertia and Sleepy-headedness;
His proverbial Dishonesty;
His predisposition to fabricate Falsehoods; and
His Apathetic Indifference to all Propositions and Enterprises of Solid Merit.

Many other differences might be mentioned; but the score and more of obvious and undeniable ones here enumerated ought to suffice for the utter confusion and shame of all those disingenuous politicians and others, who, knowing better, and who are thus guilty of the crime of defeating the legitimate ends of their own knowledge, would, for mere selfish and partisan purposes, convey the delusive impression that there is no other difference than that of color.

There are many points of general dissatisfaction and dispute, which should not, on any account, be overlooked in the discussion of the subjects here presented. One of these is, that white people, whose reason and honor have not been vitiated, object to close relationship with negroes, not wishing to live with them in the same house; not wishing to fellowship with them in the same society, assembly, or congregation; not wishing to ride with them in the same omnibus, car, or carriage; and not wishing to mess with them at the same table, whether at a hotel, in a restaurant, on a steamer, or elsewhere. Now, any and every white person who does not think and act in strict accordance with the just and pure promptings here indicated, is, in reality, a most unworthy and despicable representative of his race. Even the lower animals, the creatures of mere instinct— the beasts, the birds, and the fishes—many distinct species of which are apparently quite similar, set us daily and hourly examples of the eminent propriety of each kind forming and maintaining separate communities of their own; and so we always find them—in herds, in flocks, and in shoals. How can the negro be a fit person to occupy, in any capacity, our houses or our hotels, our theatres or our churches, our schools or our colleges, our steamers or our vehicles, or any other place or places of uncommon comfort and convenience, which owe their creation, their proper uses, and their perpetuity, to the whites alone—places and improvements about which the negro, of himself, is, and always has been, absolutely ignorant and indifferent? Neither in his own country nor elsewhere has the negro ever built a house or a theatre; he has never erected a church nor a college; he has never constructed a steamer nor a railroad, nor a railroad car — nor, except when under the special direction and control of superior intelligence, has he ever invented or manufactured even the minutest appendage of any one of the distinctive elements or realities of human progress. Yet, let this not, by any means, be understood as an argument, nor even as a hint, in behalf of slavery. It is to the great and lasting honor of the Republic that slavery in the United States is abolished forever. In losing her slaves, the South lost nothing that was worth the keeping. Had slavery only been abolished by law many years ago, our whole country would be infinitely better off to-day.

Never will it be possible for the compiler to erase from his memory the feelings of weighty sadness and disgust which overcame him, a few months since, when, while sojourning in the city of Washington, he walked, one day, into the Capitol, and, leisurely passing into the galleries of the two houses of Congress, beheld there, uncouthly lounging and dozing upon the seats, a horde of vile, ignorant, and foul-scented negroes. He was perplexed, shocked, humiliated, and indignant — and could not sit down. With merited emotions of bitterness and contempt for those narrow-minded white men, through whose detestable folly and selfishness so great an outrage against public propriety and decency had been perpetrated, he turned away — indeed, it was not in his power to contemplate with calmness that motley and monstrous manifestation of national incongruity, ugliness, and disgrace. Then it was that, for the first time in his life, he wished himself a Hercules, in order that he might be able to clean, thoroughly and at once, those Augean stables of the black ordure and Radical filth which, therein and elsewhere, had already accumulated to an almost insufferable excess. It was the powerful and long-lingering momentum of the impressions received on that occasion, more than any other circumstance, that gave definite form and resolution to the purpose (although the idea had been previously entertained) of preparing this compilation. The object of the compiler will have been well attained if the work aids materially in more fully convincing his countrymen, North, South, East and West, that negro equality, negro supremacy, and negro domination, as now tyrannically enforced at the point of the bayonet, are cruel and atrocious innovations, which ought to be speedily terminated.

FROM
Call It Sleep
HENRY ROTH

PROLOGUE

*(I pray thee ask no questions
this is that Golden Land)*

The small white steamer, Peter Stuyvesant, that delivered the immigrants from the stench and throb of the steerage to the stench and the throb of New York tenements, rolled slightly on the water beside the stone quay in the lee of the weathered barracks and new brick buildings of Ellis Island. Her skipper was waiting for the last of the officials, laborers and guards to embark upon her before he cast off and started for Manhattan. Since this was Saturday afternoon and this the last trip she would make for the week-end, those left behind might have to stay over till Monday. Her whistle bellowed its hoarse warning. A few figures in overalls sauntered from the high doors of the immigration quarters and down the grey pavement that led to the dock.

It was May of the year 1907, the year that was destined to bring the greatest number of immigrants to the shores of the United States. All that day, as on all the days since spring began, her decks had been thronged by hundreds upon hundreds of foreigners, natives from almost every land in the world, the joweled close-cropped Teuton, the full-bearded Russian, the scraggly-whiskered Jew, and among them

Slovack peasants with docile faces, smooth-cheeked and swarthy Armenians, pimply Greeks, Danes with wrinkled eyelids. All day her decks had been colorful, a matrix of the vivid costumes of other lands, the speckled green-and-yellow aprons, the flowered kerchief, embroidered homespun, the silver-braided sheepskin vest, the gaudy scarfs, yellow boots, fur caps, caftans, dull gabardines. All day the guttural, the high-pitched voices, the astonished cries, the gasps of wonder, reiterations of gladness had risen from her decks in a motley billow of sound. But now her decks were empty, quiet, spreading out under the sunlight almost as if the warm boards were relaxing from the strain and the pressure of the myriads of feet. All those steerage passengers of the ships that had docked that day who were permitted to enter had already entered—except two, a woman and a young child she carried in her arms. They had just come aboard escorted by a man.

About the appearance of these late comers there was very little that was unusual. The man had evidently spent some time in America and was now bringing his wife and child over from the other side. It might have been thought that he had spent most of his time in lower New York, for he paid only the scantest attention to the Statue of Liberty or to the city rising from the water or to the bridges spanning the East River—or perhaps he was merely too agitated to waste much time on these wonders. His clothes were the ordinary clothes the ordinary New Yorker wore in that period—sober and dull. A black derby accentuated the sharpness and sedentary pallor of his face; a jacket, loose on his tall spare frame, buttoned up in a V close to the throat; and above the V a tightly-knotted black tie was mounted in the groove of a high starched collar. As for his wife, one guessed that she was a European more by the timid wondering look in her eyes as she gazed from her husband to the harbor, than by her clothes. For her clothes were American—a black skirt, a white shirt-waist and a black jacket. Obviously her husband had either taken the precaution of sending them to her while she was still in Europe or had brought them with him to

Ellis Island where she had slipped them on before she left.

Only the small child in her arms wore a distinctly foreign costume, an impression one got chiefly from the odd, outlandish, blue-straw hat on his head with its polka dot ribbons of the same color dangling over each shoulder. . . .

They had been standing in this strange and silent manner for several minutes, when the woman, as if driven by the strain into action, tried to smile, and touching her husband's arm said timidly, "And this is the Golden Land." She spoke in Yiddish. . . .

"Well, it's all over now." She attempted to be cheerful. "It's all behind us now, isn't it, Albert? Whatever mistakes I made don't really matter any more. Do they?"

"A fine taste of what lies' before me!" He turned his back on her and leaned morosely against the rail. "A fine taste!"

They were silent. On the dock below, the brown hawsers had been slipped over the mooring posts, and the men on the lower deck now dragged them dripping from the water. Bells clanged. The ship throbbed. Startled by the hoarse bellow of her whistle, the gulls wheeling before her prow rose with slight creaking cry from the green water, and as she churned away from the stone quay skimmed across her path on indolent, scimitar wing. Behind the ship the white wake that stretched to Ellis Island grew longer, raveling wanly into melon-green. On one side curved the low drab Jersey coast-line, the spars and masts on the waterfront fringing the sky; on the other side was Brooklyn, flat, water-towered; the horns of the harbor. And before them, rising on her high pedestal from the scaling swarmy brilliance of sunlit water to the west, Liberty. The spinning disk of the late afternoon sun slanted behind her, and to those on board who gazed, her features were charred with shadow, her depths exhausted, her masses ironed to one single plane. Against the luminous sky the rays of her halo were spikes of darkness roweling the air; shadow flattened the torch she bore to a black cross against flawless light—the blackened hilt of a broken sword. Liberty. The child and his mother stared again at the massive figure in wonder.

The ship curved around in a long arc toward Manhattan, her bow sweeping past Brooklyn and the bridges whose cables and pillars superimposed by distance, spanned the East River in diaphanous and rigid waves. The western wind that raked the harbor into brilliant clods blew fresh and clear — a salt tang in the lull of its veerings. It whipped the polka-dot ribbons on the child's hat straight out behind him. They caught his father's eye.

"Where did you find that crown?"

Startled by his sudden question his wife looked down. "That? That was Maria's parting gift. The old nurse. She bought it herself and then sewed the ribbons on. You don't think it's pretty?"

"Pretty? Do you still ask?" His lean jaws hardly moved as he spoke. "Can't you see that those idiots lying back there are watching us already? They're mocking us! What will the others do on the train? He looks like a clown in it. He's the cause of all this trouble anyway!"

The harsh voice, the wrathful glare, the hand flung toward the child frightened him. Without knowing the cause, he knew that the stranger's anger was directed at himself. He burst into tears and pressed closer to his mother.

"Quiet!" the voice above him snapped.

Cowering, the child wept all the louder.

"Hush, darling!" His mother's protecting hands settled on his shoulders.

"Just when we're about to land!" her husband said furiously "He begins this! This howling! And now we'll have it all the way home, I suppose! Quiet! You hear?"

"It's you who are frightening him, Albert!" she protested.

"Am I? Well, let him be quiet. And take that straw gear off his head."

"But Albert, it's cool here."

"Will you take that off when I —" A snarl choked whatever else he would have uttered. While his wife looked on aghast, his long fingers scooped the hat from the child's head. The next instant it was sailing over the ship's side to the green waters below. The overalled men in the stern grinned at each other. The old orange-peddler shook her head and clucked.

"Albert!" his wife caught her breath. "How could you?"

"I could!" he rapped out. "You should have left it behind!" His teeth clicked, and he glared about the deck.

She lifted the sobbing child to her breast, pressed him against her. With a vacant stunned expression, her gaze wandered from the grim smouldering face of her husband to the stern of the ship. In the silvery-green wake that curved trumpet-wise through the water, the blue hat still bobbed and rolled, ribbon stretched out on the waves. Tears sprang to her eyes. She brushed them away quickly, shook her head as if shaking off the memory, and looked toward the bow. Before her the grimy cupolas and towering square walls of the city loomed up. Above the jagged roof tops, the white smoke, whitened and suffused by the slanting sun, faded into the slots and wedges of the sky. She pressed her brow against her child's, hushed him with whispers. This was that vast incredible land, the land of freedom, of immense opportunity, that Golden Land. Again she tried to smile.

"Albert," she said timidly, "Albert."

"Hm?"

"Gehen vir voinen du? In Nev York?"

"Nein. Bronzeville. Ich hud dir schoin geschriben."

She nodded uncertainly, sighed . . .

Screws threshing, backing water, the Peter Stuyvesant neared her dock — drifting slowly and with canceled momentum as if reluctant.

FROM

Joe Gould's Secret
JOSEPH MITCHELL

Joe Gould is a blithe and emaciated little man who has been a notable in the cafeterias, diners, barrooms, and dumps of Greenwich Village for a quarter of a century. He sometimes brags rather wryly that he is the last of the bohemians. "All the others fell by the wayside," he says. "Some are in the grave, some are in the loony bin, and some are in the advertising business." Gould's life is by no means carefree; he is constantly tormented by what he calls "the three H's"—homelessness, hunger, and hangovers. He sleeps on benches in subway stations, on the floor in the studios of friends, and in quarter-a-night flophouses on the Bowery. Once in a while he trudges up to Harlem and goes to one of the establishments know as "Extension Heavens" that are operated by followers of Father Divine, the Negro evangelist, and gets a night's lodging for fifteen cents. He is five feet four and he hardly ever weighs more than a hundred pounds. Not long ago he told a friend that he hadn't eaten a square meal since June, 1936, when he bummed up to Cambridge and attended a banquet during a reunion of the Harvard class of 1911, of which he is a member. "I'm the foremost authority in the United States," he says, "on the subject of doing without." He tells people that he lives on "air, self-esteem, cigarette butts, cowboy coffee, fried-egg sandwiches, and ketchup." Cowboy coffee, he says, is strong coffee drunk black without sugar. "I've long since lost my taste for good coffee," he says. "I much prefer the kind that sooner or later, if you keep on drinking it, your hands will begin to shake and the whites of your eyes will turn yellow." While having a sandwich, Gould customarily empties a bottle or two of ketchup on his plate and eats it with a spoon. The countermen in the Jefferson Diner, on Village Square, which is one of his hangouts, gather up the ketchup bottles and hide them the moment he puts his head in the door. "I don't particularly like the confounded stuff," he says, "but I make it a practice to eat all I can get. It's the only grub I know of that's free of charge."

Gould is a Yankee. His branch of the Goulds has been in New England since 1635, and he is related to many of the other early New England families, such as the Lawrences, the Clarkes, and the Storers. "There's nothing accidental about me," he once said. "I'll tell you what it took to make me what I am today. It took old Yankee blood, an overwhelming aversion to possessions, four years of Harvard, and twenty-five years of beating the living hell out of my insides with bad hooch and bad food." He says that he is out of joint with the rest of the human race because he

doesn't want to own anything. "If Mr. Chrysler tried to make me a present of the Chrysler Building," he says, "I'd damn near break my neck fleeing from him. I wouldn't own it; it'd own me. Back home in Massachusetts I'd be called an old Yankee crank. Here I'm called a bohemian. It's six of one, half a dozen of the other." Gould has a twangy voice and a Harvard accent. Bartenders and countermen in the Village refer to him as the Professor, the Sea Gull, Professor Sea Gull, the Mongoose, Professor Mongoose, or the Bellevue Boy. He dresses in the castoff clothes of his friends. His overcoat, suit, shirt, and even his shoes are all invariably a size or two too large, but he wears them with a kind of forlorn rakishness. "Just look at me," he says. "The only thing that fits is the necktie." On bitter winter days he puts a layer of newspapers between his shirt and undershirt. "I'm snobbish," he says. "I only use the *Times*." He is fond of unusual headgear—a toboggan, a beret, or a yachting cap. One summer evening he appeared at a party in a seersucker suit, a polo shirt, a scarlet cummerbund, sandals, and a yachting cap, all hand-me-downs. He uses a long black cigarette holder, and a good deal of the time he smokes butts picked up off the sidewalks.

Bohemianism has aged Gould considerably beyond his years. He has got in the habit lately of asking people he has just met to guess his age. Their guesses range between sixty-five and seventy-five; he is fifty-three. He is never hurt by this; he looks upon it as proof of his superiority. "I do more living in one year," he says, "than ordinary humans do in ten." Gould is toothless, and his lower jaw swivels from side to side when he talks. He is bald on top, but the hair at the back of his head is long and frizzly, and he has a bushy, cinnamon-colored beard. He wears a pair of spectacles that are loose and lopsided and that slip down to the end of his nose a moment after he puts them on. He doesn't always wear them on the street and without them he has the wild, unfocussed stare of an old scholar who has strained his eyes on small print. Even in the Village many people turn and look at him. He is stooped and he moves rapidly, grumbling to himself, with his head thrust forward and held to one side. Under his left arm he usually carries a bulging, greasy, brown pasteboard portfolio, and he swings his right arm aggressively. As he hurries along, he seems to be warding off an imaginary enemy. Don Freeman, the artist, a friend of his, once made a sketch of him walking. Freeman called the sketch "Joe Gould versus the Elements." Gould is as restless and footloose as an alley cat, and he takes long hikes about the city, now and then disappearing from the Village for weeks at a time and mystifying his friends; they have never been able to figure out where he goes. When he returns, always looking pleased with himself, he makes a few cryptic remarks, giggles, and then shuts up. "I went on a bird walk along the waterfront with an old countess," he said after his most recent absence. "The countess and I spent three weeks studying sea gulls."

Gould is almost never seen without his portfolio. He keeps it on his lap while he eats and in flophouses he sleeps with it under his head. It usually contains a mass of manuscripts and notes and letters and clippings and copies of obscure little magazines, a bottle of ink, a dictionary, a paper bag of cigarette butts, a paper bag of bread crumbs, and a paper bag of hard, round, dimestore candy of the type called sour balls. "I fight fatigue with sour balls," he says. The crumbs are for pigeons; like many other eccentrics, Gould is a pigeon feeder. He is devoted to a flock which makes its headquarters atop and around the statue of Garibaldi in Washington Square. These pigeons know him. When he comes up and takes a seat on the plinth of the statue, they flutter down and perch on his head and shoulders, waiting for him to bring out his bag of crumbs. He has given names to some of them. "Come here, Boss Tweed," he says. "A lady in Stewart's Cafeteria didn't finish her whole-wheat toast this morning and when she went out, bingo, I snatched it off her plate especially for you. Hello, Big Bosom. Hello, Pop-gut. Hello, Lady Astor. Hello, St. John the Baptist. Hello, Polly Adler. Hello, Fiorello, you old goat, how're you today?"

Although Gould strives to give the impression that he is a philosophical loafer, he has done an immense amount of work during his career as a bohemian. Every day, even when he has a bad hangover or even when he is weak and listless from hunger, he spends at least a couple of hours working on a formless, rather mysterious book that he calls "An Oral History of Our Time." He began this book twenty-six years ago, and it is nowhere near finished. His preoccupation with it seems to be principally responsible for the way he lives; a steady job of any kind, he says, would interfere with his thinking. Depending on the weather, he writes in parks, in doorways, in flophouse lobbies, in cafeterias, on benches on elevated-railroad platforms, in subway trains, and in public libraries. When he is in the proper mood, he writes until he is exhausted, and he gets into this mood at peculiar times. He says that one night he sat for six or seven hours in a booth in a Third Avenue bar and grill, listening to a beery old Hungarian woman, once a madam and once a dealer in narcotics and now a soup cook in a city hospital, tell the story of her life. Three days later, around four o'clock in the morning, on a cot in the Hotel Defender, at 300 Bowery, he was awakened by the foghorns of tugs on the East River and was unable to go back to sleep because he felt that he was in the exact mood to put the old soup cook's biography in his history. He has an abnormal memory; if he is sufficiently impressed by a conversation, he can keep it in his head, even if it is lengthy and senseless, for many days, much of it word for word. He had a bad cold, but he got up, dressed under a red exit light, and, tiptoeing so as not to disturb the men sleeping on cots all around him, went downstairs to the lobby.

He wrote in the lobby from 4:15 A.M. until noon. Then he left the Defender, drank some coffee in a Bowery diner, and walked up to the Public Library. He plugged away at a table in the genealogy room, which is one of his rainy-day hangouts and which he says he prefers to the main reading room because it is gloomier, until it closed at 6 P.M. Then he moved into the main reading room and stayed there, seldom taking his eyes off his work, until the Library locked up for the night at 10 P.M. He ate a couple of egg sandwiches and a quantity of ketchup in a Times Square cafeteria. Then, not having two bits for a flophouse and being too engrossed to go to the Village and seek shelter, he hurried into the West Side subway and rode the balance of the night, scribbling ceaselessly while the train he was aboard made three round trips between the New Lots Avenue station in Brooklyn and the Van Cortlandt Park station in the Bronx, which is one of the longest runs in the subway system. He kept his portfolio on his lap and used it as a desk. He has the endurance of the possessed. Whenever he got too sleepy to concentrate, he shook his head vigorously and then brought out his bag of sour balls and popped one in his mouth. People stared at him, and once he was interrupted by a drunk who asked him what in the name of God he was writing. Gould knows how to get rid of inquisitive drunks. He pointed at his left ear and said, "What? What's that? Deaf as a post. Can't hear a word." The drunk lost all interest in him. "Day was breaking when I left the subway," Gould says. "I was coughing and sneezing, my eyes were sore, my knees were shaky, I was as hungry as a bitch wolf, and I had exactly eight cents to my name. I didn't care. My history was longer by eleven thousand brand-new words, and at that moment I bet there wasn't a chairman of the board in all New York as happy as I."

Gould is haunted by the fear that he will die before he has the first draft of the Oral History finished. It is already eleven times as long as the Bible. He estimates that the manuscript contains 9,000,000 words, all in longhand. It may well be the lengthiest unpublished work in existence. Gould does his writing in nickel composition books, the kind that children use in school, and the Oral History and the notes he has made for it fill two hundred and seventy of them, all of which are tattered and grimy and stained with coffee, grease, and beer. Using a fountain pen, he covers both sides of each page, leaving no margins anywhere,

and his penmanship is poor; hundreds of thousands of words are legible only to him. He has never been able to interest a publisher in the Oral History. At one time or another he has lugged armfuls of it into fourteen publishing offices. "Half of them said it was obscene and outrageous and to get it out of there as quick as I could," he says, "and the others said they couldn't read my handwriting." Experiences of this nature do not dismay Gould; he keeps telling himself that it is posterity he is writing for, anyway. In his breast pocket, sealed in a dingy envelope, he always carries a will bequeathing two-thirds of the manuscript to the Harvard Library and the other third to the Smithsonian Institution. "A couple of generations after I'm dead and gone," he likes to say, "the Ph.D.'s will start lousing through my work. Just imagine their surprise. 'Why, I be damned,' they'll say, 'this fellow was the most brilliant historian of the century.' They'll give me my due. I don't claim that all of the Oral History is first class, but some of it will live as long as the English language." Gould used to keep his composition books scattered all over the Village, in the apartments and studios of friends. He kept them stuck away in closets and under beds and behind the books in bookcases. In the winter of 1942, after hearing that the Metropolitan Museum had moved its most precious paintings to a bombproof storage place somewhere out of town for the duration of the war, he became panicky. He went around and got all his books together and made them into a bale, he wrapped the bale in two layers of oil cloth, and then he entrusted it to a woman he knows who owns a duck-and-chicken farm near Huntington, Long Island. The farmhouse has a stone cellar.

Gould puts into the Oral History only things he has seen or heard. At least half of it is made up of conversations taken down verbatim or summarized; hence the title. "What people say is history," Gould says. "What we used to think was history — kings and queens, treaties, inventions, big battles, beheadings, Caesar, Napoleon, Pontius Pilate, Columbus, William Jennings Bryan — is only formal history and largely false. I'll put down the informal history of the shirt-sleeved multitude—what they had to say about their jobs, love affairs, vittles, sprees, scrapes, and sorrows—or I'll perish in the attempt." The Oral History is a great hodgepodge and kitchen midden of hearsay, a repository of jabber, an omnium-gatherum of bushwa, gab, palaver, hogwash, flapdoodle, and malarkey, the fruit, according to Gould's estimate, of more than twenty thousand conversations. In it are the hopelessly incoherent biographies of hundreds of bums, accounts of the wanderings of seamen encountered in South Street barrooms, grisly descriptions of hospital and clinic experiences ("Did you ever have a painful operation or disease?" is one of the first questions that Gould, fountain pen and composition book in hand, asks a person he has just met), summaries of innumerable Union Square and Columbus Circle harangues, testimonies given by converts at Salvation Army street meetings, and the addled opinions of scores of park-bench oracles and gin-mill savants. For a time Gould haunted the all-night greasy spoons in the vicinity of Bellevue Hospital, eaves-dropping on tired interns, nurses, orderlies, ambulance drivers, embalming-school students, and morgue workers, and faithfully recording their talk. He scurries up and down Fifth Avenue during parades, feverishly taking notes. Gould writes with great candor, and the percentage of obscenity in the Oral History is high. He has a chapter called "Examples of the So-called Dirty Story of Our Time," to which he makes almost daily additions. In another chapter are many rhymes and observations which he found scribbled on the walls of subway washrooms. He b.'ieves that these scribblings are as truly historical as the strategy of General Robert E. Lee. Hundreds of thousands of words are devoted to the drunken behavior and the sexual adventures of various professional Greenwich Villagers in the twenties. There are hundreds of reports of ginny Village parties, including gossip about the guests and faithful reports of their arguments on such subjects as reincarnation, birth control, free love, psychoanalysis, Christian Science,

Swedenborgianism, vegetarianism, alcoholism, and different political and art isms. "I have fully covered what might be termed the intellectual underworld of my time," Gould says. There are detailed descriptions of night life in scores of Village drinking and eating places, some of which, such as the Little Quakeress, the Original Julius, the Troubadour Tavern, the Samovar, Hubert's Cafeteria, Sam Swartz's T.N.T., and Eli Greifer's Last Outpost of Bohemia Tea Shoppe, do not exist any longer.

Gould is a night wanderer, and he has put down descriptions of dreadful things he has seen on dark New York streets—descriptions, for example, of the herds of big gray rats that come out in the hours before dawn in some neighborhoods of the lower East Side and Harlem and unconcernedly walk the sidewalks. "I sometimes believe that these rats are not rats at all," he says, "but the damned and aching souls of tenement landlords." A great deal of the Oral History is in diary form. Gould is afflicted with total recall, and now and then he picks out a period of time in the recent past—it might be a day, a week, or a month—and painstakingly writes down everything of any consequence that he did during this period. Sometimes he writes a chapter in which he monotonously and hideously curses some person or institution. Here and there are rambling essays on such subjects as the flophouse flea, spaghetti, the zipper as a sign of the decay of civilization, false teeth, insanity, the jury system, remorse, cafeteria cooking, and the emasculating effect of the typewriter on literature. "William Shakespeare didn't sit around pecking on a dirty, damned, ninety-five-dollar doohickey," he wrote, "and Joe Gould doesn't, either."

The Oral History is almost as discursive as "Tristram Shandy." In one chapter, "The Good Men are Dying Like Flies," Gould begins a biography of a diner-proprietor and horse-race gambler named Side-Bet Benny Altschuler, who stuck a rusty icepick in his hand and died of lockjaw; and skips after a few paragraphs to a story a seaman told him about seeing a group of lepers drinking and dancing and singing on a beach in Port-of-Spain, Trinidad; and goes from that to an anecdote about a demonstration held in front of a moving-picture theatre in Boston in 1915 to protest against the showing of "The Birth of a Nation," at which he kicked a policeman; and goes from that to a description of a trip he once made through the Central Islip insane asylum, in the course of which a woman pointed at him and screamed, "There he is! Thief! Thief! There's the man that picked my geraniums and stole my mamma's mule and buggy"; and goes from that to an account an old stumble-bum gave of glimpsing and feeling the blue-black flames of hell one night while sitting in a doorway on Great Jones Street and of seeing two mermaids playing in the East River just north of Fulton Fish Market later the same night; and goes from that to an explanation made by a priest of Old St. Patrick's Cathedral, which is on Mott Street, in the city's oldest Little Italy, of why so many Italian women always wear black ("They are in perpetual mourning for our Lord"); and then returns at last to Side-Bet Benny, the lockjawed diner proprietor.

Only a few of the hundreds of people who know Gould have read any of the Oral History, and most of them take it for granted that it is gibberish. Those who make the attempt usually bog down after a couple of chapters and give up. Gould says he can count on one hand or on one foot those who have read enough of it to be qualified to form an opinion. One is Horace Gregory, the poet and critic. "I look upon Gould as a sort of Samuel Pepys of the Bowery," Gregory says. "I once waded through twenty-odd composition books, and most of what I saw had the quality of a competent high-school theme, but some of it was written with the clear and wonderful veracity of a child, and here and there were flashes of hardbitten Yankee wit. If someone took the trouble to go through it and separate the good from the rubbish, as editors did with Thomas Wolfe's millions of words, it might be discovered that Gould actually has written a masterpiece." Another is E. E. Cummings, the Poet, who is a close friend of Gould's. Cummings once wrote a poem about Gould, No. 261 in his "Collected Poems," which contains the following description of the history:

. . . a myth is as good as a smile but little
*   joe gould's quote oral*
history unquote might (publishers note) be
*   entitled a wraith's*
progress or mainly awash while chiefly
*   submerged or an amoral*
morality sort-of-aliveing by innumerable
*   kind-of-deaths*

Throughout the nineteen twenties Gould haunted the office of the *Dial,* now dead, the most highbrow magazine of the time. Finally, in its April, 1929, issue, the *Dial* printed one of his shorter essays, "Civilization." In it he rambled along, jeering at the buying and selling of stocks as "a fuddy-duddy old maid's game" and referring to skyscrapers and steamships as "bric-a-brac" and giving his opinion that "the auto is unnecessary." "If all the perverted ingenuity which was put into making buzz-wagons had only gone into improving the breed of horses," he wrote, "humanity would be better off." This essay had a curious effect on American literature. A copy of the *Dial* in which it appeared turned up a few months later in a second-hand bookstore in Fresno, California, and was bought for a dime by William Saroyan, who then was twenty and floundering around, desperate to become a writer. He read Gould's essay and was deeply impressed and influenced by it. "It freed me from bothering about form," he says. Twelve years later, in the winter of 1941, in Don Freeman's studio on Columbus Circle, Saroyan saw some drawings Freeman had made of Gould for *Don Freeman's Newsstand,* a quarterly publication of pictures of odd New York scenes and personalities put out by the Associated American Artists. Saroyan became excited. He told Freeman about his indebtedness to Gould. "Who the hell is he, anyway?" Saroyan asked. "I've been trying to find out for years. Reading those few pages in the *Dial* was like going in the wrong direction and running into the right guy and then never seeing him again." Freeman told him about the Oral History. Saroyan sat down and wrote a commentary to accompany the drawings of Gould in *Newsstand.* "To this day," he wrote, in part, "I have not read anything else by Joe Gould. And yet to me he remains one of the few genuine and original American writers. He was easy and uncluttered, and almost all other American writing was uneasy and cluttered. It was not at home anywhere; it was trying too hard; it was miserable; it was a little sickly; it was literary; and it couldn't say anything simply. All other American writing was trying to get into one form or another, and no writer except Joe Gould seemed to have imagination enough to understand that if the worst came to the worst you didn't need to have any form at all. You didn't need to put what you had to say into a poem, an essay, a story, or a novel. All you had to do was say it." Not long after this issue of *Newsstand* came out, someone stopped Gould on Eighth Street and showed him Saroyan's endorsement of his work. Gould shrugged his shoulders. He had been on a spree and had lost his false teeth, and at the moment he was uninterested in literary matters. After thinking it over, however, he decided to call on Saroyan and ask him for help in getting some teeth. He found out somehow that Saroyan was living at the Hampshire House, on Central Park South. The doorman there followed Gould into the lobby and asked him what he wanted. Gould told him that he had come to see William Saroyan. "Do you know Mr. Saroyan?" the doorman asked. "Why, no," Gould said, "but that's all right. He's a disciple of mine." "What do you mean, disciple?" asked the doorman. "I mean," said Gould, "that he's a literary disciple of mine. I want to ask him to buy me some teeth." "Teeth?" asked the doorman. "What do you mean, teeth?" "I mean some store teeth," Gould said. "Some false teeth." "Come this way," said the doorman, gripping Gould's arm and ushering him to the street. Later Freeman arranged a meeting, and the pair spent several evenings together in bars. "Saroyan kept saying he wanted to hear all about the Oral History," Gould says, "but I never got a chance to tell him. He did all the talking. I couldn't get a word in edgewise."

As long as he can remember, Gould has been perplexed by his own personality. There are a number of autobiographical essays in the Oral History, and he says that all of them are attempts to explain himself to himself. In one, "Why I Am Unable To Adjust Myself To Civilization, Such As It Is, or Do, Don't, Do, Don't, A Hell Of A Note," he came to the conclusion that his shyness was responsible for everything. "I am introvert and extrovert all rolled in one," he wrote, "a warring mixture of the recluse and the Sixth Avenue auctioneer. One foot says do, the other says don't. One foot says shut your mouth, the other says bellow like a bull. I am painfully shy, but try not to let people know it. They would take advantage of me." Gould keeps his shyness well hidden. It is evident only when he is cold sober. In that state he is silent, suspicious, and constrained, but a couple of beers or a single jigger of gin will untie his tongue and put a leer on his face. He is extraordinarily responsive to alcohol. "On a hot night," he says, "I can walk up and down in front of a gin mill for ten minutes, breathing real deep, and get a jag on."

Even though Gould requires only a few drinks, getting them is sometimes quite a task. Most evenings he prowls around the saloons and dives on the west side of the Village, on the lookout for curiosity-seeking tourists from whom he can cadge beers, sandwiches, and small sums of money. If he is unable to find anyone approachable in the tumultuous saloons around Sheridan Square, he goes over to Sixth Avenue and works north, hitting the Jericho Tavern, the Village Square Bar & Grill, the Belmar, Goody's, and the Rochambeau. He has a routine. He doesn't enter a place unless it is crowded. After he is in, he bustles over to the telephone booth and pretends to look up a number. While doing this, he scrutinizes the customers. If he sees a prospect, he goes over and says, "Let me introduce myself. The name is Joseph Ferdinand Gould, a graduate of Harvard, *magna cum difficultate,* class of 1911, and chairman of the board of Weal and Woe, Incorporated. In exchange for a drink, I'll recite a poem, deliver a lecture, argue a point, or take off my shoes and imitate a sea gull. I prefer gin, but beer will do." Gould is by no means a bum. He feels that the entertainment he provides is well worth whatever he is able to cadge. He doesn't fawn, and he is never grateful. If he is turned down politely, he shrugs his shoulders and leaves the place. However, if the prospect passes a remark like "Get out of here, you bum," Gould turns on him, no matter how big he is, and gives him a shrill, nasal, scurrilous tongue-lashing. He doesn't care what he says. When he loses his temper, he becomes fearless. He will drop his portfolio, put up his fists, and offer to fight men who could kill him with one halfhearted blow. If he doesn't find an audience on the trip up Sixth, he turns west on Eleventh and heads for the Village Vanguard, in a cellar on Seventh Avenue South. The Vanguard was once a sleazy rendezvous for arty people, but currently it is a thriving night club. Gould and the proprietor, a man named Max Gordon, have known each other for many years and are on fairly good terms much of the time. Gould always hits the Vanguard last. He is sure of it, and he keeps it in reserve. Since it became prosperous, the place annoys him. He goes down the stairs and says, "Hello, Max, you dirty capitalist. I want a bite to eat and a beer. If I don't get it, I'll walk right out on the dance floor and throw a fit." "Go argue with the cook," Gordon tells him. Gould goes into the kitchen, eats whatever the cook gives him, drinks a couple of beers, fills a bag with bread crumbs, and departs.

Despite his shyness, Gould has a great fondness for parties. There are many people in the Village who give big parties fairly often. Among them are a rich and idiosyncratic old doctor, a rich old spinster, a famous stage designer, a famous theatrical couple, and numbers of painters and sculptors and writers and editors and publishers. As often as not, when Gould finds out that any of these people are giving a party, he goes, and as often as not he is allowed to stay. Usually he keeps to himself for a while, uneasily smoking one cigarette after another and stiff as a board with tenseness. Sooner or later, however, impelled by a drink or two and by the

desperation of the ill at ease, he begins to throw his weight around. He picks out the prettiest woman in the room, goes over, bows, and kisses her hand. He tells discreditable stories about himself. He becomes exuberant; suddenly, for no reason at all, he cackles with pleasure and jumps up and clicks his heels together. Presently he shouts, "All in favor of a one-man floor show, please say 'Aye'!" If he gets the slightest encouragement, he strips to the waist and does a hand-clapping, foot-stamping dance which he says he learned on a Chippewa reservation in North Dakota and which he calls the Joseph Ferdinand Gould Stomp. While dancing, he chants an old Salvation Army song, "There Are Flies on Me, There Are Flies on You, but There Are No Flies on Jesus." Then he imitates a sea gull. He pulls off his shoes and socks and takes awkward, headlong skips about the room, flapping his arms and letting out a piercing caw with every skip. As a child he had several pet gulls, and he still spends many Sundays on the end of a fishing pier at Sheepshead Bay observing gulls; he claims he has such a thorough understanding of their cawing that he can translate poetry into it. "I have translated a number of Henry Wadsworth Longfellow's poems into sea gull," he says.

Inevitably, at every party Gould goes to, he gets up on a chair or a table and delivers some lectures. These lectures are extracts from chapters of the Oral History. They are brief, but he gives them lengthy titles, such as "Drunk as a Skunk, or How I Measured the Heads of Fifteen Hundred Indians in Zero Weather" and "The Dread Tomato Habit, or Watch Out! Watch Out! Down with Dr. Gallup!" He is skeptical about statistics. In the latter lecture, using statistics he claims he found in financial sections in newspapers, he proves that "the eating of tomatoes by railroad engineers was responsible for fifty-three per cent of the train wrecks in the United States during the last seven years." When Gould arrives at a party, people who have never seen him before usually take one look at him and edge away. Before the evening is over, however, a few of them almost always develop a kind of puzzled respect for him;

they get him in a corner, ask him questions, and try to determine what is wrong with him. Gould enjoys this. "When you came over and kissed my hand," a young woman told him one night, "I said to myself, 'What a nice old gentleman.' A minute later I looked around and you were bouncing up and down with your shirt off, imitating a wild Indian. I was shocked. Why do you have to be such an exhibitionist?" "Madam," Gould said, "it is the duty of the bohemian to make a spectacle of himself. If my informality leads you to believe that I'm a rum-dumb, or that I belong in Bellevue, hold fast to that belief, hold fast, hold fast, and show your ignorance."

Gould is a native of Norwood, Massachusetts, a suburb of Boston. He comes from a family of physicians. His grandfather, Joseph Ferdinand Gould, for whom he was named, taught in the Harvard Medical School and had a practice in Boston. His father, Clarke Storer Gould, was a general practitioner in Norwood. He served as a captain in the Army Medical Corps and died of blood poisoning in a camp in Ohio during the first World War. The family was well-to-do until Gould was about grown, when his father invested unwisely in the stock of an Alaska land company. Gould says he went to Harvard only because it was a family custom. "I did not want to go," he wrote in one of his autobiographical essays. "It had been my plan to stay home and sit in a rocking chair on the back porch and brood." He says that he was an undistinguished student. Some of his classmates were Conrad Aiken, the poet; Howard Lindsay, the playwright and actor; Gluyas Williams, the cartoonist; and Richard F. Whitney, former president of the New York Stock Exchange. His best friends were three foreign students — a Chinese, a Siamese, and an Albanian.

Gould's mother had always taken it for granted that he would become a physician, but after getting his A.B. he told her he was through with formal education. She asked him what he intended to do. "I intend to stroll and ponder," he said. He passed most of the next three years strolling and pondering on the ranch of an uncle in Canada. In 1913, in an Albanian restaurant in Boston named the Scanderbeg, whose coffee he liked, he became acquainted with Theofan S. Noli, an archimandrite of the Albanian Orthodox Church, who interested him in Balkan politics. In February, 1914, Gould startled his family by announcing that he planned to devote the rest of his life to collecting funds to free Albania. He founded an organization in Boston called the Friends of Albanian Independence, enrolled a score or so of dues-paying members, and began telegraphing and calling on bewildered newspaper editors in Boston and New York City, trying to persuade them to print long treatises on Albanian affairs written by Noli. After about eight months of this, Gould was sitting in the Scanderbeg one night, drinking coffee and listening to a group of Albanian factory workers argue in their native tongue about Balkan politics, when he suddenly came to the conclusion that he was about to have a nervous breakdown. "I began to twitch uncontrollably and see double," he says. From that night on his interest in Albania slackened.

After another period of strolling and pondering, Gould took up eugenics. He has forgotten exactly how this came about. In any case, he spent the summer of 1915 as a student in eugenical field work at the Eugenics Record Office at Cold Spring Harbor, Long Island. This organization, endowed by the Carnegie Institution, was engaged at that time in making studies of families of hereditary defectives, paupers, and town nuisances in several highly inbred communities. Such people were too prosaic for Gould; he decided to specialize in Indians. That winter he went out to North Dakota and measured the heads of a thousand Chippewas on the Turtle Mountain Reservation and of five hundred Mandans on the Fort Berthold Reservation. Nowadays, when Gould is asked why he took these measurements, he changes the subject, saying, "The whole matter is a deep scientific secret." He was happy in North Dakota. "It was the most rewarding period of my life," he says. "I'm a good horseman, if I do say so myself, and I like to dance and whoop, and the Indians seemed to enjoy having me around. I was afraid they'd think I was batty when I asked for permission to measure their noggins, but they didn't mind. It seemed to amuse them. Indians are the only true aristocrats I've ever known. They ought to run the country, and we ought to be put on the reservations." After seven months of reservation life, Gould ran out of money. He returned to Massachusetts and tried vainly to get funds for another head-measuring expedition. "At this juncture in my life," he says, "I decided to engage in literary work." He came to New York City and got a job as assistant Police Headquarters reporter for the *Evening Mail.* One morning in the summer of 1917, after he had been a reporter for about a year, he was basking in the sun on the back steps of Headquarters, trying to overcome a hangover, when the idea for the Oral History blossomed in his mind. He promptly quit his job and began writing. "Since that fateful morning," he once said, in a moment of exaltation, "the Oral History has been my rope and my scaffold, my bed and my board, my wife and my floozy, my wound and the salt on it, my whiskey and my aspirin, and my rock and my salvation. It is the only thing that matters a damn to me. All else is dross."

Gould says that he rarely has more than a dollar at any one time, and that he doesn't particularly care. "As a rule," he says, "I despise money." However, there is a widely held belief in the Village that he is rich and that he receives an income from inherited property in New England. "Only an old millionaire could afford to go around as shabby as you," a bartender told him recently. "You're one of those fellows that die in doorways and when the cops search them their pockets are just busting with bankbooks. If you wanted to, I bet you could step over to the West Side Savings Bank right this minute and draw out twenty thousand dollars." After the death of his mother in 1939, Gould did come into some money. Close friends of his say that it was less than a thousand dollars and that he spent it in less than a month, wildly buying drinks all over the Village for people he had never seen before. "He seemed miserable with money in his pockets," Gordon, the proprietor of the Vanguard, says. "When

it was all gone, it seemed to take a load off his mind." While Gould was spending his inheritance, he did one thing that satisfied him deeply. He bought a big, shiny radio and took it out on Sixth Avenue and kicked it to pieces. He has never cared for the radio. "Five minutes of the idiot's babble that comes out of those machines," he says, "would turn the stomach of a goat."

During the twenties and the early thirties Gould occasionally interrupted his work on the Oral History to pose for classes at the Art Students' League and to do book-reviewing for newspapers and magazines. He says there were periods when he lived comfortably on the money he earned this way. Burton Rascoe, literary editor of the old *Tribune,* gave him a lot of work. In an entry in "A Bookman's Daybook," which is a diary of happenings in the New York literary world in the twenties, Rascoe told of an experience with Gould. "I once gave him a small book about the American Indians to review," Rascoe wrote, "and he brought me back enough manuscript to fill three complete editions of the Sunday *Tribune.* I especially honor him because, unlike most reviewers, he has never dogged me with inquiries as to why I never run it. He had his say, which was considerable, about the book, the author, and the subject, and there for him the matter ended." Gould says that he quit book-reviewing because he felt that it was beneath his dignity to compete with machines. "The Sunday *Times* and the Sunday *Herald Tribune* have machines that review books," he says. "You put a book in one of those machines and jerk down a couple of levers and a review drops out." In recent years Gould has got along on less than five dollars in actual money a week. He has a number of friends— Malcolm Cowley, the writer and editor; Aaron Siskind, the documentary photographer; Cummings, the poet; and Gordon, the night-club proprietor, are a few— who give him small sums of money regularly. No matter what they think of the Oral History, all these people have great respect for Gould's pertinacity.

Gould has a poor opinion of most of the writers and poets and painters and sculptors in the Village, and doesn't mind saying so. Because of his outspokenness he has never been allowed to join any of the art, writing, cultural, or ism organizations. He has been trying for ten years to join the Raven Poetry Circle, which puts on the poetry exhibition in Washington Square each summer and is the most powerful organization of its kind in the Village, but he has been blackballed every time. The head of the Ravens is a retired New York Telephone Company employee named Francis Lambert McCrudden. For many years Mr. McCrudden was a collector of coins from coin telephones for the telephone company. He is a self-educated man and very idealistic. His favorite theme is the dignity of labor, and his major work is an autobiographical poem called "The Nickel Snatcher." "We let Mr. Gould attend our readings, and I wish we could let him join, but we simply can't, Mr. McCrudden once said. "He isn't serious about poetry. We serve wine at our readings, and that is the only reason he attends. He sometimes insists on reading foolish poems of his own, and it gets on your nerves. At our Religious Poetry Night he demanded permission to recite a poem he had written entitled "My Religion.' I told him to go ahead, and this is what he recited:

'In winter I'm a Buddhist,
And in summer I'm a nudist.'

And at our Nature Poetry Night he begged to recite a poem of his entitled 'The Sea Gull.' I gave him permission, and he jumped out of his chair and began to wave his arms and leap about and scream, 'Scree-eek! Scree-eek! Scree-eek!' It was upsetting. We are serious poets and we don't approve of that sort of behavior." In the summer of 1942 Gould picketed the Raven exhibition, which was held on the fence of a tennis court on Washington Square South. In one hand he carried his portfolio and in the other he held a placard on which he had printed: "JOSEPH FERDINAND GOULD, HOT-SHOT POET FROM POETVILLE, A REFUGEE FROM THE RAVENS. POETS OF THE WORLD, IGNITE! YOU HAVE NOTHING TO LOSE BUT YOUR BRAINS!" Now and then, as he strutted back and forth, he would take a leap and then a skip and say to passers-by, "Would you like to hear what Joe Gould thinks of the world and all that's in it? Scree-eek! Scree-eek! Scree-eek!"

GETTING IT TOGETHER

"Getting It Together" attempts to do just
that with things as they are *circa* 1972.
Here are the points of view of some who
have presumed to take the measure of a
specific city as an entity, a total
experience. Once again, our selections
concern themselves with excesses,
hopefully with the trace of an occasional
smile. The descent from the stylistic high
of the Chamber of Commerce brochure to
the low cut of Mailer's scalpel should
provide a bracing verbal experience.

PART THREE

Miami Beach— Limitless Sightseeing

Ever see an oil palm or a monkey puzzle tree? Ever lure a brilliant red and gold macaw from a gumbo limbo to your arm to take a peanut? Ever see bottle-nosed dolphins bowling? Ever watch a jewel fish, clothed in deep blue with silver stars nibble on marine algae?

If such sightseeing is appealing take the family to Miami Beach where hotel rates and apartment rentals are at their summer bargain levels; the unique and the familiar on every hand.

Motoring vacationers have almost limitless sightseeing within an easy one-day round-trip drive of this seaside city. Those who arrive by air, rail and bus can rent a car for their holidays or take tour buses to most of the major attractions.

BUS TOURS   Half-day bus tours range from $4 to $6, including admission to the attraction at destination. An all-day trip to the Everglades National Park, including lunch, is $9.

Admission prices at the various popular sightseeing spots range from $1 to $2.50, with children usually charged about half the adult tariff. Many points of interest are free, including the Miami Beach

Photograph by DeFrancis.

Garden Center with its display of orchids and many exotic plants, the Miami Beach Bass Museum of Art, and the county-operated zoo. Entry to the Everglades park is $1 per automobile, one or more passengers.

Municipal recreation areas in Miami Beach are the familiar golf courses and sandy beaches of any coastal city, except here an hibiscus may stymie an errant drive and coconut palms grow beside the sea.

The oil palms, monkey puzzle trees and scores of other trees, shrubs and vines from all parts of the tropical world may be seen in Fairchild Garden. The garden, amid broad acres on the mainland shore of Biscayne bay, can be reached in less than an hour, and boasts the largest collection of palms in the Western hemisphere.

DOLPHINS DO TRICKS   The bottle-nosed dolphin, or porpoise if you prefer, bowl, jump through hoops and perform other tricks at the Seaquarium. There, too, if you rather not go skin or scuba diving, one can see the colorful and bizarre fishes of these waters, displayed in tanks.

The bird show is at the Parrot

Jungle, with its macaws flying freely among the trees. At the Monkey Jungle it is of course monkeys, also jumping by free among the trees but visitors walk through net-covered paths. The monkeys can't be trusted not to nip if provoked. At the Serpentarium one watches cobras and other snakes being "milked" of their venom. This is not an audience-participation show.

Skin and scuba diving parties can be arranged on boats leaving Miami Beach or at Pennekamp Coral Reef park, a comfortable two-hour drive. Choose a clear and calm day for this. A drive through the tropical fruit growing area 25 miles south of Miami Beach on the mainland is of interest, especially during summer when the mangos are ripening and can be bought at roadside stands.

There are of course many other activities for the visitor. Horse and greyhound racing, golf, tennis, the night clubs, swimming, fishing, sailing and a special free program for young people that includes contemporary music and sports events starting in late June.

Miami Beach was the scene of the 1968 Republican Convention, at which Richard Nixon was nominated for the presidency by his party. Here, Norman Mailer makes the city of Miami Beach function metaphorically for all the strange contradictions and confusions which, for him, symbolized the Republicans and, in fact, all Americans.

FROM

Miami and the Siege of Chicago
NORMAN MAILER

MIAMI BEACH

They snipped the ribbon in 1915, they popped the cork, Miami Beach was born. A modest burg they called a city, nine-tenths jungle. An island. It ran along a coastal barrier the other side of Biscayne Bay from young Miami—in 1868 when Henry Lum, a California 'forty-niner, first glimpsed the island from a schooner, you may be certain it was jungle, cocoanut palms on the sand, mangrove swamp and palmetto thicket ten feet off the beach. But by 1915, they were working the vein. John S. Collins, a New Jersey nurseryman (after whom Collins Avenue is kindly named) brought in bean fields and avocado groves; a gent named Fisher, Carl G., a Hoosier— he invented Prestolite, a millionaire— bought up acres from Collins, brought in a work-load of machinery, men, even two elephants, and jungle was cleared, swamps were filled, small residential islands were made out of baybottom mud, dredged, then relocated, somewhat larger natural islands adjacent to the barrier island found themselves improved, streets were paved, sidewalks put in with other amenities—by 1968, one hundred years after Lum first glommed the beach, large areas of the original coastal strip were covered over altogether with macadam, white condominium, white luxury hotel and white stucco flea-bag. Over hundreds, then thousands of acres, white sidewalks, streets and white buildings covered the earth where the jungle had been. Is it so dissimilar from covering your poor pubic hair with adhesive tape for fifty years? The vegetal memories of that excised jungle haunted Miami Beach in a steam-pot of miasmas. Ghosts of expunged flora, the never-born groaning in vegetative chancery beneath the asphalt came up with a tropical curse, an equatorial leaden wet sweat of air which rose from the earth itself, rose right up through the baked asphalt and into the heated air which entered the lungs like a hand slipping into a rubber glove.

The temperature was not that insane. It hung around 87 day after day, at night it went down to 82, back to the same 87 in the A.M.—the claims of the News Bureau for Miami Beach promised that in 1967 temperature exceeded 90° only four times. (Which the Island of Manhattan could never begin to say.) But of course Miami Beach did not have to go that high, for its humidity was up to 87 as well—it was, on any and every day of the Republican Convention of 1968, one of the hottest cities in the world. The reporter was no expert on tropical heats—he had had, he would admit, the island of Luzon for a summer in World War II; and basic training in the pine woods of Fort Bragg, North Carolina, in August; he had put in a week at Las Vegas during July—temperatures to 110; he had crossed the Mojave Desert once by day; he was familiar with the New York subway in the rush hour on the hottest day of the year. These were awesome immersions—one did not have to hit the Congo to know what it was like in a hothouse in hell—but that 87° in Miami Beach day after day held up in competition against other sulphuric encounters. Traveling for five miles up the broken-down, forever in-a-state-of-alteration and repair of Collins Avenue, crawling through 5 P.M. Miami Beach traffic in the pure miserable fortune of catching an old taxi without air conditioning, dressed in shirt and tie and jacket—formal and implicitly demanded uniform of political journalists—the sensation of breathing, then living, was not unlike being obliged to make love to a 300-pound woman who has decided to get on top. Got it? You could not dominate a thing. That uprooted jungle had to be screaming beneath.

Of course it could have been the air conditioning: natural climate transmogrified by technological climate.

They say that in Miami Beach the air conditioning is pushed to that icy point where women may wear fur coats over their diamonds in the tropics. For ten miles, from the Diplomat to the Di Lido, above Hallandale Beach Boulevard down to Lincoln Mall, all the white refrigerators stood, piles of white refrigerators six and eight and twelve stories high, twenty stories high, shaped like sugar cubes and ice-cube trays on edge, like mosques and palaces, shaped like matched white luggage and portable radios, stereos, plastic compacts and plastic rings, Moorish castles shaped like waffle irons, shaped like the baffle plates on white plastic electric heaters, and cylinders like Waring blenders, buildings looking like giant op art and pop art paintings, and sweet wedding cakes, cottons of kitsch and piles of dirty cotton stucco, yes, for ten miles the hotels for the delegates stood on the beach side of Collins Avenue: the Eden Roc and the Fontainebleau (Press Headquarters), the Di Lido and the De Lano, the Ivanhoe, Deauville, Sherry Frontenac and the Monte Carlo, the Cadillac, Caribbean and the Balmoral, the Lucerne, Hilton Plaza, Doral Beach, the Sorrento, Marco Polo, Casablanca, and Atlantis, the Hilyard Manor, Sans Souci, Algiers, Carillon, Seville, the Gaylord, the Shore Club, the Nautilus, Montmartre, and the Promenade, the Bal Harbour on North Bay Causeway, and the Twelve Caesars, the Regency and the Americana, the Diplomat, Versailles, Coronado, Sovereign, the Waldman (dig!), the Beau Rivage, the Crown Hotel, even Holiday Inn, all oases for technological man. Deep air conditioning down to 68°, ice-palaces to chill the fevered brain—when the air conditioning worked. And their furnishings were monumentally materialistic. Not all of them: the cheaper downtown hotels like the Di Lido and the Nautilus were bare and mean with vinyl coverings on the sofas and the glare of plastic off the rugs and tables and tiles, inexpensive hotel colors of pale brown and buff and dingy cream, sodden gray, but the diadems like the Fontainebleau and the Eden Roc, the Doral Beach, the Hilton Plaza (Headquarters for Nixon), the Deauville (Hq for Reagan) or the Americana —Rockefeller and the New York State

delegation's own ground—were lavish with interlockings, curves, vaults and runs of furnishings as intertwined as serpents in the roots of a mangrove tree. All the rivers of the very worst taste twisted down to the delta of each lobby in each grand Miami Beach hotel—rare was the central room which did not look like the lobby of a movie palace, imitation of late-Renaissance imitations of Greek and Roman statues, imitations of baroque and rococo and brothel Victorian and Art Nouveau and Bauhaus with gold grapes and cornucopias welded to the modern bronze tubing of the chair, golden moldings which ran like ivy from room to room, chandeliers complex as the armature of dynamos, and curvilinear steps in the shape of amoebas and palettes, cocktail lounge bars in deep rose or maroon with spun-sugar white tubes of plaster decor to twist around the ceiling. There was every color of iridescence, rainbows of vulgarity, aureoles of gorgeous taste, opium den of a middle-class dollar, materialistic as meat, sweat, and the cigar. It is said that people born under Taurus and Capricorn are the most materialistic of us all. Take a sample of the residents in the census of Miami B.— does Taurus predominate more than one-twelfth of its share? It must, or astrology is done, for the Republicans, Grand Old Party with a philosophy rather than a program, had chosen what must certainly be the materialistic capital of the world for their convention. Las Vegas might offer competition, but Las Vegas was materialism in the service of electricity— fortunes could be lost in the spark of the dice. Miami was materialism baking in the sun, then stepping back to air-conditioned caverns where ice could nestle in the fur. It was the first of a hundred curiosities—that in a year when the Republic hovered on the edge of revolution, nihilism, and lines of police on file to the horizon, visions of future Vietnams in our own cities upon us, the party of conservatism and principle, of corporate wealth and personal frugality, the party of cleanliness, hygiene, and balanced budget, should have set itself down on a sultan's strip.

Chicago is the second largest city in America and is beautiful or ugly and small-townish or sophisticated, depending upon your point of view—as the following two pieces indicate. The first selection comes from a pamphlet distributed to tourists by the Chicago Convention Bureau, Inc.

Chicago: Discover the Great Indoors

The best place for some people to get away from it all is right in the middle of it all.

Are you one of those people? Then Chicago is waiting for you. Sightseeing. Theatre. Sports. Shopping. Nightlife. Symphony. Museums. Elegant dining. The world's best everything.

A city of spectacular architecture unequaled anywhere in the world. With a 100-story John Hancock Center underscoring its heritage from Louis Henry Sullivan, Frank Lloyd Wright, Mies van der Rohe, Bertrand Goldberg, dozens of other master builders and designers.

Privacy if you want it. Relaxation if you need it. Celebration if you're ready for it. Come discover the great indoors. Just turn the page.

And find yourself in a crowd.

Don't spend all your time discovering the great indoors.

Get outside. Walk around. Look at things. It's okay, you're a visitor, remember?

Walk through Grant Park at night and see Buckingham Fountain change colors right before your eyes. Or hear a live concert at the band shell. Maybe sit by the lake for a while and watch the yachts. And the girls.

Stroll along the lake shore for a particularly scenic view.

Chicagoans love the outdoors. And on any summer day, you'll find the natives sunning along Oak Street Beach. Beautiful. Just beautiful. Bring your swim suit and join in.

Chicago is a city of lush parks and greenery. Unexpected little open plazas invite you to pause and admire the flowers. Trees grow on Michigan Avenue. Fall days sparkle with bright foliage. And in winter, it all turns into a frosty fairyland.

If you've never been close to a Picasso original, go straight to the plaza in front of the Civic Center. You'll see the world's tallest (about six stories) and most controversial work of art. Picasso's gift to Chicago. Bring your camera; they'll never believe this back home.

You'll find an international flavor in Chicago. The city revels in its melting-pot heritage. The Polish wear green on St. Patrick's Day and march in the parade. Chinatown restaurants serve authentic spaghetti. Something special's always going on. Pageants. Festivals. Folk dances. Have you ever watched a Frenchman dance the Polka? Come to Chicago.

Here's one city where you can go out for dinner and wind things up at breakfast. That's Chicago nightlife for you. Non stop.

As you may know, Chicago has long been the cultural center of mid-America. Here, you can attend the ballet. The opera. Legitimate theatre. The symphony. Or a puppet show.

Lincoln and Garfield Parks stay tropical year 'round. Indoors, of course—in the conservatories. Palm trees here are taller than Miami's. The Japanese gardens rival Tokyo's.

Here Norman Mailer looks at Chicago as a symbol of mid-America. The city was the site of the Democratic Convention of 1968 a short time after the Republican Convention in Miami Beach (see page 50).

FROM
Miami and the Siege of Chicago
NORMAN MAILER

CHICAGO

Chicago is the great American city. New York is one of the capitals of the world and Los Angeles is a constellation of plastic, San Francisco is a lady, Boston has become Urban Renewal, Philadelphia and Baltimore and Washington wink like dull diamonds in the smog of Eastern Megalopolis, and New Orleans is unremarkable past the French Quarter. Detroit is a one-trade town, Pittsburgh has lost its golden triangle, St. Louis has become the golden arch of the corporation, and nights in Kansas City close early. The oil depletion allowance makes Houston and Dallas naught but checkerboards for this sort of game. But Chicago is a great American city. Perhaps it is the last of the great American cities.

The reporter was sentimental about the town. Since he had grown up in Brooklyn, it took him no time to recognize, whenever he was in Chicago again, that the urbanites here were like the good people of Brooklyn —they were simple, strong, warm-spirited, sly, rough, compassionate, jostling, tricky and extraordinarily good-natured because they had sex in their pockets, muscles on their back, hot eats around the corner, neighborhoods which dripped with the sauce of local legend, and real city architecture, brownstones with different windows on every floor, vistas for miles of red-brick and two-family wood-frame houses with balconies and porches, runty stunted trees rich as farmland in their promise of tenderness the first city evenings of spring, streets where kids played stick-ball and roller-hockey, lots of smoke and iron twilight. The clangor of the late nineteenth century, the very hope of greed, was in these streets. London one hundred years ago could not have looked much better.

Brooklyn, however, beautiful Brooklyn, grew beneath the skyscrapers of Manhattan, so it never became a great city, merely an asphalt herbarium for talent destined to cross the river. Chicago did not have Manhattan to preempt top branches, so it grew up from the savory of its neighborhoods to some of the best high-rise architecture in the world, and because its people were Poles and Ukrainians and Czechs as well as Irish and the rest, the city had Byzantine corners worthy of Prague or Moscow, odd tortured attractive drawbridges over the Chicago River, huge Gothic spires like the skyscraper which held the Chicago *Tribune,* curves and abutments and balconies in cylindrical structures thirty stories high twisting in and out of the curves of the river, and fine balustrades in its parks. Chicago had a North Side on Lake Shore Drive where the most elegant apartment buildings in the world could be found—Sutton Place in New York betrayed the cost analyst in the eye of the architect next to these palaces of glass and charcoal colored steel. In superb back streets behind the towers on the lake were brownstones which spoke of ironies, cupidities and intricate ambition in the fists of the robber barons who commissioned them—substantiality, hard work, heavy drinking, carnal meats of pleasure, and a Midwestern sense of how to arrive at upper-class decorum were also in the American grandeur of these few streets. If there was a fine American aristocracy of deportment, it was probably in the clean tough keen-eyed ladies of Chicago one saw on the streets off Lake Shore Drive on the near North Side of Chicago.

Not here for a travelogue—no need then to detail the Loop, in death like the center of every other American city, but what a dying! Old department stores, old burlesque houses, avenues, dirty avenues, the El with its nineteenth-century dialogue of iron screeching against iron about a turn, and caverns of shadow on the pavement beneath, the grand hotels with their massive lobbies, baroque ceilings, resplendent as Roman bordellos, names like Sheraton-Blackstone, Palmer House, red fields of carpet, a golden cage for elevator, the unheard crash of giant mills stamping new shapes on large and obdurate materials is always pounding in one's inner ear—Dreiser had not written about Chicago for nothing.

To the West of the Lake were factories and Ciceros, Mafia-lands and immigrant lands; to the North, the suburbs, the Evanstons; to the South were Negro ghettos of the South Side—belts of Black men amplifying each the resonance of the other's cause—the Black belt had the Blackstone Rangers, the largest gang of juvenile delinquents on earth, 2,000 by some count—one could be certain the gang had leaders as large in potential as Hannibal or Attila the Hun—how else account for the strength and wit of a stud who would try to rise so high in the Blackstone Rangers?

Further South and West were enclaves for the University of Chicago, more factories, more neighborhoods for Poles, some measure of more good hotels on the lake, and endless neighborhoods—white neighborhoods which went for miles of ubiquitous dingy wood houses with back yards, neighborhoods to hint of Eastern Europe, Ireland, Tennessee, a gathering of all the clans of the Midwest, the Indians and Scotch-Irish, Swedes, some Germans, Italians, Hungarians, Rumanians, Finns, Slovaks, Slovenes—it was only the French who did not travel. In the Midwest, land spread out; not five miles from the Loop were areas as empty, deserted, enormous and mournful by night as the outer freight yards of Omaha. Some industrial desert or marsh would lie low on the horizon, an area squalling by day, deserted by night, except for the hulking Midwestern names of the boxcars and the low sheds, the warehouse buildings, the wire fences which went along the side of unpaved roads for thousands of yards.

The stockyards were like this, the famous stockyards of Chicago were at night as empty as the railroad sidings of the moon. Long before the Democratic Convention of 1968 came to the Chicago Amphitheatre,

indeed eighteen years ago when the reporter had paid his only previous visit, the area was even then deserted at night, empty as the mudholes on a battlefield after a war has passed. West of the Amphitheatre, railroad sidings seemed to continue on for miles, accompanied by those same massive low sheds larger than armories, with pens for tens of thousands of frantic beasts, cattle, sheep, and pigs, animals in an orgy of gorging and dropping and waiting and smelling blood. In the slaughterhouses, during the day, a carnage worthy of the Disasters of War took place each morning and afternoon. Endless files of animals were led through pens to be stunned on the head by hammers, and then hind legs trussed, be hoisted up on hooks to hang head down, and ride along head down on an overhead trolley which brought them to Negroes or whites, usually huge, the whites most often Polish or Hunkies (hence the etymology of Honkie—a Chicago word) the Negroes up from the South, huge men built for the shock of the work, slash of a knife on the neck of the beast and gouts of blood to bathe their torso (stripped of necessity to the waist) and blood to splash their legs. The animals passed a psychic current back along the overhead trolley—each cut throat released its scream of death into the throat not yet cut and just behind, and that penultimate throat would push the voltage up, drive the current back and further back into the screams of every animal upside down and hanging from that clanking overhead trolley, bare electric bulbs screaming into the animal eye and brain, gurglings and awesome hollows of sound coming back from the open plumbing ahead of the cut jugular as if death were indeed a rapids along some underground river, and the fear and absolute anguish of beasts dying upside down further ahead passed back along the line, back all the way to the corrals and the pens, back even to the siding with the animals still in boxcars, back, who knew—so high might be the psychic voltage of the beast—back to the farm where first they were pushed into the truck which would take them into the train. What an awful odor the fear of absolute and unavoidable death gave to the stool and stuffing and pure vomitous shit of the beasts waiting in the pens in the stockyard, what a sweat of hell-leather, and yet the odor, no, the titanic stench, which rose from the yards was not so simple as the collective diarrhetics of an hysterical army of beasts, no, for after the throats were cut and the blood ran in rich gutters, red light on the sweating back of the red throat-cutters, the dying and some just-dead animals clanked along the overhead, arterial blood spurting like the nip-ups of a little boy urinating in public, the red-hot carcass quickly encountered another Black or Hunkie with a long knife on a long stick who would cut the belly from chest to groin and a stew and a stink of two hundred pounds of stomach, lungs, intestines, mucosities, spleen, exploded cowflop and pigshit, blood, silver lining, liver, mother-of-pearl tissue, and general gag-all would flop and slither over the floor, the man with the knife getting a good blood-splatting as he dug and twisted with his blade to liberate the roots of the organ, intestine and impedimenta still integrated into the meat and bone of the excavated existence he was working on.

Well, the smell of the entrails and that agonized blood electrified by all the outer neons of ultimate fear got right into the grit of the stockyard stench. Let us pass over into the carving and the slicing, the boiling and scraping, annealing and curing of the flesh in sugars and honeys and smoke, the cooking of the cow carcass, stamp of the inspector, singeing of the hair, boiling of hooves, grinding of gristle, the wax-papering and the packaging, the foiling and the canning, the burning of the residue, and the last slobber of the last unusable guts as it went into the stockyard furnace, and up as stockyard smoke, burnt blood and burnt bone and burnt hair to add their properties of specific stench to fresh blood, fresh entrails, fresh fecalities already all over the air. It is the smell of the stockyards, all of it taken together, a smell so bad one must go down to visit the killing of the animals or never eat meat again. Watching the animals be slaughtered, one knows the human case—no matter how close to angel we may come, the butcher is equally there. So be it. Chicago makes for hard

minds. On any given night, the smell may go anywhere—down to Gary to fight with the smog and the coke, out to Cicero to quiet the gangs with their dreams of gung ho and mop-up, North to Evanston to remind the polite that *inter faeces et urinam* are we born, and East on out to Lake Michigan where the super felicities in the stench of such earth-bound miseries and corruptions might cheer the fish with the clean spermy deep waters of their fate.

Yes, Chicago was a town where nobody could ever forget how the money was made. It was picked up from floors still slippery with blood, and if one did not protest and take a vow of vegetables, one knew at least that life was hard, life was in the flesh and in the massacre of the flesh —one breathed the last agonies of beasts. So something of the entrails and the secrets of the gut got into the faces of native Chicagoans. A great city, a strong city with faces tough as leather hide and pavement, it was also a city where the faces took on the broad beastiness of ears which were dull enough to ignore the bleatings of the doomed, noses battered enough to smell no more the stench of every unhappy end, mouths—fat mouths or slit mouths—ready to taste the gravies which were the reward of every massacre, and eyes, simple pig eyes, which could look the pig truth in the face. In any other city, they would have found technologies to silence the beasts with needles, quarter them with machines, lull them with Muzak, and have stainless steel for floors, aluminum beds to take over the old overhead trolley—animals would be given a shot of vitamin-enrichment before they took the last ride. But in Chicago, they did it straight, they cut the animals right out of their hearts —which is why it was the last of the great American cities, and people had great faces, carnal as blood, greedy, direct, too impatient for hypocrisy, in love with honest plunder. They were big and human and their brother in heaven was the slaughtered pig—they did not ignore him. If the yowls and moans of his extinction was the broth of their strength, still they had honest guts to smell him to the end—they did not flush the city with Odorono or Pinex or No-Scent, they swilled the beer and assigned the hits and gave America its last chance at straight-out drama. Only a great city provides honest spectacle, for that is the salvation of the schizophrenic soul. Chicago may have beasts on the street, it may have a giant of fortitude for Mayor who grew into a beast—a man with the very face of Chicago—but it is an honest town, it does not look to incubate psychotics along an air-conditioned corridor with a vinyl floor.

Brooklyn: The Sane Alternative
PETE HAMILL

From an old Brooklyn street, the spires of Manhattan are like a vision of "some strange, exotic city across the river."

One cold spring I found myself alone in Rome, in a small room high up over Parioli, trying to write. The words came thickly, sluggishly, and none of them were any good. I quit for the day. For a while I read day-old copies of *Paese Sera,* the Communist daily, and the Paris *Herald,* and then, bored, I turned on the radio, lay down on the lumpy couch, and, half-listening, stared out at the empty sky. The music was the usual raucous Italian stew, mixed with screaming commercials, and I fell into a heavy doze. Then, suddenly, absurdly, I came awake, as an old song started to play. *She kicked out my windshield. She hit me over the head. She cussed and cried. And said I'd lied. And wished that I was dead. Oh! Lay that pistol down, Babe. .* It was "Pistol Packin' Mama," by Tex Ritter, and how it came to be played that afternoon, 20 years after Anzio, I'll never know. But I did not think about the hard young men of that old beachhead, or about their war, or even about cowboys in flight from homicidal girlfriends. I thought about Brooklyn.

When I was a kid growing up in Brooklyn, "Pistol Packin' Mama" was the first record we ever owned. My brother Tommy and I bought it for a dime in a secondhand book-and-record shop on Pearl Street under the Myrtle Avenue El, and we played it until the grooves were gone. The week before we bought it, my mother had arrived home with an old-wine-colored hand-cranked Victrola, complete with picture of faithful dog and master's voice, and a packet of nail-like needles. It was given the place of honor in the living room, in the old top-floor right at 378 Seventh Avenue; that is, it was placed on top of the kerosene stove for the duration of the summer, and it was almost as heavy as the five-gallon drums we hauled home in the winter snow to feed the stove (steam heat, then, was a luxury assigned to the Irish with property). We thought that phonograph was a bloody marvel.

The purchase of "Pistol Packin' Mama" was something else again. We did not really lust after hymns of violence; we weren't country-and-western buffs (we always preferred Charles Starrett, the Durango Kid, who was all business, to the saps like Roy Rogers and Gene Autry, who played banjo as they rode after outlaws). It was something more complicated. We bought "Pistol Packin' Mama" because it was the first hard, solid evidence we had until then about the existence of the world outside Brooklyn.

We studied geography in school, of course, with all those roll-down maps of the world, those dull figures about copra production, the uses of sisal and, of course, the location of the Holy Land. But Brooklyn was not on those maps. *New York* was, but to us, New York was some strange, exotic city across the river, where there were people who rooted for the Giants and the Yankees. Brooklyn was not there. Even Battle Creek, Michigan, where we sent a hundred Kellogg boxtops, was on the map. Brooklyn was not. The people who secretly ruled the earth did not recognize us, and we did not really recognize them. So to own a copy of that awful record was like establishing diplomatic relations with the rest of the world; "Pistol Packin' Mama" had been a *hit*—broadcast from a million radios—and for Tommy and me to have a copy of it, to hold it in our hands, to turn it over (the flip side was something that went "Rosalita, you are the rose of the baaaanjo!"), to be able to play it at our leisure and not wait to hear it at the whim

of those people who secretly ruled the earth
— that was breaking out.

Lying on that couch in Rome, I had
already learned that you never break out of
anything, that it was ludicrous to think that
you could solve anything by setting out on
journeys. The last time I had gone there,
Brooklyn had seemed shabby and worn-
out: not just in the neighborhood where I
grew up, but everywhere. There was
something special, almost private, about
being from Brooklyn when I was growing
up: a sense of community, a sense of being
home. But I hadn't lived there for a long
time, and when I did go it seemed always
for a disaster: to see the corpses of men,
baked by the heat, being carried out of the
Constellation as it burned in the snow at the
Navy Yard; to visit, like a ghoul, the
mothers of dead soldiers; to cover the latest
hostilities between the Gallo and Profaci
mobs; to talk with the father of an eight-
year-old boy who had pushed a girl off a
roof in Williamsburg. Only the dead know
Brooklyn, Thomas Wolfe had written. For a
while it seemed that way. The place had
come unraveled, like the spring of a clock
dropped from a high floor. Nevertheless,
that night in Rome I started getting ready
to go home.

The Brooklyn I came home to has
changed. For the first time in 10 years, it
seems to have come together. In Park
Slope, people like David Levine, Jeremy
Larner, Joe Flaherty, Sol Yurick have
moved into the splendid old brownstones;
the streets seem a bit cleaner; on some
streets, citizens are actually planting
trees again, with money they have raised
themselves through block associations
and block parties. Art galleries are opening.
Neighborhoods like Bay Ridge and South
Brooklyn now have boutiques and head
shops. People who have been driven out of
the Village and Brooklyn Heights by the
greed of real-estate operators are learning
that it is not yet necessary to decamp for
Red Bank or Garden City. It is still
possible in Park Slope, for example, to rent
a duplex with a garden for $200 a month,
a half-block from the subway; still possible
to buy a brownstone in reasonably good
condition for $30,000, with a number of

fairly good houses available for less, if you
are willing to invest in reconditioning them.
Hundreds of people are discovering that
Brooklyn has become the Sane Alternative:
a part of New York where you can live a
decent urban life without going broke,
where you can educate your children
without having the income of an Onassis,
a place where it is still possible to see the
sky, and all of it only 15 minutes from Wall
Street. The Sane Alternative is Brooklyn.

Impressions can be backed up by any
number of statistics. Today, Brooklyn is the
fourth-largest city in the United States.
It has more people than 26 states, contains
one out of every 65 people born in this
country. For 30 years there have been jokes
about the tree that grew in Brooklyn; in fact,
the borough contains 235,000 trees, which
is a hell of a lot more than you will find in
the high-rise ghettos of the Upper East Side.
Brooklyn's purchasing power in 1968 rose
to $6,600,000,000, up $347,000,000 over
the previous year. In 1967, wholesale and
retail trade in the borough amounted to
$5,400,000,000; there was a payroll of
$2,400,000,000 for 704,800 jobholders.
In a study called "The Next Twenty Years,"
the New York Port Authority predicts a 7.7
per cent growth in jobs by 1985, while
population will grow at only 2 per cent.
According to a 1965 Dun and Bradstreet
report, Brooklyn is now the nation's fourth-
largest industrial county, third-largest food
consumer, and fourth-largest user of goods
and services. The median income ($5,816)
is still $175 less than that in Manhattan;
but the median age of the 2,627,420
citizens is 33.5, lower than New York City's
as a whole (35) and lower than the median
(34) in the metropolitan region that includes
Westchester, Rockland, Nassau and
Suffolk Counties.

But no set of statistics can adequately
explain what has happened to Brooklyn in
the years since the end of the Second World
War. They don't explain its decline. They
don't explain its renaissance.

For me, Brooklyn is the great proof of the
theory that many of the problems of the
American city are emotional. If you were
born in Brooklyn, as I was, you learned
something about this quite early. Through

most of its early history, Brooklyn was really a kind of bucolic suburb, dedicated to middle-class values, solid and phlegmatic. Its citizens owned small farms. They opened small manufacturing plants, especially on the Manhattan side of Prospect Park, which is the section of Brooklyn that today most resembles the dark industrial image of the 19th century. When the subways pushed out past Prospect Park into Flatbush and beyond, Brooklyn became the bedroom for the middle class. Its first period of shock and decline came after the 1898 Mistake, when the five boroughs were united into Greater New York under the supposedly benevolent dictatorship of Manhattan. Until then, if we are to believe old newspapers, Brooklynites were proud and industrious citizens who planted their own trees, who gloried in their independence. Most of them opposed the 1898 Mistake; but the deal was pushed through the State Legislature by the Republicans, who thought that the large number of Republicans in Brooklyn would help them wrest control of the entire city from Tammany Hall. (In those days, of course, Republicans were in the tradition of Lincoln, not Goldwater and Thurmond.)

After the 1898 Mistake, some sections of Brooklyn started to change radically. In the 19th-century part of town, the poor Irish and the poor Italians started moving in; they filled the old-law cold-water-flat tenements; they ran speakeasies during Prohibition; some of them learned how to make money with murder. The poor Jews moved into Williamsburg and Brownsville, where they also learned something about the rackets. The respectable people, as they thought of themselves, fled to Flatbush and Bensonhurst and even out into the wilds of Flatlands. But there was a long period of stability that almost lasted through the Second World War.

The first cracks in that stability showed up during the war, when a lot of fathers were away fighting and a lot of mothers were working in war plants. Some Brooklynites had been shocked at the revelation about Murder, Incorporated, the brutal Brooklyn-based Jewish-Italian mob whose members killed for money. But when the teenage gangs started roving Brooklyn

during the war, then some citizens thought the end was near (you could abide Murder, Inc., of course, if your other institutions — family, church, jobs — remained stable). In Bedford-Stuyvesant, the first black gangs, the Bishops and the Robins, began to assemble down on Sands Street; the Navy Yard Boys were already rolling sailors and shipyard workers; the Red Hook Boys came out of the first projects and the side streets around the Gowanus Canal; the Garfield Boys, from Garfield Place in South Brooklyn, expanded into the South Brooklyn Boys, and became the training ground for many of the soldiers who are now in the Brooklyn chapters of the Mafia. In my neighborhood, the Shamrock Boys became the Tigers, and they fought the South Brooklyn Boys with an expertise in urban guerrilla warfare (on both sides) that the Black Panthers would be advised to study. I don't know if there ever really was a gang called the Amboy Dukes (I am told by buffs that there was), but Irving Shulman's *The Amboy Dukes* became the bible for a lot of these kids; they studied the sayings of Crazy Shack the way the motorcycle gangs later studied Lee Marvin and Brando in *The Wild One.*

The gangs were wild, often brutal; there were more than a few knifings and gang rapes, and a number of killings, especially after the war, when veterans started bringing home guns as souvenirs; in shop classes in the high schools, students spent more time making zip guns out of pieces of pipe than they did making bookcases or pieces of sinks. The gun — especially if it was a *real* gun — became a thing of awe. The first time I ever saw Joe Gallo (they called him Joe the Blond in those days) he was in the Ace Pool Room upstairs from his father's luncheonette on Church Avenue; someone, I think it was an old friend named Johnny Rose, whispered to me, "Don't ever say nuthin' about him: he's *packin'*."

The gangs started breaking up in the '50s. First, the Korean War took most of the survivors away, all of those kids who had been too young for the Second World War. By the time they came home they were sick of fighting; they married, and some of them moved away. But while they were gone, something else had arrived in Brooklyn: drugs. What the Youth Board and the cops had not been able to do, heroin did. More of them died from O.D.'s than ever died in the gang wars. Prison took a lot of them, and for some odd reason, the ones who had managed to escape arrests and habits became cops. Only two really new gangs started in the '50s: the Jokers and a gang from my neighborhood which called itself Skid Row. The Jokers lost a lot of members to drugs, and a few of them were involved in a brutal stomp-killing. I still see some of the Skid Row kids around. My brother Tommy was a member for a while; by the time he was in CCNY, three of the gang were already dead from heroin.

The whole terrible period of the gangs, followed by the introduction of heroin, changed a lot of citizens' attitudes about Brooklyn. Those who had escaped the Lower East Side now started talking about escaping Brooklyn. Events seemed to have moved beyond their control. You could do the best you were capable of doing: work hard, hold two jobs, get bigger and better television sets for the living room, watch steam heat replace kerosene stoves, see the old coal stoves in the kitchens dragged out to be replaced by modern gas ovens, and still people in their teens were found dead in the shrubs of Prospect Park, their arms as scarred as school desks. "We gotta get outa Brooklyn." You heard it over and over in those days. It wasn't a matter of moving from one neighborhood to the next; the transportation system was too good for all that; it was out "to the island" or to California or Rockland County. The idea was to get out.

Leaving was made easier by four central factors in the period of postwar decline in Brooklyn. All, in their special ways, were emotional. The four factors: 1) the folding of the *Brooklyn Eagle;* 2) the departure of the Brooklyn Dodgers for California; 3) the long years of insecurity and the final folding of the Brooklyn Navy Yard; 4) the migration of southern Negroes, most of whom settled in Brooklyn, not Manhattan.

The *Eagle* was not the greatest newspaper in New York in its day; there were after all, eight others (the *Times, Herald Tribune, News, Mirror, World-*

Telegram, Post, Journal-American, and the *Sun)* and for years Brooklyn had two other papers—the *Citizen* and the *Times-Union.* But the *Eagle* was a pretty good paper for what it was attempting to do, and all it ever really attempted was to cover Brooklyn. I used to deliver it after school, which is why one shoulder is lower than the other, but along with a lot of other people I used to read it. I don't have the slightest idea what its editorial policies were, though I imagine they were conservative, since its owner eventually folded it up instead of submitting to the Newspaper Guild. I used to read the comics and the sports pages and odd features like Uncle Ray's Corner, which was all about the lifestyle of the mongoose, and other matters. The best comic strips were *Invisible Scarlet O'Neil,* who had some kind of special vein in her arm which she pressed to become invisible, and *Steve Roper,* which was about a magazine reporter. Of the sportswriters, I only remember Harold C. Burr, who had a gnarled face pasted above his column and looked something like Burt Shotton, who was interim Pope of the Dodgers while Leo Durocher sat out a suspension, and Tommy Holmes, who joined the staff of the *Herald Tribune* after the *Eagle* folded.

But even though the *Eagle* was not a great paper, it had a great function; it helped to weld together an extremely heterogeneous community. Without it, Brooklyn became a vast network of hamlets, whose boundaries were rigidly drawn but whose connections with each other were vague at best, hostile at worst. None of the three surviving metropolitan newspapers really covers Brooklyn now until events—Ocean Hill-Brownsville, for example—have reached the stage of crisis; the *New York Times* has more people in Asia than it has in Brooklyn, and you could excuse that, certainly, on grounds of priorities if you did not also know that this most powerful New York paper has three columnists writing on national affairs, one writing on European affairs, and none at all writing about this city.

Without the *Eagle,* local merchants floundered for years in their attempt to reach their old customers; two large Brooklyn department stores—Namm's and

Loeser's — folded up. If you were looking for an apartment or a furnished room in Brooklyn, there was no central bulletin board. School sports are still largely ignored in the metropolitan papers, as Pete Axthelm pointed out so vividly in these pages a few months ago about the great Boys' High teams; Boys' High is in Brooklyn, for God's sake, in *Bedford-Stuyvesant!* How could you expect to get your reporter back alive? But the *Eagle* covered school sports with a vengeance, and the rivalries between various high schools were strong and alive. Today, they don't seem to matter much; hell, even the old ladies who used to yank the *Eagle* from my hand to read the obituaries don't have that consolation anymore.

Nobody really covers the Brooklyn Borough President's office anymore (as I suppose nobody has covered the Bronx Borough President since the absorption of the *Bronx Home News* by the *Post*). Nobody covers the borough as a whole. When Hugh Carey announced that he was running for mayor, not many New Yorkers knew who he was, despite the fact that he is one of the most important members of the New York City Congressional delegation, and comes from the borough with the strongest Democratic party machine. He is from Brooklyn: nobody knows his name. (The void left by the loss of the *Eagle* has been increasingly filled in recent years by the weekly neighborhood papers, of which the *Park Slope News-Home Reporter* is by far the best I've seen. During the school strike, it ran the single best account of the anger and bitterness on local levels of any paper in the city.) In any other city its size, there would be at least two newspapers. Brooklyn has none.

The loss of the Dodgers was an even deeper emotional shock to the people of Brooklyn, because it affected so many more people than the *Eagle's* demise did. Kids, for example. I remember an afternoon in the fall of 1941, when I was 6, sitting in the midst of a crowd of thousands on the steps of the just-opened central branch of the Brooklyn Public Library. A few days before, the Dodgers had won the National League pennant. All through the '30s, they were the clowns of the league: an

outfielder named Babe Herman had been hit on the head with a fly ball; three Dodger runners once ended up on third base at the same time; a player named Casey Stengel once came to bat, tipped his hat, and a bird flew out. But in 1941 they won the pennant, and Brooklyn welcomed them home like champions. All the schools were closed. There was a motorcade from the Brooklyn Borough Hall right up Flatbush Avenue to Ebbets Field, and in the huge crowds people were laughing and cheering and crying, lost in that kind of innocent euphoria that always comes when underdogs win out against all odds. (Imagine what will happen in this town when the Mets finally win a pennant.) All of them were there: Kirby Higbe, Hugh Casey, Dolf Camilli, Durocher himself, Pee Wee Reese, the great and tragic Pete Reiser: all of them smiling and waving in the bright sunshine. I was 6, and even I knew who they were.

Well, they lost the World Series that year to the hated Yankees, when Mickey Owen dropped a third strike. But nobody gave up on them. "Wait till nex' year" became the perennial battle cry, and for the next 15 years they were one of the finest baseball clubs in the country. Then suddenly, with the stealth of a flat thief, Walter O'Malley took them away. They were still making money at Ebbets Field, despite the old ballpark's rickety condition and despite television. Dodger fans, after all, were *loyal.* But the Dodgers, in O'Malley's opinion, were just not making *enough* money. One barren spring, Ebbets Field was left empty and dark, the dugouts abandoned, the infield turning to brittle dust, the great greensward of the outfield gone brown and mottled, the bleachers, where so much laughter, joy and sorrow had been staged, whipped by a cold wind. Today the old ballpark is gone. Still another housing project is planted on its site, with only a brass plaque to tip a chiseled hat to a rowdy and innocent past.

The operative word in the whole matter of the Dodgers is *innocent.* Baseball was a sport then, and if you came from Brooklyn, baseball meant the Dodgers. There were always some nonconformists; I remember a guy named Jackie McEvoy who rooted for the Giants and Buddy Kelly, who later died in Korea, rooting for the Yankees. But the Dodgers really were "The Pride of Brooklyn" and Dixie Walker really was "The People's Cherce." This vast confraternity of baseball maniacs held that borough together in a very special way; first, they provided common ground: Italians, Irish, blacks, Jews, Poles, all went to the games. Second, they provided something to talk about that did not involve religion, politics or race. And most importantly, they helped refute the canards about Brooklyn that puzzled so many of us when we were kids: the tree, the Brooklyn accent, the William Bendix type in all the movies, etc.

Dodger fans believed in myths. They were romantics, of course, hoping that the impossible could be made possible, but often they settled for small victories. If the headline on the back page of the *Daily News* said FLOCK BEAT JINTS 3-2, then all was well with the world. It was no small surprise that when Bobby Thomson hit The Home Run off Ralph Branca to win the 1951 pennant for the Giants, several people in Brooklyn committed suicide.

I suppose that such emotions over a group of grown men playing a boy's game seem rather ludicrous today. But the people of Brooklyn had this one thing, this one simple belief: that ballplayers were the best people on earth. And in the evenings, thousands of fans, literally, would walk across Prospect Park to the night games, past the Swan Lake and the Zoo and out onto Flatbush Avenue, joined together by this odd faith in people named Snider and Furillo and Campanella and Cox. They were *part* of an experience larger than themselves, something that involved gray scoreboards, Red Barber, peanuts, special cops, the Brooklyn Sym-Phony, the crowds on the streets outside, Gladys Gooding at the organ, the roar at the crack of the bat, Pete Reiser breaking his skull against the concave outfield wall, Snider dropping home runs into the gas station on Bedford Avenue, black men laughing with white men in the bleachers when Robinson took his jittery lead to second, beer, hot dogs, laughter. Laughter. The Dodgers were called Dem Bums, and the laughter came in part from knowing that they were not.

And when they left, the people of Brooklyn were shocked. As deeply shocked as they had been by almost any other public act in their time. They had given the Dodgers love. It never mattered to the fans that the Dodgers also made a lot of money. Hell, they *should* make a lot of money. The important thing was the game, the field of play, the heroes. But O'Malley took them away. For money. Nothing else. Sheer, pure greed. And for a lot of people that was the end of innocence. Romantics are always betrayed in the end, and O'Malley did a savage job of betrayal.

The Brooklyn Navy Yard was crucial to Brooklyn for at least one very good reason: it gave us work. It even gave me work. In 1951, during the Korean War, I went to work at Shop 17 in Building 63 of the Navy Yard as an apprentice sheet-metal worker. The number of men working there had declined from a peak of 70,000 during the Second World War to about 40,000, but the Yard was still the largest single employer in the borough. I hardly know the boy I was then; in memory it was a rough wild time, with a lot of drinking in the saloons of Flushing Avenue, much laughter with welders, and kindness from various people who said I was a bloody fool to be working with my hands when I could still go back and finish high school. I had one great job, with a thin, coughing black man who was a welder-burner and who stopped working every half-hour to drink milk. He said it coated his lungs against the filings of burnt metal. He coughed a lot anyway. We were working on an aircraft carrier named the *Wasp,* which was being re-fitted to accommodate jet aircraft. All the old bulkheads had to be removed, to be replaced with sturdier walls. His job was to burn around the edges of the bulkheads with an acetylene torch. My job was to pile into the bulkheads with a huge 20-pound hammer and knock them flat. It was an orgy of sheer animal fury, setting yourself, swinging ferociously, beating and smashing those bulkheads until they fell, while the thin black man coughed and laughed. "You some crazy white boy," he would say.

But all of us working there, even in the

early '50s, knew that the Navy Yard could not make it. To begin with, it was not a very economic place to build ships. It could be used for repair work, of course, but the big jobs—the new carriers, the atomic submarines—almost all went to private industry, or to shipyards where the workers were a little hungrier. In the Navy Yard you were a federal civil servant; it was very tough to get rid of you over small matters. The professionals at the Yard did a good day's work, but for a lot of the people who saw it as a day's pay, there wasn't much work done at all. At Shop 17, they would punch in at 8 a.m. and immediately dash to the men's room on the second floor. They would then grab an empty stall (not an easy matter), put an arm on the toilet-paper roll, and pass out for an hour. Later, they would go down to the floor, check out to the tool room, and spend an hour smoking. There might be a little work done, but by 11:30 it was back to the men's room to start washing up for lunch. After lunch, the pattern repeated itself, except that washing up to go home often started at 4 p.m., a full hour before checking out. There was something beautiful about the sheer audacity of those malingerers, but it also spelled the doom of the Yard. The 70,000 dwindled to 10,000 and finally to none. When Robert McNamara finally ordered the Yard closed, there was great public hand-wringing; nobody who ever worked there was at all surprised.

In addition to the loss of immediate jobs, there were other things involved for the people of Brooklyn. Many small factories and businesses lived off the Yard as subcontractors. In the immediate vicinity of the Yard there were bars, gas stations, naval outfitters, whose lives were intimately involved. In the long years of rumor and uncertainty, many gave up and moved on. The workers themselves were wary of signing leases, buying homes, purchasing anything on credit; they simply did not know when the ax would fall. A number of smaller businessmen in Brooklyn felt that if the Navy Yard could not make it, with its natural advantages, its federal subsidy, then *they* never could make it. The Navy Yard in the years of its decline, became still another emotional symbol. Brooklyn without the

Yard was not Brooklyn. It was as simple as that.

The black migration hit Brooklyn harder than any other part of the city. There were pockets of Puerto Ricans in Brooklyn, clustered around Smith Street in Boerum Hill, around the Williamsburg Bridge, and out in Sunset Park. But the really large numbers of Puerto Ricans had gone to East Harlem and the South Bronx. The southern black man came to Brooklyn.

There were several reasons for this. It was far more difficult for a badly-educated rural black man to get an apartment in Harlem than it was in Bedford-Stuyvesant. Harlem was a society, the black capital of America, with its already well-defined institutions: churches, numbers runners, landlords, restaurants, artists, after-hours places, con men, musicians, etc. Bed-Stuy was much looser, much less structured. In Bed-Stuy you didn't have to be hip.

Bed-Stuy was also easier to block-bust. A number of black real-estate operators (in addition to whites) made fortunes busting Bed-Stuy. They often employed white salesmen, who would purchase a house in a white street, move in a black family, and then start calling up everyone else on the street. Since many of these areas had two-family houses, or old elegant brownstones, this was much easier to do in Brooklyn than it was in Harlem, where old-law tenements were the rule. Less money was involved, and more heartbreak, especially for the unfortunate hard-working black man who thought he had escaped the ghetto only to find that it was coming out behind him.

So Bedford-Stuyvesant exploded. Whites began leaving by the hundreds. In places like Brownsville, they left because Brownsville had almost always been a slum, and the second generation that was making it did not see any need for further loyalty. Others simply saw the whole thing as hopeless: Brooklyn, which in their youth had been the city of trees and free spaces and security, was being torn apart by drugs and gang wars. The *Eagle* was gone, the Dodgers had departed: *Take the money and get out while you can.* There was racial fear involved, of course, but it would be too easy to explain it all away that way. It was race plus despair plus insecurity about money plus desires for the betterment of one's children plus—the most important plus—the loss of a feeling of community.

As Bedford-Stuyvesant expanded (any street that was occupied by blacks became Bedford-Stuyvesant, whether it was in Clinton Hill or Crown Heights), fear expanded. In Park Slope, across Flatbush Avenue from Bed-Stuy, real-estate operators started breaking up the fine old brownstones into black boarding houses. Most were occupied by transients, as boarding houses have always been occupied, and they simply didn't care what neighbors thought about them. The streets became littered with broken bottles and discarded beer cans; the yards filled with garbage; drug arrests increased; hookers worked the avenues; there were knifings and shootings, and soon the merchants on Flatbush Avenue started folding up and moving away. No insurance could cover what they stood to lose. When the Peconic Clam Bar on the corner of Flatbush and Bergen Street closed up because of too many stick-ups, the game looked finished. The Peconic Clam Bar was across the street from Brooklyn Police Headquarters.

And then, suddenly, Brooklyn seemed to reverse itself. You still cannot get a taxi to take you from the Village to any neighborhood remotely near Bed-Stuy. But the borough has halted its own decline, stopped, brought the panic and the despair almost to an end.

Again, the reasons are complicated, and have certain emotional roots. The wound of the Dodgers' departure seems finally healed; the arrival of the Mets gave the old Dodger fans something to cheer for, and there are no more of the old *Brooklyn* Dodgers now playing for the Los Angeles team. Baseball itself has declined in interest: it's slow, dull, almost sedate these days, especially on television. Pro football excites more people in the Brooklyn saloons, and it is a measure of the anti-Establishment, anti-Manhattan feelings of Brooklynites that they all seem to root for the Jets (not all, of course, not all, but the romantics do).

Word also began to drift in from the suburbs: things were not all well out there. Those who left Brooklyn because the schools were overcrowded soon found that the schools were also overcrowded in Babylon. Those who fled the terrors of drugs soon found that there were drugs in Rahway and Red Bank and Nyack too, and that flight alone would not avoid that peril. There was cultural shock. A childhood spent leaning against lampposts outside candy stores could not be easily discarded, especially on streets where there were no candy stores, where the bright lights did not shine into the night, where the laughter of the neighborhood saloon was not always available. People started longing for the Old Neighborhood. "These people can't even make a egg cream right." "I tried to get a bits-eye-oh out here an' it tastes like a pair a Keds." When I would go out to California on various assignments, I learned that I would be serving as a courier from the Real World; guys who had gone out to Costa Mesa and San Jose and L.A. 20 years before wanted me to bring *veal,* real-thin-honest-to-Jesus veal cutlets so they could make veal Parmigiana the way it is supposed to be made. In the suburbs late at night, people would sit in their living rooms and talk about boxball, devilball, buck-buck-how-many-horns-are-up? (called Johnny Onna Pony by the intellectuals), ringalevio, and always, always, stickball. Remember the time Johnny McAleer hit three spaldeens over the factory roof? Or the time Billy Rossiter swung at a ball, that bat flew out of his hands, hit an old lady on the head, and went through the window on 12th Street? Remember the Arrows, and the great money games they had on 13th and Eighth? Nostalgia worked its sinister charms. The Old Neighborhood wasn't much, but it wasn't this empty grub-like existence in the suburbs, struggling with mortgages and crabgrass and PTA meetings and water taxes and neighbors who had never shared one common experience with you. A little at a time, people started to drift back. It was not, and is not, a flood. But it has begun.

For younger people, the suburbs seemed to hold a special horror. If you were a writer, and you were faced with a move to the suburbs, you would rather go all the way into exile: to Mexico or Ireland or Rome. You could not live in the Village or Brooklyn Heights, because the real-estate scoundrels had made those places special preserves for the super-affluent (you *could* live in those places, of course, but the things you would have to do to afford it would make it impossible to live with yourself). Younger people started looking over the neighboring terrain. They cracked Cobble Hill first, reclaiming a number of fairly good buildings. Then Park Slope started to open up; the boarding houses were bought for as little as $14,000, cleaned out, re-built and re-wired. That was only four and five years ago. Today, the prices are slowly being driven up, and the great fear is that the real-estate people will take over this place too.

The New People, as they are called, saw Brooklyn fresh. They had not known it before, so they knew nothing about its decline. Most important, they carried with them no old emotional wounds. Instead they saw it as a place with great broad boulevards like Eastern Parkway and Ocean Parkway (once, my brother and I walked out Ocean Parkway all the way to Avenue T because we read in the papers that Rocky Graziano lived there; we sat around on benches for hours, but we never saw Rocky, who was the middleweight champion of the world.) They recognized that Greenwood Cemetery, which contains the bones of such diverse worthies as Boss Tweed and William S. Hart, was one of the great urban glades, a spot with lush foliage, sudden hills, bizarre statuary (at night, when we were kids, we would sneak into the cemetery to try to catch the giant turtles which lived in its ponds; the ghosts sent us running). They know that the Brooklyn Museum is one of the finest in the country, with a great collection of graphics, a splendid African collection, some superb American Indian pieces, and paintings by Ryder, Jack Levine, etc. (we went there to see the mummies, to walk into the bowels of the mock pyramid, dreading the Pharaoh's curse, remembering every terror of that great picture *The Mummy's Hand*.) They know that Prospect Park is

a masterpiece of landscape architecture, the park that learned from the mistakes of Central Park, which by comparison is bland and flat, and they know that during the Revolutionary War, George Washington had a command post in its hills (but they've never been inside Devil's Cave, nor did they know what happened in the night in the shrubs along the Indian War Path, and they don't know the spot where Yockomo was shot to death near the Swan Lake by Scappy from South Brooklyn, and they weren't there the night that Vito Pinto dove into the Big Lake at three in the morning and found himself wedged in the mud three inches below the surface, and they never saw Jimmy Budgell come tearing down the horse path on a strawberry roan like one of the Three Musketeers). They know that the great arch at Grand Army Plaza contains a fine piece of sculpture by Frederick Remington, that there is an abandoned tunnel under the Plaza, that the main branch of the Brooklyn Public Library is one of the best in the city (and when I was a kid I used to look up at the carved legend on the wall that begins HERE ARE ENSHRINED THE LONGING OF GREAT HEARTS . . . and spent one long summer hoping that someday I would be a Great Heart too and that maybe books were the key). They saw Brooklyn in a way that we had not seen it when we were young, and they saw it in a way that Brooklyn had not seen itself, perhaps, since the years before the 1898 Mistake. I just wish that they could have been there that afternoon at the now-shuttered 16th Street Theatre, when Tim Lee (now at the *Post*) and his brother Mike were taken by their mother for the usual Saturday matinee of three Republic westerns. At one point, a Superman chapter came on, and Mike Lee stood up, and shouted at the top of his lungs: "Hey, Ma! I can see the crack of his *ass!*" His mother beat him mercilessly with a banana that was part of the lunch, and then took them all home.

The New People are part of the emotional cure. There are other, more practical cures under way. For one thing, the migration of southern blacks seems to have come to an end; it has at least been reduced to a trickle. More importantly, Bedford-Stuyvesant has been developing its own institutions. Quietly and steadily, the Bedford-Stuyvesant Restoration Corporation, which was started through the efforts of Robert Kennedy, has been working very hard at bringing jobs to the area. IBM has already announced that it will build a manufacturing plant there. Plans are under way to build a new Boys' High. The city has committed itself to building a community college in the area. Through one of the two corporations set up by Senator Kennedy, a $75,000,000 mortgage loan fund has been put together and a job-training program for 1,200 persons is under way. With federal help, three firms (Advance Hudson Mounting and Finishing Co.; Campus Graphics Inc.; Day Pac Industries Inc.) have begun a $30,000,000 project of plant construction that will employ 1,435 people. Say what you will about the Black Panthers, they probably have a small point to make about ghetto businesses owned by whites; through reform of the insurance laws, more and more black businesses are starting in New York, the vast majority of them in Brooklyn. The development of the Black Pearl taxi system is an example of the building of institutions; let the white cabdrivers bitch and complain and issue dark warnings about cabdrivers in "gypsy" cabs who might have criminal records. The fact is, the Black Pearl cabs (and others not connected with Black Pearl) have made it possible for black residents of Bedford-Stuyvesant to travel the way a lot of other New Yorkers travel, and the money is staying in the area.

In addition, thousands of Puerto Ricans have settled in Brooklyn, in flight from the urban demolition that passes for slum clearance in Manhattan and the Bronx. There are now more Puerto Ricans in Brooklyn than in any of the other five boroughs, and they have brought with them their many virtues: the instinct to open small businesses, the almost visceral need to hold a family together, a sense of community. Sure, the Puerto Ricans play their radios loud, they play dominoes in the street and they drink a lot of beer out of one-pound bags (at a party once, someone asked my friend Jose Torres to go out for "24 bags of beer"). But for me, that has

made Brooklyn a more exciting, more lively place. You can measure a city by the life in its streets, and the Puerto Ricans have brought life with them: abundant, rowdy and baroque.

It is true that parts of Brownsville now look like Hamburg in 1945. Entire blocks have been abandoned to the rats and the wind. Old temples from the days when this was a Jewish area are now boarded up, or have given way to Baptist churches. The Gym at Georgia and Livonia, where Bummy Davis used to train while the Murder, Inc. goombahs looked on benevolently, is now gone; a big sign saying FORTUNOFF'S FOR MAH-JONGG SETS covers the windows, and you wonder how many people in the neighborhood play mah-jongg these days. (Milton Gross from the *Post* lived around that neighborhood, and I wonder if he was there that day 25 years ago when my father took me out to watch Davis with a bunch of other fight buffs in somebody's old Packard.) Near P.S. 174, there is one of those Mondrianesque cityscapes — blue, yellow, pink squares that were once the walls of kitchens and bedrooms, where people loved each other, and quarreled late at night, and cried angrily at the meanness of poverty, and then moved on. You can still see an occasional Dairy Appetizing store out there, and Carlucci's on the Brownsville end of Eastern Parkway is still one of the best Italian restaurants anywhere. But there remains this feeling of walking through purgatory. Street after street has been leveled. Only later do you discover that much of this demolition is part of a Model Cities plan, and that those streets will again be alive with children, and perhaps even trees. (But where are all the people now? Where on God's poor earth did they go?) In Ocean Hill-Brownsville (the school district, not strictly the neighborhood) there is a revolution of sorts under way. It is led by people like Rhody McCoy, his governing board and the Rev. John Powis of Our Lady of Presentation R.C. Church. They are working at the hardest part of any revolution: the part that goes beyond posture and mere defiance to accomplishment. They understand what the Board of Education and various other bureaucracies staffed by suburbanites don't understand: that the key is community. If they lose, Brooklyn loses, the city loses, we all lose.

The Brooklyn Navy Yard seems to be on its way back. A group called CLICK (Commerce, Labor, Industry Corporation of Kings) — started by people like Stanley Steingut, Brooklyn Borough President Abe Stark and Congressman Hugh Carey — has joined the City of New York (mainly the Economic Development Administration, with the help of another Brooklynite, Commerce Commissioner Ken Patton of Park Slope), to bring the Yard back to life. They hope eventually to provide between 30,000 and 40,000 jobs in the Yard by attracting civilian investment. They have signed a contract with Sea Train Inc., which will employ more than 3,000 workers in its first 18 months. The Yard, which covers 170 acres, already houses several small companies, such as the Rotodyne Manufacturing Company, which employs 130 workers building industrial ovens. The city is processing dozens of other applications. It might not come back to even the last payroll (1963: $201,000,000) for quite a while. But the beginning has been made. The governing factor in the city's decisions to rent space is that the space must be used for jobs. They will not rent space for warehouses, and have already turned down one request from the Federal Bureau of Prisons, which wanted 12 acres for a jail.

Not far from the Yard, the Pratt Center for Community Improvement is drawing plans for the revitalization of the entire neighborhood near the Yard: Fort Greene, Williamsburg, Bedford-Stuyvesant. Among many other plans, they hope to set up a series of nurseries along major bus routes leading to the Yard, so that working mothers from Bed-Stuy will be able to drop off small children on their way to work and pick them up on the way home.

Out in Flatlands, a new Industrial Park is being built on 96 acres, to provide 7,000 jobs, and three plants are already under construction. The Brooklyn waterfront continues to outstrip the Manhattan waterfront in construction of new piers and rehabilitation of old ones. Two new department stores are planned for downtown Brooklyn, and the Brooklyn store of Abraham & Straus has now passed Bloomingdale's in net sales. The Downtown Brooklyn Civic Center is now complete, and if the architecture rather resembles Abe Stark Stalinist in manner, it is at least new and it functions. Coney Island seems to me to be in decline, with the amusement area shrinking, old saloons like Scoville's gone, the old bungalows on the side streets battered away, many proud houses gone seedy and squalid. But I'm told that last year Coney Island had its best year financially since 1947. The 12-acre site of Steeplechase Park will become a public park backing on the beach, and the aquarium is planning a 5,000-seat whale and dolphin area.

The Brooklyn Academy of Music has gone through a real rebirth in the past two years, something that startles old Brooklynites who thought of the Academy as a shambling pile located down the street from the Raymond Street Jail, and given over to travel lectures about the sex life of West Papuans. Today the Academy has become the dance center of the United States, possibly of the world. And it is avoiding the Lincoln Center aura of gilded society and class distinctions by giving special rates and tickets to poverty agencies, so that young people from all over the city can see modern dance, often for the first time. For those of us who used to go downtown to meet friends coming out of jail, to pick up girls at the dances at the Granada Hotel or to box at the YMCA gym on Hanson Place, it all seems very strange; not many of us ever thought that the Academy would be thriving and the Raymond Street Jail would be closed.

There remain real problems in Brooklyn. There is still desperate poverty in the slums. Many urban renewal projects are still exercises in urban demolition. There are still too many decrepit, aging public schools, and the parochial school system remains a fragmenting anachronism. Eugene Gold, the Brooklyn District Attorney and one of the best of a new breed of elected officials in Brooklyn, told me that drugs and violence remain major problems.

"I would say that drugs contribute in one way or another to about 50 to 70 per cent of the borough's crime," Gold said recently. "I don't mean simply arrests for pushing or possessing drugs. I mean, in addition, drugs as the cause of other crimes: burglaries, stick-ups, muggings and the rest. We have a drug problem in *every* part of this city. When I go into Bedford-Stuyvesant to talk to people, as I do as often as I'm asked, they have one concern: how to stop crime. How to stop drugs. It's a real problem."

My own observation is that heroin seems to have declined. Most of the old junkies from my neighborhood are either dead or in prison, and the ones who remain are thought of as freaks. But marijuana is everywhere, and pills are easily available. Unfortunately, this is not just the problem of Brooklyn. The suburbs have the problem too. Last year, when I was spending some time in good old rightwing conservative Orange County in Southern California, drug arrests among young people had gone up almost 50 per cent in one year. There is no way to escape drugs by moving out. In California, they even arrested Jesse Unruh's son on a pot charge.

It seems to me that despite the problems, Brooklyn has become the only sensible place to live in New York. Much has changed since I was a boy, but what the hell. If you consider jars of mixed peanut butter and jelly as the final sign of the decline of a great nation, people my age think the same thing about that modern abomination, the manufactured stickball bat. It is, after all, a terrible thing to deprive a kid of the chance to acquire lore, and the lore of the stickball bat is arcane and mysterious. Nevertheless, on the first day of spring this year, with a high bright sun moving over Prospect Park and a cool breeze blowing in from the harbor, I bought one of the abominations, and a fresh spaldeen, and talked some of the local hippies into playing a fast game. It was the first time I had played since moving away from Brooklyn, and in one small way I wanted to celebrate moving back.

We played in the old skating rink at Bartel Pritchard Square, and the young lean kids with the long hair simply could not hit the ball. They might have been playing cricket. But the first time up, I smacked one long and high, arcing over the trees, away over the head of the furthest outfielder. On the old court at 12th Street and Seventh Avenue, it would have been away over the avenue, at least three sewers, and probably more. Standing there watching the ball roll away in the distance, I realized again that despite all the drinking, sins, strange cities, remorse, betrayals, and small murders, there was still a part of me that had never left Brooklyn, that wanted desperately to stay, that was still 14 years old and playing stickball through long and random days and longing to be a Great Heart. I hoped that Carl Furillo, wherever he was, was shagging flies with an honored antique glove, and hearing the roars in his ears from the vanished bleachers.

The next time up, I grounded out, but it didn't really matter.

"The Making of a Yippie" seems to be about a *man* (which it is, of course), but it's also about a city, in this case Cincinnati, Ohio. Jerry Rubin's reactions to Cincinnati and the high school he attended there were among the forces which turned him into a Yippie leader.

The Making of a Yippie
J. ANTHONY LUKAS

In the sneaker-scuffed hallway of Walnut Hills High School, between matching Grecian statues of discus and javelin throwers, Cincinnati plainclothesmen had thrown up a skirmish line. More policemen were clustered by the green lockers in front of the principal's office. It was Homecoming Day for Jerry Rubin, Class of 1956, and when Jerry comes home, Cincinnati doesn't take any chances.

Ray Brokamp, the Walnut Hills principal, was being particularly careful, for Jerry's return to his Alma Mater could hardly have come at a more embarrassing moment. Cincinnati was scheduled to vote a month later on a school levy. Three of the last four had been voted down and school officials feared that if the Yippie leader were allowed to speak at Walnut Hills it could damage chances for the new levy. So, despite repeated requests by his student supporters, Jerry was warned that he would be arrested if he tried to speak on campus.

Ambling up the driveway toward the massive brick school that morning last April, Jerry leered impishly as he savored the intriguing possibilities before him. Already facing three indictments, he didn't want another one; but he figured old Brokamp would try to avoid a messy arrest too. So, if he played it right he could stage a classic bit of Yippie theatre which would enhance his reputation as the Court Jester of the Revolution. "Wow," he chortled with demonic glee, "it could be beautiful. 'Yippie Leader Goes Back to School. Students Defy Principal to Greet Alumnus.' Beautiful! Pure theatre!" His stumpy (five-foot-six, one-hundred-fifty-pound) frame was costumed for the part in buckskin half boots, brown corduroy pants, a red-and-yellow-striped polo shirt studded with buttons reading "Teens for Decency," "Yippie," and "Cleaver for President," and a red American Indian headband holding back his explosion of reddish-brown hair which tangled with his walrus moustache and wiry beard. As usual, he was trailed by a platoon of reporters, photographers and television cameramen.

At first, the theatre was subdued. When Jerry strolled through the school door, a husky man barred his way and directed him to the principal's office, where Mr. Brokamp said he would be permitted to stay only long enough for an interview with the *Chatterbox,* the school paper he had once edited. Addressing him in a gently bantering tone as "Warden Brokamp," Jerry pointed to a white-wigged George Washington on the wall. "George was one of the first long hairs and remember, warden, he loved democracy so much he refused to be king."

By the time he finished his interview, hundreds of students were swarming in the driveway outside. Some were Jerry's enthusiastic supporters, a small group associated with a high-school underground magazine called *Ideoplastos* (Greek for *The Power of Ideas*). Among these was Andy Schwartz, the Student Council president, who sported a large cardboard button on his chest reading "The Forbidden Fruit. Rubin After School Today." Most of those outside were just waiting to board the yellow school buses, but when someone yelled "Here's Rubin!" they crowded round, seeking autographs, asking what he thought of Cincinnati these days, or just getting a look at "a real live Yippie."

And as Jerry swept down the driveway he carried many of the curiosity-seekers with him. Soon more than a hundred and fifty students (of the school's twenty-seven hundred) were strung out behind him as he tramped across a lawn scattered with dandelions, through a shady park and along the sidewalk of Victory Parkway where drivers speeding past peered out at the curious caravan. After about a mile, Jerry led them into the garden of the Friends Meeting House, a big, grey house once the home of Jerry's family lawyer, where he had celebrated many Seders. ("Why is tonight different from all other nights?" he gleefully mimicked the Seder service as he walked up the driveway. "Because this is Al Katz's house and I feel inhibited.")

But in the garden Jerry was anything but inhibited. He was in his best Yippie form as he surveyed the students sprawled among the clover and violets, their geometry and history books cast carelessly aside as they gazed up at him.

"This isn't a class," he began. "I'm not going to talk like a teacher. Because to me schools are jails. Especially Walnut Hills. Walnut Hills is an elite school, which takes the children of the privileged from all over the city. It's a place where the rich teach the rich to replace them. Well, everything I'm doing now comes right out of Walnut Hills. Because when I was here I was so bottled up, just working for grades to get into college, respecting teachers who weren't worth respect. All these last years for me have been an effort to win back the innocence and enthusiasm that I had as a baby. That's what's happening in the last six years. We're creating a new culture. How many of you kids are going to college?"

Many students, who had been laughing appreciatively at Jerry's jibes, raised their hands. Taken aback, Jerry recovered quickly: "That's okay. College is a good place to sit-in, get high, demonstrate, lock up the deans. . . .

"But you've got problems right there," he mused, chewing on a blade of grass. "Did you see all those police at the school? It was the closest thing I've seen to Chicago. And all because they were afraid I was going to show part of my body?" Rolling up his shirt sleeve he stuck out a bony arm. "I've got an elbow." Kids rolled merrily on the grass.

"I might bring an elbow. But I wouldn't come into the school with napalm, guns, planes. They were afraid of obscenity. The only profane word I know is decency. It sounds like I'm spouting revolution— which I'm going to—but all I'm spouting now is the First Amendment."

The kids applauded. Then a slim boy with a dandelion chain draped over his shoulder-length hair rose and said: "We ought to do something about the school. Everybody knows about the study-hall doors being locked so you can't even go out and get a drink of water. We ought to do something about that."

"What can we do?" a girl asked.

"One day we just get up and walk out," the boy answered, and many of the students clapped loudly.

Jerry smiled. "After today," he said, "maybe a little breathing space can be opened up at Walnut Hills. If you can get some, I'll come back anytime."

"Graduation speaker!" someone shouted.

"Yeh, how about that!" Jerry cried delightedly. "Wow! Beautiful!"

After most of the audience had gone home, Jerry and his most ardent supporters gathered around a TV set to watch the news coverage of his day. When the announcer on Channel 5 declared, "Yippie Leader Makes Like Pied Piper," everybody laughed and broke into wild applause. Jerry beamed. Then the announcer ran down other major

headlines: "Harvard Reoccupied. Cornell Declared Under Emergency. Purdue Students Seize Building."

"Another day in America," Jerry said with a little smile.

That evening, Jerry, his girl friend Nancy, his younger brother Gil, and a few friends paid a visit to his family. Jerry's parents had died years before, but there were three uncles—Sid, Harry and Maurice Katz—and assorted cousins and in-laws around. The Katzes had never appreciated Jerry's style, particularly some of his irreverent jibes at the folks at home. Once, several years before, Jerry had complained to a newspaper interviewer about the oppressiveness of Cincinnati's Jewish "subculture." A lot of people in town thought subculture meant inferior culture and that took some explaining. Then, just a few months before, Jerry told a Cincinnati *Enquirer* reporter in Washington, "I hated Cincinnati . . . I was bored. I had to get away from Cincinnati provincialism so I could be free and seek the truth." And the Katzes had been hearing about that ever since—little remarks dropped at the barbershop or the country club, like, "I saw they had a big write-up on your nephew, the Hippie-Yippie-Dippie," or "I don't know, Cincinnati always seemed pretty good to me, but I guess your nephew likes Moscow better."

But the Katzes were curious about their nephew. So some showed up for a small family reunion that night at Sid's house— a split-level ranch house in the Golf Manor section of town. When Jerry knocked on the door, it was opened by Sid. But what a Sid! He was dressed in a brightly colored Mexican coat; a blue tie fastened around his forehead; an electric guitar hung around his neck with a black skull-and-crossbones flag propped over it. Jerry guffawed and hugged Sid, who had always been by far his favorite uncle.

Sid had once been a tap-dancer in vaudeville, strutting his stuff along the old Pantages and RKO circuits. Occasionally he had played M.C. too, polishing an endless supply of patter jokes. Slower on his feet now, a little pudgy, he sold movie advertising, the spots which show in small-town theatres or drive-ins extolling the wonders of oven cleaners or Cross-Your-Heart bras. But he still twisted his bushy moustache into big stage winks and fenced at the world with the same Georgie Jessel thrusts.

"You know," he told Jerry after they were settled in his down-stairs den. "I can't get away from you. Thelma and I were down in Florida this winter. We go into this store and there's incense so thick you couldn't see your hand before your face. Finally, we pushed through the fog and there on the wall is a bigger-than-life-size picture of you."

Jerry threw up his hands and hugged Nancy. "As far as I'm concerned," he shouted, "Sid Katz is the first Yippie. Absolutely. He's a Yippie."

Mildred, Harry's wife, turned to Jerry with annoyance in her voice. "Are you laughing all the time, Jerry, or are you serious about all this stuff?"

"When you're laughing the most you're the most serious," Jerry said, draining his second Scotch and water.

"Well, if you're serious you shouldn't act like you do," Mildred said. "All that hair. The dirt. Everybody looks at you like you're a maniac. Now I believe in some of the things you do, but. . . ."

"Aunt Mil," Jerry interrupted. "Did you vote in the last elections?"

"No. Who could I vote for? There wasn't anybody to vote for."

"Then you voted right. You voted for Pigasus, the pig we nominated. We counted all the non-voters as voting for Pigasus."

"Oh, Jerry," Mildred said with a sigh. "That's not life. Some day you've got to learn to compromise."

"I'm never going to compromise," Jerry barked, "about anything!"

"You've told us everything you're against," said Marcia Bortz, one of Jerry's cousins. "But what are you for?"

"I'm for free—everything."

"Chaos," Mildred said. "That's what it would be. Chaos."

One of the brothers-in-law turned to Jerry. "Nobody has a right to eat free. These people on welfare want everything free. You should see what they do. I own a lot of real estate in town and a few weeks ago they went on a rent strike against me."

"Well, maybe you deserved it," Jerry said. "Are they slums?"

"Slums! They've got hardwood floors, air-conditioning. . . ."

The phone rang. Jerry, halfway through his third Scotch, picked it up and crooned, "Youth International Party."

Thelma, her arm suspended halfway toward the receiver, gasped, "How are we ever going to recover from this?"

"Did you hear that?" the brother-in-law said. "He called me a slum lord!"

"Don't you see," Jerry was saying, "capitalism itself has to be destroyed. Capitalism killed my father. He worked harder than anybody in this room. . . ."

"That's ridiculous," said Sherri, Sid's daughter, who is married to a successful young real-estate man. "My husband works as hard as anybody," she said, flashing real anger.

"If you ever had to go out and get a real job," snapped Marcia, "you'd feel different."

"A slum lord?" the brother-in-law said. "He's a maniac!"

"You know," somebody said, "they'll make a movie out of this with Sinatra and they won't even call us in for side parts."

When Jerry was fourteen, his grandmother had a stroke and, since there was nobody else to take care of her, the Rubins moved back with the old people— this time at 1816 Catalina Avenue in Bond Hill, a solidly Jewish middle-class area about two miles further out. The new house, which was to be Jerry's home until he left Cincinnati, was a two-story brick box with green shutters and a little white portico supporting a porch on which his grandfather and grandmother would sit in folding chairs on sunny afternoons. Again the Rubins lived upstairs and the Katzes downstairs, but this time the Katzes were feebler and needed more attention. Jerry recalls that the smell of approaching death pervaded the house.

That fall Jerry entered Walnut Hills High School—two years after he should have. Walnut Hills, which drew the best students from all over the city, started in the seventh grade. But Jerry, whose elementary school record had been mediocre, failed the entrance exam. This was a devastating blow. He remembers breaking into tears when he heard the exam results. Most of his friends were going on to Walnut Hills and for the next two years he had to attend Samuel Ach Junior High School, a rougher, racially mixed and academically lackluster school further downtown.

This hit Jerry particularly hard because it seemed to reinforce the class distinctions which he began to see between the Rubin and the Katz sides of the family. "They had better cars; they had better furniture; they went to better restaurants; and then this." Lower-middle-class Jews generally went to Samuel Ach while the upper middle class often went to Walnut Hills. And Johnny Katz, Maurice's son who was Jerry's age, had made Walnut Hills in the seventh grade. Nobody let Jerry forget that.

The family encouraged competition among the various cousins, but particularly between Johnny and Jerry because they were so close in age. Jerry recalls his parents' painful reminders that "Johnny's doing so well," or that "What you do reflects on us" (a remark he particularly resented and equates today with charges that the radicals' behavior reflects on America's good name). Johnny, in turn, resented his grandfather's favoritism of Esther's children, which became clear one Hanukkah when he gave Jerry a bicycle and Johnny a silver dollar. Yet the boys managed somehow to become friends. They went to the neighborhood Forest Theatre (a movie house which Johnny recalls as "the Midwest distributor of ringworm") and on Saturday afternoons they'd ride the Reading Avenue bus downtown to a matinee at one of the big movie palaces, then browse through the library or look for weird items in the pawnshops along Vine Street.

Yet the competition was still keen, and Jerry was determined to follow Johnny to the big school on the Hill. For two years he worked with only this in mind. He remembers "snowing" his teachers by

writing extra papers and doing extra homework. "When I wanted something I'd really go after it. I'd overkill." After eighth grade, he coasted into Walnut Hills.

Then, as now, Walnut Hills was ranked one of America's best high schools. Harold Howe II, later the Federal Commissioner of Education, was the principal and the school had a superb record for placing its graduates in the country's best colleges. For Jerry it was an achievement just to get in. But he brought to school a gnawing sense that he didn't belong there.

"I didn't arrive with any inherited prestige. I didn't know most of the people there. Most of them came from better parts of town. They'd all been friends together. I came from the lesser part of town. They were just richer and there was like an inferiority relationship there. I had to prove myself."

His proving ground was the *Chatterbox,* the weekly student newspaper. Jerry's attraction to newspapers grew directly out of baseball. Once he had abandoned his ambition to play professional ball, he decided to be what the sports pages called a "scribe." Jerry covered a few games for the mimeographed paper at Samuel Ach, and at Walnut Hills quickly became the school's ace sportswriter. Every afternoon he was out covering one team or another and every week the paper carried at least one Rubin by-line. By his junior year he was elected sports editor, a position usually held by a senior. Johnny Katz recalls that Jerry tried to turn him into a sports-writer: "I wrote 'coach' once and he said I should never say that, always say 'mentor.' Then I wrote 'cross-country runners' and he said always write 'hill-and-dale-men!' He had the lingo down pat."

But already his interests were broadening toward the rest of newspapering. "I wanted to be where the action was. At first that meant sports. Then it meant other kinds of action." His senior year, Jerry became coeditor of the *Chatterbox,* along with a quiet girl named Shiela Karam.

"Jerry ran the paper," recalls Alexander Gleason, the *Chatterbox*'s faculty adviser.

"He was so cocky, so sure of himself, that he made Shiela play second fiddle. She deeply resented that and often broke into tears when Jerry ignored her. Jerry could be very abrupt and even arrogant. Mind you, he was good. He'd been elected on the basis of his drive, his devotion to the paper, and his sheer professionalism. He bought the style book of The New York *Times* and made people conform to that. He was a perfectionist, a taskmaster, a bug on accuracy and details. But he could be terribly intolerant of somebody who wasn't as good as he was. If somebody goofed, he'd ride roughshod over them, and his sharp cutting voice and exasperated gestures made it worse. He'd blow his top, yell, pound the table. I'd say, 'Jerry, take it easy.' But he'd say, 'They shouldn't be here if they're no good.' He particularly had it in for Dick Levy, the sports editor, who he thought was doing a lousy job. Jerry really lacerated him. It was brutal, vicious."

Jerry drove his colleagues hard in his determination to win an "all-American" rating from the National Scholastic Press Association. He was crushed when the paper fell ninety points shy of the seventeen hundred required for that honor (it was judged "a neat, appealing paper which might be able to use a bit more zip in its makeup").

During his year as editor, the *Chatterbox*'s editoral page was hardly incendiary. On Memorial Day it urged students to show "worship and reverence" for the fifty school graduates killed in World War II. A front-page editoral urged support for the Student Council's "Clean-Up Week." Another chided students for discourtesy in assemblies. But there was a streak of iconoclasm. Although Jerry had joined Sigma Delta Chi (the best Jewish fraternity), by his senior year he was a strong opponent of fraternities (called "social clubs" at Walnut Hills). On November 15, 1955, he mobilized a majority of the paper's staff behind an editoral urging sophomores not to rush the clubs. The editoral noted that, "Most of the clubs segregate and discriminate by race and religion. They teach their members to live only with the same general type of person. . . . Through this types of discrimination the social club becomes the breeding ground for prejudice and discrimination on a larger scale." The clubs' supporters replied that the clubs were traditional at Walnut Hills. So Jerry struck back in another editorial: "It would seem unquestionable that traditions are not valuable but detrimental when they prohibit clear thinking and obstruct the establishment of new, constructive customs."

Except for this anti-fraternity campaign, Jerry was by no means a rebel at Walnut Hills. He wore clip-on bow ties and flannel shirts when most others at the school were wearing reps and oxford button-downs (Johnny Katz is sure this was not a sign of rebellion but because Jerry "just didn't know any better.") He didn't get along well with most upper-middle-class Jews at school (his closet friends were two outsiders—Yigael Goldfarb and Bennett Samuels), but this was because he still didn't feel comfortable with them, not because he yet consciously rejected their values.

Yet Jerry believes today that in one sense he was a rebel—"because I had something I believed in with incredible passion and inflexibility and totalness and worked around the clock and dedicated myself totally to. That added up to rebellion at a place where popularity and social status were everything. Nobody was supposed to take anything he did all that seriously. But I was a total reporter fanatic, asking all kinds of questions, writing them down. I was a character. I wasn't overtly snubbed or anything, but I was always on the fringes of the real 'in' group because I was just too intense."

Jerry went at journalism every moment he could find. One summer he attended a five-week course at the National High School Institute of Journalism at Northwestern and ranked first in the class of sixty student editors. His junior year, he and another student began providing sports statistics on local high-school teams to the Cincinnati newspapers. All weekend, they would work on the complex summaries, hunched over their adding machine and charts. Then Jerry would rush to get copy ready for the *Chatterbox*'s Thursday deadline.

Sometime in between he sandwiched some schoolwork. Understandably, his work was erratic—A's and B's in subjects like English and History, which interested him; often D's in Math, the sciences and languages, which bored him. Because of the low marks, Jerry failed to get elected the winter of his senior year to the Quill and Scroll Society, an honor awarded for journalistic achievement (and a minimum academic record). He was bitterly disappointed and raised his grades enough to be elected the following spring.

In his senior class poll, Jerry didn't win any of the traditional categories—"most likely to succeed," "most popular," or "best all round"—but he was voted the "busiest" boy in the class.

Half a century ago Sinclair Lewis satirized the way in which small and medium-sized cities wanted to prove themselves "Big Cities." He called the phenomenon "boosterism" (among other things), and he wrote about it most succinctly in *Babbitt*. The town of Zenith may have been fictional (though some say that it was modeled after Minneapolis), but the spirit of boosterism remains alive in America's smaller cities. Ironically, people today are desperately anxious to get away from the problems of the biggest cities; yet a place like Albuquerque, in the sunny escape-land of the Southwest, proudly proclaims that it is "a maze" of superhighways. The excerpts which follow are from brochures published by chambers of commerce and are intended to be taken seriously. They give us insight into how some Americans in some smaller cities see themselves.

Midland, Texas

Standing TALL on the southern edge of the Staked Plains of West Texas is the beautiful, friendly, smiling City of Midland, which looms for miles as a guide to persons traversing this expansive plains country.

Midland, a comparatively new city, established in 1885, stands TALL in skyscraper office buildings, in economy, in finance, in industry, in education, in business, in culture, in religious influence and in leadership . . . It also stands TALL in people—happy, friendly, go-getter type people—who always stand ready to greet, welcome and aid visitors and newcomers to their ranks.

Midland is the Headquarters City of the vast Permian Basin Empire of West Texas and Southeast New Mexico . . . recognized as one of the nation's leading petroleum centers. It also is the headquarters of a huge, prosperous ranching, livestock and farming territory.

Attractive business and industrial districts and beautiful, well-kept residential areas —all with a new and modern touch—appeal to tourists, business visitors and home-seekers.

Midland, sitting TALL in the saddle (as they say in the cattle country), will make you feel perfectly at home from the very beginning. Why not try it sometime . . .

. . . A FRIENDLY SMILE AWAITS YOU IN THE LAND OF THE HIGH SKY   Midland, Texas, an attractive, prosperous and progressive city in the Land of the High Sky, is a delightful place in which to reside . . . or just to visit . . . in a wholesome, healthful, enjoyable atmosphere . . . amid pleasant surroundings, favorable location, direct business and commercial enterprises of a wide variety.

A visitor from a foreign land once described Midland as "A smiling city . . . a community where residents always greet you with a smile!" . . . You'll like Midland!

And that's the way it is in this ever-growing community which serves a vast territory rich in petroleum, livestock, agriculture and industrial resources. It is one of the nation's leading oil and gas centers.

POPULATION: In 1900, Midland's population was 1,800; by 1940 it had increased to 9,352; by 1950 to 21,713; and by 1960 to 62,625. Estimated 1963 population is 64,151. Midland's 188.4 per cent population increase from 1950 to

1960 placed the county number 13 on the list of the fastest growing counties in the United States.

ECONOMY: Oil—in 1923 oil was discovered in the area now known as the Permian Basin and center of the Nation's greatest oil reserve. Midland serves as the business headquarters of this vast West Texas and Southeastern New Mexico oil field section. More than 750 oil companies and affiliate offices operating in Midland.

CITY GOVERNMENT: Midland's form of government is city manager-council.

LOCATION: Midland is situated on the southern edge of the Staked Plains halfway between Ft. Worth and El Paso.

ALTITUDE AND AREA: Midland's altitude is surprisingly high—2,779 feet. The corporate city limits comprise a land area of 23.8 square miles.

BUSINESS STATISTICS:

Assessed Valuation	$131,010,160	(1962)
Postal Receipts	1,098,998	(1962)
Retail Sales City	96,598,000	(1962)
Bank Deposits	157,106,614	(1962)
Building Permits	17,320,949	(1962)

UTILITIES: The water system is municipally owned. Texas Electric Service Company and Pioneer Natural Gas Company supply electricity and gas to the city.
Basic rates:

Water—1st 2,000 gal. minimum charge	$1.75
Electricity—1st 15 kwh minimum charge	1.20
Gas—1st 2,000 cubic feet minimum charge	1.65

COST OF LIVING:

Total Retail Sales	$96,598,000.00
Cost per Household	4,829.90

(Housing not included. 20,000 household units. 3.5 people per household according to 1960 census.)

INCOME:

Total Effective Buying Income	$197,674,757.00
Per Capita	3,156.00
Per Household	9.883.00

Greeley, Colorado

UNLIMITED RECREATION Living the Good Life could easily be a fulltime job in Greeley and northern Colorado. In addition to all the natural wonders of the mountains, Greeley has a complete recreation program designed to meet the needs of all its citizens.

Fishing in cool mountain streams where the rainbow trout is King is a year-round pastime. Hiking to hidden lakes and glades, hunting for elk, deer and antelope, climbing to a mountain top and skiing in the winter time—you can enjoy vacation fun every day of the year if you live in Greeley.

Spectator sports, too, abound in Northern Colorado. Within an hour's drive are numerous high school events, five college and university athletic programs, professional football and baseball and many other sports.

A full-time recreation director is retained by the city to direct its recreation program for all ages. The program offers swimming, social and square dancing, handicrafts, band and orchestra, indoor and outdoor sports, camping, skiing, Young American athletics and a Youth Center composed of some 2,000 members.

Almost any summer day is a good time to venture to Greeley's vast expanse of parks and playgrounds located in all sections of town. Greeley also has an active program for adding more parks and playgrounds as new subdivisions are built.

An 18-hole municipal golf course, an 18-hole Country Club course and a 9-hole three-par Elks course cater to golf enthusiasts. And Greeley has just opened a new municipal swimming pool.

A FAMILY COMMUNITY Environment is important in raising a family. The community, as well as the family, helps mold the character of tomorrow's generations. In this respect, Greeley is ideal for the young family.

Realizing its important role in the community, the police department has a progressive program of crime *prevention* as well as protection which has resulted in one of the lowest crime rates of any city in the nation. Its juvenile program is particularly outstanding.

Medical protection is also important to the family. The Weld County General Hospital and a large number of clinics offer a complete scope of medical and dental services.

The hospital, constructed in 1952 and expanded several times since, is a thoroughly modern structure with a 320-bed capacity. It has established Greeley as the medical center for northern Colorado and southern Wyoming and has helped in attracting an outstanding group of physicians and surgeons.

Combine these fine law and

medical protection programs with Greeley's excellent schools, community activities program, wide recreational opportunities and its clean, solid community, and you have a wonderful place in which to live and raise a family. When you visit Greeley just look around and you'll agree. . . .

Life is Really
Tops in Greeley

Brookings, South Dakota

BROOKINGS: A PACE SETTER
If you'll excuse a little local pride, Brookings, S. D., combines quite a mixture of modern retail stores, the largest institution of higher education in South Dakota, expanding residential areas, several small industries and a wide variety of recreational facilities along with an A-1 public school system, two medical clinics, a new $1½-million municipal-county hospital and a half-million-dollar retirement center.

It was the first all-fluorescent lighted city in the nation. It's located in the rich farming land of the Big Sioux River valley, and is a trade center for more than 80,000 people living within a radius of 35 miles. The climate of the area is of the temperate continental type, with a July average of 71.8° F. and a January average of 13.1° F.

These are just a few of the many reasons that 13,491 men, women and children will give you for making Brookings "home." Actually, they'll each give you 13,491 more reasons why they like it here, if you ask.

Others will point to the federal Northern Grain Insect Research Laboratory or the new animal diagnostic center as examples of the applied science that makes Brookings a center of another sort—and they'll tell you about South Dakota State University with its seven colleges of instruction (agriculture, engineering, home economics, nursing, pharmacy, arts and science, in addition to the graduate school) and its spacious 1,400-acre campus.

A friendly town, the trading center for a rich farming community of about 5,000 square miles, Brookings takes pride in its young ideas and constant re-evaluation of what it is doing and where it is going. It has, because of this, maintained the "small town" atmosphere and yet kept pace with the changing times. Neither isotopes nor ice cream socials are foreign to the city's 12,000 residents.

Leisure time in Brookings means taking part in sporting events, community activities,

recreation and cultural enlightenment.

A wide and handsome interstate highway is a glistening white frame on the city's eastern edge. Brookings is at the crossroads to the Great Lakes of South Dakota and the Black Hills to the west. It is located 60 miles from the state's largest city.

What's The Big Idea?
We Confess—We sometimes fail to see the forest for the trees.

Will you lend a hand? The "idea city" isn't perfect, we're the first to confess. Very often a first impression is the most valuable and lasting. We want the "idea city" to be perfect and we want you to be a part of our success story. If you visit Brookings, or pass through, keep your eyes and ears peeled for improvements we might be striving for. Then let us know. We respect your judgment and opinions.

Jackson, Mississippi

THE EXCITING FACE AND PACE OF JACKSON TODAY
Jackson—Mississippi's sparkling Capital City—more and more is becoming widely recognized as a community

that combines in a unique and wonderful way good business and pleasant living. A noted radio newscaster has made the comment that nowhere is the South's exciting economic

renaissance more apparent than here in Jackson. Long-time residents, newcomers and visitors alike in Jackson all feel the dynamic surge of a city that seems to be headed for spectacular growth and expansion in the years just ahead.

Both the face and pace of Jackson have changed enormously in recent years. New buildings, homes, streets and highways are bringing a fresh and dramatic look to all parts of the city. And yet, along with this economic and physical growth, Jackson continues to retain much of the charm, friendliness and graciousness of an earlier day.

With its pleasant climate and ideal location, and as the vigorous Capital City of a state that shows such exceptional promise for progress, there is no doubt that Jackson is now emerging as one of the elite cities not only of the South but of the nation—with an unusually bright potential for the future.

Perhaps what you see in these pages can pave the way for an "on-the-scene" visit to our city soon—either for business or pleasure. We welcome every opportunity of proving to you that *Jackson means business . . . and the good life, too.*

"THE BEST OF BOTH WORLDS"   Do you think that you can't get rid of big-city headaches without giving up the metropolitan conveniences? Would you enjoy business life in a modern, progressive city, and family life in a quiet suburb, without commuting eighty miles in-between? Then look south, young man (and others) . . . look south to Jackson, Mississippi, because it's your kind of town!

Even though you may be prepared not to find any of the familiar story-book relics of the Old South in Jackson, as a first-time visitor you could well be surprised at what you *do* find here: a vigorous city of a quarter-million, whose population is dedicated to progress on all fronts. And there is a decidedly unique spirit among Jackson's citizens, a combination of the traditional gentle pace and neighborliness of the South, with a great enthusiasm for the challenges and demands of modern business. Observers agree that Jacksonians have

struck an admirable balance of the best of both worlds, and it has been successful.

Perhaps it is this balance which makes life in Jackson appealing for so many. Despite its metropolitan atmosphere, the city has avoided the problems which sometimes make urban life hardly worth the struggle. Traffic is rarely a problem in Jackson; you can drive from most residential areas to the downtown business district within fifteen minutes. A long-range street improvement program assures that future traffic will flow just as smoothly.

Jackson can claim rank as a clean city, in all senses of the phrase, morally and physically. Its crime rate is among the lowest in the nation, both in major crimes and juvenile delinquency. Jacksonians worship at some 230 churches, representing all major denominations. In addition, Jackson is the administrative center of most church organizations in the state.

FINISHING TOUCH   The Arts Festival, held each April, is only the finishing touch to Jackson's cultural season. Throughout the fall, winter, and spring, Jacksonians have plentiful opportunities to attend plays, concerts, and operas. Two theatre groups, the Little Theatre and New Stage present a full bill of productions each year. Nationally-famous artists and musical groups are brought to Jackson by local concert managers, and the city's own Symphony Orchestra presents six regular subscription concerts and numerous special concerts during the season. Jackson's Symphony is recognized as among the leading urban orchestras of the country.

Jackson's Opera Guild and Ballet Guild are important forces in the cultural life of the city, often working together in productions of opera from all periods. Exhibitions of art and photography are held at the Municipal Art Gallery, where the Mississippi Art Association sponsors a monthly showing.

The new $2-million dollar Municipal Auditorium was opened in 1968, providing the city with a spacious center for the performing arts. Located in the downtown business section, the facility seats 2500 in comfort and elegance.

Jacksonians don't neglect the youngsters when it comes to providing them with the finer things of life. Programs for children are presented frequently by the Orchestra, and the numerous libraries (there is one within two miles of every home in Jackson) present special readings from children's classics each week. Use of the libraries by children is encouraged, and the juvenile departments are well-stocked.

"WALK TO SCHOOL . . . ALL THE WAY THROUGH A PH.D." Education is readily available to Jackson families. In fact, it is possible for students in some areas of the city to literally walk to classes, from grammar school through the Ph.D. and M.D. levels.

One of the most noticeable facts of Jackson's Public School System is that statistics about it change rapidly. The growing web of top-quality schools now includes 39 elementary schools, 11 junior high schools, and 8 senior high schools. These facilities represent an investment of $45 million, and are operated on a $14 million annual budget. Numerous parochial and private schools also serve the Jackson area.

Quality of instruction has risen steadily in recent years, both in the number of subjects offered and in methods of teaching. Science, mathematics, and foreign languages have received special emphasis, and language labs have been expanded to provide a more meaningful learning experience in these areas.

Mississippi's Educational TV System, operative in 1969, is centered in Jackson. This, the nation's first full color Educational TV installation, will be a major factor in upgrading education throughout the state.

A high percentage of

Jacksonians over the age of twenty-five hold college degrees. Three senior colleges within the city — Millsaps, Belhaven, and Jackson State — offer opportunities for every student to receive college training. Many young Jacksonians who have taken advanced degrees at the nation's leading universities have returned to live, teach, and practice their professions.

HEALTHY BUSINESS CLIMATE Business finds Jackson a very hospitable environment, and few cities of this size can claim a more energetic business community. Retail business thrives. Sales per household in Jackson compare favorably with the national average; over twenty percent of Jackson families have incomes of $10,000 per year or more.

Jackson is an ideal distribution center for the southeastern and midwestern markets, and some 250 manufacturers have taken advantage of this location by establishing plants here. Added attractions for industry include an abundance of plant sites, plentiful labor, water, and electric power, and modern transportation facilities.

JACKSON TOMORROW But highways are only a small part of the exciting prospects ahead for the Jackson of tomorrow. In the planning stages, on the drawing boards, and actually under construction are projects which will shape the future of the city. Confident that the years ahead will be years of growth, Jackson is clearly preparing for tomorrow with a spirit that will not be denied.

One such project is the state's multi-million dollar Research and Development Center, now under construction at Jackson. When completed, it will not only house the state's R&D offices, but will serve as the State Universities Center and as the home of the Educational TV System. Graduate Schools of the three state universities will be located here, solidifying Jackson's position as the educational center of the state. Facilities of the Research and Development operation will be available to industry for help in finding new products and markets for Mississippi-based industries.

Other "centers" are planned for Jackson, also — including a new Governmental Center which will provide additional space and services for the functions of state government. A Cultural Center is on the drawing board; interested business groups are raising funds which will be matched by the municipality to build the Mississippi Arts Center, to be adjacent to the new Municipal Auditorium. This facility will include an additional 600-seat theatre, office space for several cultural organizatons, rehearsal space, and gallery space for exhibitions and displays.

Services in the city are also scheduled for expansion, especially in the area of medical care. Three major hospitals have expansion plans in progress. St. Dominic's Hospital plans a 200-bed addition, together with adequate service area which will make the hospital a 600-bed facility. The Mississippi Baptist Hospital is planning an entirely new building, and University Hospital and Medical Center has a long-range plan of expansion both in its hospital and teaching and research facilities.

All together, The Jackson of tomorrow promises to be an exciting city in which to live and work, packed with opportunities and challenges for all. In future growth, as well as in the dynamic spirit of the present city, it is clear that the slogan of the Jackson Chamber of Commerce is true: "Jackson means business . . . and the good life, too."

STUDENTS

Students have always had trouble with their public image—highly placed people have clucked over student behavior for centuries. In Chaucer's *Canterbury Tales,* for example, Oxford students of nearly six hundred years ago appeared as bawdy, scruffy, and unscrupulous, given to making fools of their elders; in more recent times men of the greatest importance have seen some students as "bums." The exacerbating differences used to exist only between "town and gown," but recently the conflict has escalated to a point where student behavior is a hot political issue on the national level.

Ironically, not so long ago students were rather admired, or at least envied, not for their idealism or hard work, but for their brainless nincompoopery, driving around in funny-looking cars and drinking sodas at the corner malt shop. Movies depicted intellectual students as pitiful social misfits, and witless "jocks" (or All-American football heroes) became the ideal of every *real* American. All of this during World War II, when chilling numbers of these same youth were dying to "make the world safe for Democracy," a democracy which, incidentally, saw little wrong with sororities and fraternities which specifically excluded members of minority groups. In other words, when students seemed best to the larger world, one might legitimately say that they were morally and intellectually most dead. It seems that students should be seen, not heard, if Middle America is to approve.

In making himself heard the student has forfeited his traditional immunity from the punishments meted out by the masters of law and order. Society once winked at the "kids' pranks"—when they got a little drunk or "hazed" each other—but now that students are out on the streets finding fault with the system, the situation has changed. Uniformed men in the hallways, the crack of rifle fire, and the letting of blood have come to symbolize the campus to many Americans in the last few years. A Gallup poll in mid-1970 uncovered the amazing fact that student unrest was the matter of greatest concern to the majority of Americans—not the war in Vietnam, not racial strife, but students. "Why can't they work for change *within* the system" the puzzled and infuriated average man asks—forgetting that students are not a part of the system (though, oddly enough, the colleges are), because they have no voice in it.

The shift from complacency to involvement has been very rapid, to the general dismay of society. Perhaps, however, students will really take the place in society for which their intelligence and education have prepared them. Perhaps, too, the colleges will fulfill their functions more adequately than they have in the past. Chances are your college motto contains the word "truth" somewhere. Perhaps in the uneasiness of these days the truth will become a little easier to perceive.

PART FOUR

School Days
CHUCK BERRY

Up in the morning and out to school
The teacher is teaching the golden rule
American History and Practical Math
You study them hard, hoping to pass
Working your fingers right down to the
    bone,
The guy behind you won't leave you alone.

Ring Ring goes the bell
The cook in the lunchroom ready to sell
You're lucky if you can find a seat
You're fortunate if you have time to eat
Back in the classroom open your books
Even the teacher don't know how mean
    she looks.

Soon as three o'clock rolls around
You finally lay your burden down
Close your books, get out of your seat
Down the halls and into the street
Up to the corner and round the bend
Right to the juke joint you go in.

Rock the coin right into the slot
You've gotta hear something that's really
    hot.
With the one you love you're making
    romance
All day long you've been wanting to dance,
Feeling the music from head to toe,
Round and round and round you go.

Hail Hail Rock and Roll!
Deliver me from the days of old.
Long Live Rock and Roll!
The beat of the drums hot and cold
The feeling is there body and soul.

FROM
Stop Time
FRANK CONROY

THE STREET

I was already late, having completely missed home-room period, so there was

Photograph by Thomas Boyle.

no great harm in waiting a bit longer. I bought a hot dog and watched two boys from the morning session pitching pennies against the wall of Stuyvesant High School. The sun was high, filling half the street, and I moved out from under the vendor's striped umbrella to get its warmth. My heart was calm. Nothing could be done about my lateness and in the meantime there was the street, wonderfully quiet in the steady sunlight, the sharp taste of yellow mustard in my mouth, and the slow rhythms of the game to contemplate. For a few moments I was free, relieved of thought, temporarily released from the faint sickness inside me. Although I refused to admit it, I was getting sick. Delicate changes were going on—the subtle adjustments of a mind that feels itself threatened but cannot localize the threat, the hidden wariness toward all things and all people, a certain suspension of sensibility, like holding one's breath in a moment of crisis and finding when the danger passes there is no need of breath, that one can live without air.

"Get in there, you cocksucker," said one of the boys. Toeing the line, his body bent like a racer waiting for the gun, he launched his coin in a flat arch and smiled as it came to rest a half inch from the wall. "Wins."

"Can I shoot?"

They looked at me quickly. "Okay."

"He has to go first, though," the other boy said.

We threw coins for a while, unhurried, all of us relaxed and easy in the sun. The hot-dog vendor leaned against his cart, half asleep, his chin in his hands. I was about even when the two boys called a halt and set off toward First Avenue. They turned the corner arguing about a disputed play and I started up the steps, my shadow climbing crookedly ahead of me.

THE FIRST FLOOR

I could have sneaked in through one of the side exits, of course, but there wasn't much point since the new attendance taker in home room was above taking bribes and had doubtless included my name in the late list. Approaching the wide table at the head of the main corridor I felt a familiar gathering-of-self at the day's first encounter with the enemy, represented in this instance by the student serving as late monitor. He looked up from his books and gave me a smile. "Again, huh?"

"That's right." I was happy to see him instead of Mr. Schmidt, the teacher who sometimes served, because as fellow students we had a bond that transcended my sins. We shared the stoicism of the helpless, the dreamy *sangfroid* of the abused, playing out our respective roles with tongue in cheek as if to say there's more to me than meets the eye. As a good student he was glad to see me acting out his fantasies of rebellion, while I, the reprobate, was heartened to discover that even the good students were unhappy, that they hated school no less than myself, each in his own way.

"Three times this week and it's only Thursday."

"You have to stick with it to be champ." But my heart sank. I hadn't remembered, and three times in a single week was dangerous. The Dean might feel he should do something.

"Well, I hope you like Seward. That's where they'll send you."

He wasn't being superior, it was a flat statement of fact.

"I don't give a shit what they do."

He shrugged and pulled a pad of forms under his eyes, signed, and ripped off the sheet. "It's first period. You missed home room." . . .

The five-minute warning bell had rung. I sat with my ankles on the railing reading a novel about the Second World War. I should have used the time to do my homework, but the appeal of Nazis, French girls, K rations, and sunlight slanting through the forest while men attempted to kill one another was too great. I read four or five hours every night at home, but it was never quite as sweet as in school, when even a snatch read as I climbed the stairs seemed to protect me from my surroundings with an efficacy that bordered on the magical. And if the story dealt with questions of life and death, so much the better. How could I be seriously worried

about having nothing to hand in at Math when I was pinned in a shallow foxhole, under a mortar barrage, a dead man across my back and an hysterical young lieutenant weeping for his mother by my side? I could not resist the *clarity of the world* in books, the incredibly satisfying way in which life became weighty and accessible. Books were reality. I hadn't made up my mind about my own life, a vague, dreamy affair, amorphous and dimly perceived, without beginning or end.

A boy pushed open the door and looked in. My function as monitor was to keep unauthorized people from going in and out, a responsibility I ignored, and when I turned my head it was with the pleasant anticipation of the law-breaker about to flout authority.

"Conroy?"

"Yes." Too bad. I could tell he was licit from his tone. Shouts drifted up from the gym floor.

He waved a slip of paper. "Two-oh-eight. Right away." I accepted the pass and began gathering my books.

How strange that when the summons came I always felt good. The blood would rush through my body, warming me with its cheerful, lively heat. If there was a slight dryness in my mouth there was also a comfortable tingling of the nerves, a sharpening of the reflexes, and a sense of heightened awareness. The call produced a mild euphoria, not out of any perverse desire to be punished but in anticipation of a meeting with fate, in expectation of plunging deeper into life. The Dean was less the Dean and more my dead father than either of us suspected at the time. I sustained a fantastic belief that the mechanical clichés of our disciplinary interviews were only the prelude to eventual mutual recognition. His threats seemed of no more importance than the how-do-you-dos and so-nice-to-meet-yous one mouthed to any new person, and in my eagerness to begin a real exchange I hardly heard them. I misread the boredom and irritation in his face, thinking it came from frustration at the slow pace of love, investing his dry soul with juices that had doubtless drained before I was born. The truth, that among the thousands of students I was no more than a number to him, that he was so overworked he couldn't possibly have remembered me from one time to the next without his records, that in fact everything between us was totally procedural—that truth was unthinkable.

THE SECOND FLOOR

Three boys were on the bench. I sat down with them and watched the floor for a moment, not, as a naïve observer might have thought, to dramatize penitence, but simply to maintain my privacy in an important moment. Drawn close by their delinquency, the other boys whispered and passed notes, holding off fear with artificial camaraderie. I kept quiet, acclimating slowly to the electric air, knowing that where there was danger there might also be salvation.

I never rehearsed a defense. I must have thought the Dean preferred a boy who walked in and took his medicine to one who groveled, however cleverly. And of course when the moment of recognition came, when the barriers fell and we stood revealed, I didn't want to be in the midst of an elaborate lie. To hasten the emergence of love I could only be completely honest. Lies might make it difficult for him to reach me, and vice-versa.

I wanted to be won over by him, but not cheaply. If he won me cheaply he might betray me. The sense in which I knew this is hard to explain. It wasn't a principle I'd deduced from experience, it was knowledge without thought. Had someone asked me at the time what it meant to be betrayed by another person I couldn't have answered. Without being able to conceive betrayal I none the less protected myself against it, unconsciously, in my expectation of a commitment from the other person equal to my own. A perfectly valid stance between individuals but a tragic absurdity between a child and authority.

A side door I'd never noticed before opened and a student came out smiling. I caught a glimpse of a man at a desk, and for no reason at all I became convinced he was a policeman.

"Fischberg," the Dean's secretary called without looking up. The boy next to me left the bench and went through the side door. I heard the man inside tell him to close it.

The smiling student picked up a pass from the secretary and started out. As he passed I touched his arm. "Who's that in there?"

"I don't know. Some jerk asking if I had a happy home life."

"No talking there!"

A soft buzz sounded on the secretary's intercom. "Next," she said.

There was a momentary paralysis on the bench.

"Well, what are you waiting for?" She shuffled some papers on her desk.

"Conroy? Is one of you Conroy?"

I walked to the Dean's door and went in.

"All right Conroy, step over here."

I crossed the carpet and stood in front of his desk. He took off his glasses, rubbed the bridge of his nose, and put them on again. After a moment he pushed against the edge of the desk and swiveled away to face the wall, leaning back with a sigh and then letting his chin come down slowly like a man dozing off.

"Why were you late?" he asked the wall.

"There was no reason, I guess."

"No reason?"

"I mean I don't have an excuse."

"You didn't miss your bus? You didn't forget your transit pass? The subways didn't break down?"

"No sir."

"I suppose not, since you've been late three times this week, You can't possibly have an excuse so you don't give one. Isn't that right?" He stared at the wall.

I didn't answer.

"Isn't that right?" he asked again in exactly the same flat tone.

"If you say so, sir."

He turned his head to look at me for a moment, his face expressionless, and then went back to watching the wall. "I don't have time for trouble-makers, Conroy. I get rid of them."

"I don't know why I'm late so often. I try to get here on time but somehow it just happens."

"Don't make a mystery out of it, Conroy.

You're late because you're lazy and inattentive."

I could feel myself beginning to close down inside, as if my soul were one of those elaborate suitcases street peddlers use to display their wares, the kind that fold up from all directions at the approach of the law.

He lifted some papers from his desk. "You're nothing but trouble. Constantly late if you get here at all, inattentive in class, disrespectful to your teachers, twice reprimanded for gambling . . ."

"It was just pitching pennies, sir."

"I know what it was. Don't interrupt."

"Yes sir."

"At this moment you are failing three subjects."

"We haven't had any tests yet. I'm sure I'll pass the tests."

He looked up, his eyes narrowing in irritation. "You're failing three subjects. That leaves the decision up to me. You stay here or you get transferred to another school. You're in that category now."

I turned away, instinctively hiding the fear that might be on my face. Getting kicked out of Stuyvesant would be a catastrophe surpassing anything in my experience, perhaps because it seemed to eliminate the possibility of turning over a new leaf. I disbelieved in self-betterment. By turning a new leaf I meant no more than avoiding the more obvious forms of trouble.

Secretly, I did hope that things would get better. That I didn't know *how* they'd get better was balanced by my inability to understand why they were bad in the first place. It was a delicate world in which one had to move carefully, dealing with elements one understood vaguely if at all, knowing only that some elements seemed to sustain life and some to threaten it. Getting thrown out of school would disrupt things profoundly. I would no longer be able to experiment with those balanced elements, probing them gingerly here and there, adding some, taking away some, trying, in the least dangerous way, to find out what they were. In a trade school, my bridges burned behind me, I imagined myself in total isolation and darkness, unable to reorganize, unable to make the slightest adjustments in the course of my life, finally and irrevocably in the hands of a disinterested fate.

"What do you think I should do?" he asked.

"I want to stay. I can make it."

"What the hell is the matter with you, Conroy?"

I looked down at the edge of the desk. Something strange was happening. I seemed to be at two removes from reality, crouching behind my own body like a man manipulating a puppet through a curtain. "I don't know." My arms were reaching in through my back to make me talk. "That's the truth."

"If you don't," he said slowly, "you had better find out."

I climbed back into myself and nodded.

He opened the drawer of his desk and took out a small notebook. "Early report for two weeks. Get here fifteen minutes before the first bell and sign in with the hall monitor." He uncapped his pen and made a notation. "Leave plenty of time. Miss once and you're out. Understand?"

"Yes sir."

"That's all." He didn't look up. . . .

THE THIRD FLOOR

Miss Tuts, a tiny red-haired woman, stood at the side of the room screaming at the boy in front of the blackboard. "No, no, no! Didn't you hear what I said? *Soixante-duex! Soixante-deux!* And write it out, don't just put the numbers."

The boy turned slowly to the board and raised the chalk. Hesitantly he began to write.

"Wrong," she yelled. "Sit down. You didn't prepare the lesson." Her figure was black against the big windows as she paced back and forth with quick little steps. "Bernstein! Put the vocabulary for today on the board. And don't forget the verbs."

Bernstein stood up, a perfect pear. "Just the French?"

"Yes," she cried irritably. "Do I have to explain every day?"

Someone laughed in the back.

"Quiet!"

Bernstein finished one column quickly and started on the next, writing the words in exactly the same order in which they'd appeared in the textbook. He could memorize effortlessly, and the pride with which he repeated the same trick day after day had not endeared him to his classmates.

"Bernstein sucks," the boy next to me said quietly.

"Did you say something, Aaronson?"

"No, Miss Tuts."

"Stand up and translate the first column."

"Le shawmbra, the room. Le lee, the bed . . ."

Someone hit Bernstein on the back with a ball of paper as he turned away from the board. Laughter from the rear of the room. Aaronson went on without skipping a beat. "Revay, to dream. Se lavay, to wash . . ."

"Who threw that?" Miss Tuts screamed, running to the front of the room. "Who threw that paper?"

Looking uncomfortable, Bernstein returned to his seat.

"Le shapoe, the hat. La . . ."

She slammed her hand on the desk. "Shut up! Sit down! Now, who threw that paper?"

Silence.

Plunk! Someone plucked the short-metal prong under the seat with his thumbnail. Plunk! Answers started coming in from different parts of the room. Plunk! Plunk!

"Stop it! Stop it this instant!"

Plunk! Plunk!

"I'll send you all to the Dean! The entire class!"

We laughed as she stalked out. Her threat was empty. It had been used too often.

THE FOURTH FLOOR

Dr. Casey was a big man, well over six feet tall with the build to go with it, but he was getting old. His square face was touched with the gray skin tone of age, and except for rare moments of anger his eyes had lost the flash of life. He stared out over his desk expressionlessly, his hands clasped before him. He talked from the first bell to the last, and no one interrupted him. As long as he talked we didn't have to work. We'd discovered there was no need to listen. We could catch up on homework for other classes, read, or do the crossword puzzle. He didn't care as long as we were

quiet and looked busy. Perhaps he even thought we were taking notes.

"I put my sons through Harvard. Both of them. But they're gone now. Things change, that's what you people don't realize. When you're my age it becomes quite clear. Things change, things change constantly and the very things that seem most secure are actually changing very slowly, sometimes so slowly you can't see what's happening even though it's staring you in the face. You must stay alert at all times. Never believe the way things look. The garbage collectors believe everything is simple and that's why they're garbage collectors. You have to look behind the masks, you have to get behind the lies. Most of it is lies, you know. I am aware of that fact." He tapped the surface of the desk with his knuckles. "I can see through the lies because I've lived a full life. I didn't waste my time. In the First World War I was in graves registration. I saw things I can't tell you about. Things so horrible good taste prevents me from mentioning them. You people of course have no idea. That's why I'm here. That's why I'm here. That's why I'm sitting up here at this desk giving my life for your vicarious perusal." He stared out over the lowered heads of the boys and cleared his throat with a tremendous bellow. It was highly overdone, a self-conscious mannerism the boys had learned to ignore. Each day more and more phlegm was rolled more and more lovingly, as if he were testing our unconcern, as if, as the gesture became totally operatic, he were daring us to call his bluff. "My field was etymology. Where words came from. Words, after all, are the tools they use to break us down. I resist them because I know more about words than they do. Every educated man should know about words." He paused to let the thought sink in. "Then when they spew out their poison and their vomit I see it for what it is. Filth! Nothing more or less than that! And we are surrounded by it, gentlemen. The secretions of corrupted minds are the juices that nourish modern society, just as the blood of animals nourishes our bodies. Pus runs free over the body politic. Graft and corruption are everywhere. They've approached me many times, I assure you, whining and wheedling before me, making their filthy offers, trying to break me down. Well they can try for a thousand years and my answer will be the same. They can shove their special arrangements. They can shove their recommendations, gold watches and testimonial dinners. Let them eat their own swill." He spoke softly, as if withdrawn into himself, as if the strength of his feelings had driven him back to a point where he was no more than an observer of his own actions. Leaning far back in his chair, his long legs extended straight out into the aisle, he peered through loosely clasped fingers, his entire body motionless as a corpse. "None of it surprises me. None of it. They show us one man riding another, riding him like a horse, like a beast of burden. That stuff gets through. They call it art. They spit on the nobility of the human body. They lower themselves to the level of animals. Below animals. A man riding a man is going too far. I call them dogs from the bottom of my soul."

The school day is over. A mood of manic hilarity fills every classroom as we wait for the final bell. The aisles are crowded with laughing, shouting boys. The teachers, already on their way home mentally, sit behind their desks with lowered heads and occupy themselves with small unnecessary tasks.

Despite the confusion we're ready to go at the signal. Our books are packed. Our jackets are on. We pour through the door and out into the hall with a collective sigh. We rush for the stairs, dodging in and out among the slower boys. The noise is terrific. On the stairs we really let loose. Screams and yells float up from the lower floors. Fists bang against the metal side panels in continuous thunder. Down, down, down, rushing past the painted numbers, swinging round like crack the whip at the landings, leaping steps when there's room, pushing the boy in front, being pushed from behind, all of us mad with freedom. Down, down. So easily, so effortlessly. The stream carries us safely past the third, the second, the first, and out into the immense throng streaming through the banks of open doors to the street. We flow over the sidewalk and

between the parked cars onto the asphalt. In the darkness faces are indistinct. Matches flash for cigarettes. Around the corner the avenue gleams with neon. Most of us have already forgotten the five hours inside school because for most of us school is less than nothing. We spread like a liquid over the neighborhood and disappear into the subways.

FROM
The Student As Nigger
JERRY FARBER

Students are niggers. When you get that straight, our schools begin to make sense. It's more important, though, to understand why they're niggers. If we follow that question seriously enough, it will lead us past the zone of academic bullshit, where dedicated teachers pass their knowledge on to a new generation, and into the nitty-gritty of human needs and hang-ups. And from there we can go on to consider whether it might ever be possible for students to come up from slavery.

A student is expected to know his place. He calls a faculty member "Sir" or "Doctor" or "Professor"—and he smiles and shuffles as he stands outside the professor's office waiting for permission to enter. The faculty tell him what courses to take (in my department, English, even electives have to be approved by a faculty member); they tell him what to read, what to write, and, frequently, where to set the margins on his typewriter. They tell him what's true and what isn't. Some teachers insist that they encourage dissent but they're almost always jiving and every student knows it. Tell the man what he wants to hear or he'll fail your ass out of the course.

When a teacher says "jump," students jump. I know of one professor who refused to take up class time for exams and required students to show up for tests at 6:30 in the morning. And they did, by God! Another, at exam time, provides answer cards to be filled out—each one enclosed in a paper bag with a hole cut in the top to see through. Students stick their writing hands in the bags while taking the test. The teacher isn't a provo; I wish he were. He does it to prevent cheating. Another colleague once caught a student reading during one of his lectures and threw her book against the wall. Still another lectures his students into a stupor and then screams at them in a rage when they fall asleep.

Even more discouraging than this Auschwitz approach to education is the fact that the students take it. They haven't gone through twelve years of public school for nothing. They've learned one thing and perhaps only one thing during those twelve years. They've forgotten their algebra. They're hopelessly vague about chemistry and physics. They've grown to fear and resent literature. They write like they've been lobotomized. But, Jesus, can they follow orders! Freshmen come up to me with an essay and ask if I want it folded and whether their name should be in the upper right hand corner. And I want to cry and kiss them and caress their poor tortured heads.

Students don't ask that orders make sense. They give up expecting things to make sense long before they leave elementary school. Things are true because the teacher says they're true. At a very early age we all learn to accept "two truths," as did certain medieval churchmen. Outside of class, things are true to your tongue, your fingers, your stomach, your heart. Inside class, things are true by reason of authority. And that's just fine because you don't care anyway. Miss Wiedemeyer tells you a noun is a person, place or thing. So let it be. You don't give a rat's ass; she doesn't give a rat's ass.

The important thing is to please her. Back in kindergarten, you found out that teachers only love children who stand in nice straight lines. And that's where it's been at ever since. Nothing changes except to get worse. School becomes more and more obviously a prison. Last year I spoke to a student assembly at Manual Arts High School and then couldn't get out of the goddamn school. I mean there was NO WAY OUT. Locked doors. High fences. One of the inmates was trying to make it over a fence when he saw me coming and froze in panic. For a moment, I expected

sirens, a rattle of bullets, and him clawing the fence.

What school amounts to, then, for white and black kids alike, is a 12-year course in how to be slaves. What else could explain what I see in a freshman class? They've got that slave mentality: obliging and ingratiating on the surface, but hostile and resistant underneath.

As do black slaves, students vary in their awareness of what's going on. Some recognize their own put-on for what it is and even let their rebellion break through to the surface now and then. Others— including most of the "good students"— have been more deeply brainwashed. They swallow the bullshit with greedy mouths. They honest-to-God believe in grades, in busy work, in General Education requirements. They're pathetically eager to be pushed around. They're like those old greyheaded house niggers you can still find in the South who don't see what all the fuss is about because Mr. Charlie "treats us real good."

College entrance requirements tend to favor the Toms and screen out the rebels. Not entirely, of course. Some students at Cal State L.S. are expert con artists who know perfectly well what's happening. They want the degree or the 2-S and spend their years on the old plantation alternately laughing and cursing as they play the game. If their egos are strong enough, they cheat a lot. And, of course, even the Toms are angry down deep somewhere. But it comes out in passive rather than active aggression. They're unexplainably thick-witted and subject to frequent spells of laziness. They misread simple questions. They spend their nights mechanically outlining history chapters while meticulously failing to comprehend a word of what's in front of them.

The saddest cases among both black slaves and student slaves are the ones who have so thoroughly introjected their masters' values that their anger is all turned inward. At Cal State these are the kids for whom every low grade is torture, who stammer and shake when they speak to a Professor, who go through an emotional crisis every time they're called upon during class. You can recognize them easily at finals time. Their faces are festooned with fresh pimples; their bowels boil audibly across the room. If there really is a Last Judgement, then the parents and teachers who created these wrecks are going to burn in hell.

So students are niggers. It's time to find out why, and to do this, we have to take a long look at Mr. Charlie.

The teachers I know best are college professors. Outside the classroom and taken as a group, their most striking characteristic is timidity. They're short on balls.

Just look at their working conditions. At a time when even migrant workers have begun to fight and win, college professors are still afraid to make more than a token effort to improve their pitiful economic status. In California state colleges the faculties are screwed regularly and vigorously by the Governor and Legislature and yet they still won't offer any solid resistance. They lie flat on their stomachs with their pants down, mumbling catch phrases like "professional dignity" and "meaningful dialogue."

I'm not sure why teachers are so chickenshit. It could be that academic training itself forces a split between thought and action. It might also be that the tenured security of a teaching job attracts timid persons and, furthermore, that teaching, like police work, pulls in persons who are unsure of themselves and need weapons and the other external trappings of authority.

At any rate teachers ARE short on balls. And, as Judy Eisenstein has eloquently pointed out, the classroom offers an artificial and protected environment in which they can exercise their will to power. Your neighbors may drive a better car; gas station attendants may intimidate you; your wife may dominate you; the State Legislature may shit on you; but in the classroom, by God, students do what you say—or else. The grade is a hell of a weapon. It may not rest on your hip, potent and rigid like a cop's gun, but in the long run it's more powerful. At your personal whim—any time you choose—you can keep 35 students up for nights and have the pleasure of seeing them walk into the classroom pasty-faced and red-eyed carrying a sheaf of typewritten pages, with title page, MLA footnotes and margins set at 15 and 91.

The general timidity which causes teachers to make niggers of their students usually includes a more specific fear— fear of the students themselves. After all, students are different, just like black people. You stand exposed in front of them, knowing that their interests, their values, and their language are different from yours. To make matters worse, you may suspect that you yourself are not the most engaging of persons. What then can protect you from their ridicule and scorn? Respect for Authority. That's what. It's the policeman's gun again. The white bwana's pith helmet. So you flaunt that authority. You wither whisperers with a murderous glance. You crush objectors with erudition and heavy irony. And, worst of all, you make your own attainments seem not accessible but awesomely remote. You conceal your massive ignorance—and parade a slender learning.

There is a kind of castration that goes on in schools. It begins, before school years, with parents' first encroachments on their children's free unashamed sexuality and continues right up to the day when they hand you your doctoral diploma with a bleeding, shriveled pair of testicles stapled to the parchment. It's not that sexuality has no place in the classroom. You'll find it there but only in certain perverted and vitiated forms.

So you can add sexual repression to the list of causes, along with vanity, fear and will to power, that turn the teacher into Mr. Charlie. You might also want to keep in mind that he was a nigger once himself and has never really gotten over it. And there are more causes, some of which are better described in sociological than in psychological terms. Work them out, it's not hard. But in the meantime what we've got on our hands is a whole lot of niggers. And what makes this particularly grim is that the student has less chance than the black man of getting out of his bag. Because the student doesn't even know he's in it. That, more or less, is what's happening in higher education. And the results are staggering.

For one thing damn little education takes

place in the schools. How could it? You can't educate slaves; you can only train them. Or, to use an even uglier and more timely word, you can only program them.

Educational oppression is trickier to fight than racial oppression. If you're a black rebel, they can't exile you; they either have to intimidate you or kill you. But in high school or college, they can just bounce you out of the fold. And they do. Rebel students and renegade faculty members get smothered or shot down with devestating accuracy. In high school, it's usually the student who gets it; in college, it's more often the teacher. Others get tired of fighting and voluntarily leave the system. Dropping out of college, for a rebel, is a little like going North, for a Negro. You can't really get away from it so you might as well stay and raise hell.

How do you raise hell? That's a whole other article. But just for a start, why not stay with the analogy? What have black people done? They have, first of all, faced the fact of their slavery. They've stopped kidding themselves about an eventual reward in that Great Watermelon Patch in the sky. They've organized; they've decided

to get freedom now, and they've started taking it.

Students, like black people, have immense unused power. They could, theoretically, insist on participating in their own education. They could make academic freedom bilateral. They could teach their teachers to thrive on love and admiration, rather than fear and respect, and to lay down their weapons. Students could discover community. And they could learn to dance by dancing on the IBM cards. They could make coloring books out of the catalogs and they could put the grading system in a museum. They could raze another set of walls and let education flow out and flood the streets. They could turn the classroom into where it's at—a "field of action" as Peter Marin describes it. And, believe it or not, they could study eagerly and learn prodigiously for the best of all possible reasons—their own reasons.

They could. Theoretically. They have the power. But only in very few places, like Berkeley, have they even begun to think about using it. For students, as for black people, the hardest battle isn't with Mr. Charlie. It's with what Mr. Charlie has done to your mind.

Not very long ago people thought of college campuses as ivory towers isolated from the troubles that plagued society in general. The dozen pieces which follow deal with one urban campus revolution, that at Columbia in April 1968. The issues which set off two weeks of intermittent violence and confusion were many, but the central one was characteristically urban: the use of scarce park land in a black ghetto for facilities (in this case a new gymnasium) for a university which was largely white. New leaders emerged and the language of revolution flowered. The "long hairs" confronted the "Establishment," and the battle lines were drawn. Even now the combatants remain largely the same, and the revolution continues—inspired and sometimes directed from the once quiet ivory towers.

300 Protesting Columbia Students Barricade Office of College Dean

Three-hundred chanting students barricaded the Dean of Columbia College in his office yesterday to protest the construction of a gymnasium in Morningside Park and a defense-oriented program participated in by Columbia University. The protest against

the gymnasium extended at one time to the building site, where students tore down a section of fence before being driven off by 30 policemen. The students say that construction of the gymnasium would be "racist" because it would deprive Negroes in the area of recreational facilities. The charge against the defense program, the Institute for Defense Analysis, was that it supported the war effort in Vietnam. The protest, organized by the leftist Students for a Democratic Society, had the

support of other Columbia campus groups. Representatives of several Negro organizations unrelated to Columbia joined the protest. Among the groups were the Harlem chapter of the Congress of Racial Equality, the Harlem Committee for Self-Defense, the United Black Front, and the New York chapter of the Student Nonviolent Coordinating Committee, which is headed nationally by H. Rap Brown. The protest began shortly after noon when about 500 students gathered around the sundial in front of Low Memorial Library, Columbia University's main administrative building. From the sundial, the demonstrators surged up the steps toward the Low building to take their protest directly to the administration.

The Low building was closed, however, and the demonstrators were turned back by university security guards. Behind the guards stood about 150 members of a counter-demonstration group, the conservative-oriented Students for a Free Campus.

The S.D.S.-led students gathered around Mark Rudd, Columbia's S.D.S. president, who read a letter from David B. Truman, vice president of the university, offering to meet with the group immediately in the McMillan Theater, on the Columbia campus.

The boisterous group shouted down the offer. The students then marched to the site of the new gymnasium, at 113th Street and Morningside Drive, where they tore down a section of chain link fence around the area being cleared for the $11.6-million gymnasium. The police moved in, wielding billy clubs, and arrested one student, Fred Wilson.

The protesters marched four blocks back to the university campus, where Mr. Rudd again addressed the group at the sundial. "We're going to have to take a hostage to make them let go of I.D.A. and let go of the gym," he shouted.

With that, Mr. Rudd led the group to Hamilton Hall, the administrative building for Columbia College, the undergraduate arm of the university.

A Protest 'Forever'

At Hamilton Hall, Mr. Rudd took a stand in front of acting Dean Henry S. Coleman's office. He said Mr. Coleman had been selected as the group's hostage.

Mr. Coleman, formerly director of admissions at Columbia, became acting dean in June, 1967, when Mr. Truman, then dean of Columbia College, was named vice

president and provost of the university.

Mr. Rudd urged the group to remain in Hamilton Hall and outside Mr. Coleman's office, until its demands were met, and vowed that the group would stay there "forever" if necessary.

Dean Coleman was not in his office at the time. He appeared a few minutes later, elbowing his way through the crowd, and stood next to Mr. Rudd at the door of his office. Mr. Rudd asked the crowd: "Is this a demonstration?" and the crowd boomed back, "Yes!"

The university recently instituted a rule banning any demonstrations in buildings on the campus, and so the question and answer were obviously meant to point up the group's defiance of the rule.

"Are we going to stay here until our demands are met?" Mr. Rudd asked, and again, there was a booming "yes" from his followers. The demonstrators then chanted, for several minutes, "Hell no, we won't go."

Dean Coleman, who stood and listened to the chanting, finally said, "I have no control over the demands you are making, but I have no intention of meeting any demands under a situation such as this."

A voice from the crowd shouted "get on the phone." Dean Coleman replied, "I have no intention of calling the president or vice president of the university under conditions such as this."

The group started singing "We shall not be moved." Leaders of the protest urged the demonstrators to remain in the hall outside Dean Coleman's office, and they promised that food and drink were on the way. Dean Coleman turned and entered his office.

Soon boxes containing soft drinks, carrots, bananas, cake and oranges were brought in.

After the demonstrators had been outside his office for more than an hour, Dean Coleman came out and said, "I repeat, I have no control over your demands."

He warned, "It's getting too

crowded here and we're going to have trouble." The Dean then went back into his office. The student leaders drew up a written list of demands.

The demonstration was spearheaded by an informal steering committee established at 2 P.M. by representatives of the Society of Afro-American Students, the Students for a Democratic Society and the Columbia Citizenship Council, a group that does tutorial work in the neighborhoods surrounding Columbia.

In addition to demanding that Columbia end construction of the Morningside Park gymnasium and sever its links with the Institute of Defense Analysis, the steering committee also called upon the university to:

¶Terminate all disciplinary actions pending against students as a result of previous demonstrations against the gym and grant a general amnesty to all participants in the current protest.

¶Lift the ban on campus demonstrations.

¶Resolve all future disciplinary action against students at open hearings before students and faculty members.

¶Use its good offices to obtain dismissals of charges against those who participated in demonstrations at the gymnasium site in the past.

Six students are on probation at Columbia as a result of their participation in protests at the gymnasium site and several persons, including the Rev. A. Kendall Smith, have been arrested.

Dean Coleman, after reviewing the demands, told the students that Mr. Truman had seen the demands and was willing to meet in Wollman Auditorium "now." A steering committee of the protesters met briefly and turned down the offer of the meeting, unless they received a written guarantee of amnesty for the protesters.

Mr. Truman later, in an interview in his office in Low Library, said the answer to the amnesty demand was "no."

He said he was prepared to have the demonstrators remain in Hamilton Hall "until they get tired."

Once the students had taken over Hamilton Hall, no campus security guards were in evidence and there were no city police anywhere on the campus. By the early morning, the number of demonstrators had grown to about 400.

Shortly after the blockade of the dean's office began, red crepe and posters bearing the likenesses of Lenin, Ernesto Che Guevara and Malcolm X, the black nationalist who was assassinated in Harlem, were pasted on the walls.

A group of eight Negro youths stood guard outside Dean Coleman's office. At about 10 P.M., a group of Columbia students scuffled briefly with the guards.

One student showed a copy of a leaflet that he said was being distributed in Harlem. It said: "Stop Columbia from taking over Harlem. Black students at Columbia are holding a dean captive and have taken control of the administration building . . . Go to Columbia and help the black students NOW . . ."

At 11:15 P.M., Dean Coleman said he intended to stay in his office "throughout the night if necessary." He refused any other comment.

There were at least two other Columbia faculty members who remained in the dean's office.

Outside the office, Omar Ahmed, an organizer for the United Black Front said: "We have been running a long campaign against Columbia. This is part of the continuing attack. This is going to be a very hot summer for Columbia University."

Mr. Ahmed said his group intended to "keep up the pressure on the gym, on Harlem Hospital and on Delano Village, which Columbia University bought."

Delano Village is a Harlem housing development bought by Columbia to house staff mem-mers of Harlem Hospital, which is affiliated with Columbia.

Black organizations charge Columbia has evicted Negroes to make room for hospital personnel. The organizations also blame Columbia for allegedly poor conditions at Harlem Hospital.

The Student Nonviolent Coordinating Committee, one of the most militant black organizations in the country, urged "all people who understand the urgency of this struggle to support the students, community people and their allies."

"It should be crystal clear that the issue at stake is the control by local people of their community and the institutions within their community, and the right of black people to protest injustices perpetrated upon them by institutions such as Columbia University," S.N.C.C. said.

The group's spokesman said that I.D.A. "works on military projects aimed at the oppression of the people of Vietnam" and "develops riot equipment to commit mass genocide against black people here in the U.S."

Groups Invited

William Sales, a 25-year-old Columbia graduate student who is working on a doctorate in international affairs and who is a member of the five-man steering committee leading the protest, said all off-campus groups participating in the demonstration had been invited by the steering committee, which is composed entirely of students.

While demonstrators filled the corridors of Hamilton Hall, some playing guitars and others sharing blankets and engaging in discussions, Mr. Sales summarized his feelings about Columbia's relations with its neighboring black community.

"They're trying," he said, "to Bogart Harlem," explaining that he meant act toward Harlem like Humphrey Bogart, the late movie star.

Shortly after 1 A.M., about 50 counterdemonstrators gathered around a statue of Alexander Hamilton about 20 feet from the besieged building

and sang choruses of "The Ballad of the Green Berets," a song extolling the heroism of Special Forces troops fighting in Vietnam.

Fred Wilson, the 19-year-old student arrested at the gymnasium site, was charged with assault, criminal mischief and resisting arrest. He was said to have knocked down three policemen when they tried to stop him from pulling down the fence.

Plans for the construction of the gymnasium have been troubling members of the Negro community as well as some city officials and Columbia alumni. The building is to be erected on a steep rocky slope in Morningside Park, which separates Columbia, on Morningside Heights, from Harlem.

The university signed a 100-year lease with the city for the site in 1961, with rent set at $3,000 a year. The arrangement provided that Columbia build a separate gymnasium and swimming pool for the Harlem community.

Columbia's relations with its neighbors in Harlem have been strained for several years.

One of the problems has been Columbia's expansion, which has resulted in the university's acquisition of more than 100 buildings in the last few years and the eviction of many long-time residents of low-cost rent-controlled housing.

Concerned about crime in its area, Columbia bought many hotels that were well-known havens for prostitutes and narcotics addicts and attempted to evict these tenants, but some community groups objected, saying Columbia should have undertaken the rehabilitation rather than the eviction of the residents . . .

Columbia Closes Campus After Disorders

Office of President Is Seized—Dean Freed but Protest Widens

Columbia University students expanded their protest early today, invading two more buildings after the Morningside Heights campus was closed following a second day of tumultuous demonstrations.

By early this morning, the demonstration involved Hamilton, Fayerweather and Avery halls as well as the Low Memorial Library office of Dr. Grayson Kirk, the university president. Dr. Kirk's office was seized yesterday, a day also marked by the release of Acting Dean Henry Coleman, who had been held captive in his Hamilton Hall office for more than 24 hours.

With the demonstration growing in magnitude, the police established a command post on the Columbia campus at the request of university authorities for the first time in three years.

Classes Canceled

The closing of the campus was ordered last night and resulted in the cancellation of classes for 1,500 students. Later Dean David B. Truman, vice president of the university, said classes today would be held as scheduled.

Campus activities in general were carried out normally yesterday, as only about 150 students of the 27,500 enrolled at the university were involved in the seizure.

But a university spokesman said sessions scheduled for Hamilton Hall, where one-third of the college's classes are held, had been canceled yesterday.

Many students were openly resentful of the demonstration, and last night, as a light rain fell, about 200 gathered outside Low Library, which houses President Kirk's office, chanting: "Get'em out. Get'em out." . . .

Until yesterday, no city policemen had been summoned to the Columbia campus since May 8, 1965, when about 200 demonstrators forced the postponement of a ceremony at which commissions were being distributed to members of the university's Naval Reserve Officers Training Corps.

Twenty policemen were invited to the campus by the university to restore order during the 1965 demonstration.

Previously, the police have gone to the Columbia vicinity during panty raids, but a Columbia spokesman said such outbreaks were largely focused on streets bordering the university so that the police did not have to enter the Columbia campus.

By 9:30 P.M., between 25 and 50 city policemen were on the campus to protect campus property, according to the office of J. W. Whiteside, director of buildings and grounds for the university.

According to the police, city policemen normally do not enter private property, such as a university campus, unless invited. Should the police have evidence of a crime on a campus, the police said, they would respond without invitation from university officials.

The protest began shortly after noon Tuesday with an attempt to take the issues directly to the administration by storming the offices in Low Library. Turned back by guards, the demonstrators proceeded to the site of the new gymnasium, off the campus at 113th Street and Morningside Drive, where they tore down a section of chain-like fence around the area being cleared for the $11.6-million structure.

A short time later, the protestors, led by Mark Rudd, campus president of Columbia's Students for a Democratic Society, marched to Hamilton Hall, the ivied main building that is the headquarters for Columbia College, the men's undergraduate school, where Dean Coleman was later blockaded in his office.

Hamilton Hall, which is near Amsterdam Avenue at 116th Street, was occupied by the largely white membership of S.D.S., joined by Negro students and some Harlem residents. When at about 5 A.M. the Negroes asked the whites to leave, declaring that the whites were not committed enough to radical action, including violence, Mr. Rudd led a group of about 60 white students to Low Library, north of 116th Street, midway between Broadway and Amsterdam Avenue.

Late in the afternoon the Students for a Democratic Society held a strategy session to plan further action. Mr. Rudd advocated the seizure of more campus buildings, but was voted down by those who wanted to concentrate on lobbying with other students in support of the society's demands.

Mr. Rudd left the crowded meeting in a rush. He announced he had resigned, but later reconsidered, attributing his announcement to the strain of the last two days.

Meanwhile, members of the society had proposed a student strike today.

Many members of the S.D.S. are deeply troubled over their relationship to the Negro students and Harlem residents who ejected them from Hamilton Hall. Some felt it was necessary for the Negroes to take control.

"It's very important for blacks to have their own thing, to develop solidarity," said a graduate student in sociology.

"Blacks have to assume their own positions of leadership," added John Hendrickson, a law student, "and this is one way of doing it."

"We just didn't have the same commitment," added Henry Reichman, a junior, who had been sleeping in the lounge of a dormitory. "Some of the blacks were actually willing to die. It made me wonder what my commitment really was, and it frightened me."

When the whites moved on Dr. Kirk's office, some gained access by brushing past security guards and entering the front door. Others clambered up an outside grating and entered a window.

Among the students inside was Linda LeClair, the 20-year-old New Hampshire girl who was the focus of attention on the university's campus last week when she was reprimanded by Barnard College authorities for living off campus with her boyfriend.

President Kirk was not in his office when it was seized, but he was on campus and appeared at the closed faculty meeting late in the day.

Inside Dr. Kirk's office, some students hurled papers and books to the floor, damaged fixtures in the private bathroom, helped themselves to a supply of cigars and pasted to the window signs reading "Liberated Area. Be Free to Join Us."

The students also pasted up photographs of President Kirk that they found in the office.

One was decorated with a red mustache.

The opposition of other students to the demonstration evidenced itself in direct action at one point when Mr. Rudd appeared at a window in Dr. Kirk's office to say that the demonstrators were ready to stay indefinitely. Eggs were thrown from the crowd on the sidewalk below. The eggs missed their target and splattered on the building's granite face. . .

The pieces above are reproduced as they appeared in *The New York Times* while the events were taking place. Below, a Columbia student, a participant in the "disorders," gives us his own quite personal point of view on the same incidents. Kunen's reminiscences are followed by more *Times* reportage.

FROM

The Strawberry Statement
JAMES SIMON KUNEN

THE SHIT HITS THE FAN

Columbia used to be called King's College. They changed the name in 1784 because they wanted to be patriotic and *Columbia* means *America.* This week we've been finding out what America means.

Every morning now when I wake up I have to run through the whole thing in my mind. I have to do that because I wake up in a familiar place that isn't what it was. I wake up and I see blue coats and brass buttons all over the campus. ("Brass buttons, blue coat, can't catch a nanny goat" goes the Harlem nursery rhyme.) I start to go off the campus but then remember to turn and walk two blocks uptown to get the only open gate. There I squeeze through the three-foot "out" opening in the police barricade, and I feel for my wallet to be sure I've got the two I.D.'s necessary to get back into my college. I stare at the cops. They stare back and see a red armband and long hair and they perhaps tap their night sticks on the barricade. They're looking at a radical leftist.

I wasn't always a radical leftist. Although not altogether straight, I'm not a hair person either, and ten days ago I was writing letters to Kokomo, Indiana, for Senator McCarthy; my principal association with the left was that I rowed port on crew. But then I got involved in this movement and one thing led to another. I am not a leader, you understand. But leaders cannot seize and occupy buildings. It takes great numbers of people to do that. I am one of those great numbers. What follows is the chronicle of a single revolutionary digit.

MONDAY, APRIL 22:   A mimeograph has appeared around the campus charging SDS with using coercion to gain its political ends. SDS is for free speech for itself only, it is charged. SDS physically threatens the administration. SDS breaks rules with impunity while we (undefined) are subject to dismissal for tossing a paper airplane out a dorm window. Aren't you TIRED, TIRED, TIRED of this? Will Mark Rudd be our next dean? Do something about it. Come to the SDS rally tomorrow and *be prepared.* At first anonymous, the leaflet reappears in a second edition signed Students for a Free Campus. The jocks have done it again. As with the demonstrations against Marine campus recruiting in the spring of '67, threats of violence from the right will bring hundreds of the usually moderate to the SDS ranks just to align themselves against jock violence. I personally plan to be there, but I'm not up tight about it. At the boat house, a guy says he's for the jock position. Don't get me wrong, I say, I'm not against beating up on a few pukes, I just don't think you should stoop to their level by mimeographing stuff. We both go out and kill ourselves trying to row a boat faster than eight students from MIT will be able to.

TUESDAY, APRIL 23: Noon. At the sundial are 500 people ready to follow Mark Rudd (whom they don't particularly like because he always refers to President Kirk as "that shithead") into the Low Library administration building to demand severance from IDA, an end to gym construction, and to defy Kirk's recent edict prohibiting indoor demonstrations. There are around 100 counterdemonstrators. They are what Trustee Arthur Ochs Sulzberger's newspapers refers to as "burly white youths" or "students of considerable athletic attainment"—jocks. Various deans and other father surrogates separate the two factions. Low Library is locked. For lack of a better place to go we head for the site of the gym in Morningside Park, chanting "Gym Crow must go." I do not chant because I don't like chanting.

I have been noncommittal to vaguely against the gym, but now I see the site for the first time. There is excavation cutting across the whole park. It's really ugly. And there's a chain link fence all around the hole. I don't like fences anyway so I am one of the first to jump on it and tear it down. Enter the New York Police Department. One of them grabs the fence gate and tries to shut it. Some demonstrators grab him. I yell "Let that cop go," partly because I know that the night sticks will start to flagellate on our heads, which they proceed to do. One of my friends goes down and I pull him out. He's on adrenaline now and tries to get back at the cops but I hold him, because I hit a cop at Whitehall and I wished I hadn't very shortly thereafter.*

After the usual hassle, order is restored and the cops let Rudd mount a dirt pile to address us. As soon as he starts to talk he is drowned out by jackhammers but, at the request of the police, they are turned off. Rudd suggests we go back to the sundial and join with 300 demonstrators there, but we know that he couldn't possibly know whether there are 300 demonstrators there and we don't want to leave. He persists and we defer.

Back at the sundial there is a large crowd. It's clear we've got something going. An offer comes from Vice-President Truman to talk with us in McMillin Theatre but Rudd, after some indecision, refuses. It seems we have the initiative and Truman just wants to get us in some room and bullshit till we all go back to sleep. Someone suggests we go sit down for awhile in Hamilton, the main college classroom building, and we go there. Sitting down turns to sitting-in, although we do not block classes. Rudd asks, "Is this a demonstration?" "Yes!" we answer, all together. "Is it indoors?" "Yes!"

An immediate demand is the release of the one student arrested at the park, Mike Smith, who might as well be named John Everyman, because nobody knows him. To reciprocate for Mike's detention, Dean Coleman is detained.

At four o'clock, like Pavlov's dog, I go to crew, assuring a long-hair at the door that I'll be back. At practice it is pointed out to me that the crew does not have as many WASPS as it should have according to the population percentage of WASPS in the nation, so don't I think that crew should be shut down? I answer no, I don't think crew should be shut down.

Back at school at eight I prepared to spend the night at Hamilton. My friend Rock is there. We decide that we are absolutely bound to meet some girls or at

*In October of 1967, there was a series of "Stop the Draft Week" demonstrations at Whitehall, the Army Induction Center for Manhattan. At about 6 A.M. on a Thursday morning a blue cossack rode his lumbering steed at me on the sidewalk. It was just too early in the morning to get run over by a horse. I slugged him (the cop) in the thigh, which was as high as I could reach, and was immediately brought to bay and apprehended by a detective, who smashed me in the knee with a movie camera, and later let me go when he deduced from my name that I was Irish, which I'm not.

least boys since there are 300 of them in the lobby. Every ten minutes he yells to me, "Hey, did you make any friends yet?" I say no each time, and he says that he hasn't either, but he's bound to soon.

I go upstairs to reconnoiter and there is none other than Peter Behr of Linda LeClair fame chalking on the wall, "Up against the wall, motherfucker, . . .' from a poem by LeRoi Jones." I get some chalk and write "I am sorry about defacing the walls, but babies are being burned and men are dying, and this University is at fault quite directly." Also I draw some SANE symbols and then at 2:30 A.M. go to sleep.

WEDNESDAY, APRIL 24, 5:30 A.M. Someone just won't stop yelling that we've got to get up, that we're leaving, that the blacks occupying Hamilton with us have asked us to leave. I get up and leave. The column of evicted whites shuffles over to Low Library. A guy in front rams a wooden sign through the security office side doors and about 200 of us rush in. Another 150 hang around outside because the breaking glass was such a bad sound. They become the first "sundial people." Inside we rush up to Kirk's office and someone breaks the lock. I am not at all enthusiastic about this and suggest that perhaps we ought to break up all the Ming Dynasty art that's on display while we're at it. A kid turns on me and says in a really ugly way that the exit is right over there. I reply that I am staying, but that I am not a sheep and he is.

Rudd calls us all together. He looks very strained. He elicits promises from the *Spectator* reporters in the crowd not to report what he is about to say. Then he says that the blacks told us to leave Hamilton because they do not feel that we are willing to make the sacrifices they are willing to make. He says that they have carbines and grenades and that they're not leaving. I think that's really quite amazing.

We all go into Kirk's office and divide into three groups, one in each room. We expect the cops to come any moment. After an hour's discussion my room votes 29–16 to refuse to leave, to make the cops carry us out. The losing alternative is to escape through the windows and then go organize a strike. The feeling is that if we get busted, *then* there will be something to organize a

strike about. The man chairing the discussion is standing on a small wooden table and I am very concerned lest he break it. We collect water in wastebaskets in case of tear gas. Some of it gets spilled and I spend my time trying to wipe it up. I don't want to leave somebody else's office all messy.

We check to see what other rooms have decided. One room is embroiled in a political discussion, and in the other everyone is busy playing with the office machines.

At about 8:30 A.M. we hear that the cops are coming. One hundred seventy-three people jump out the window. (I don't jump because I've been reading *Lord Jim*.) That leaves twenty-seven of us sitting on the floor, waiting to be arrested. In stroll an inspector and two cops. We link arms and grit our teeth. After about five minutes of gritting our teeth it dawns on us that the cops aren't doing anything. We relax a little and they tell us they have neither the desire nor the orders to arrest us. In answer to a question they say they haven't got MACE either.

In through the window like Batman climbs Professor Orest Ranum, liberal, his academic robes billowing in the wind. We laugh at his appearance. He tells us that our action will precipitate a massive right-wing reaction in the faculty. He confides that the faculty had been nudging Kirk toward resignation, but now we've blown everything; the faculty will flock to support the President. We'll all be arrested, he says, and we'll all be expelled. He urges us to leave. We say no. One of us points out that Sorel said only violent action changes things. Ranum says that Sorel is dead. He gets on the phone to Truman and offers us trial by a tripartite committee if we'll leave. We discuss it and vote no. Enter Mark Rudd, through the window. He says that twenty-seven people can't exert any pressure, and the best thing we could do would be to leave and join a big sit-in in front of Hamilton. We say no, we're not leaving until our demands on the gym, IDA and amnesty for demonstrators are met. Rudd goes out and comes back and asks us to leave again, and we say no again. He leaves to get reinforcements. Ranum leaves. Someone comes in to take pictures. We all cover our faces with different photographs of Grayson Kirk.

It's raining out, and the people who are climbing back in are marked by their wetness. Offered a towel by one of the new people, a girl pointedly says "No, thank you, I haven't been out." Rationally, we twenty-seven are glad that there are now 150 people in the office, but emotionally we resent them. As people dry out, the old and new becomes less differentiable, and I am trying for a field promotion in the movement so that I will not fade into the masses who jumped and might jump again.

The phone continues to ring and we inform the callers that we are sorry, but Dr. Kirk will not be in today because Columbia is under new management. After noon, all the phones are cut off by the administration.

At 3:45 I smoke my first cigarette in four months and wonder if Lenin smoked. I don't go to crew. I grab a typewriter and, though preoccupied by its electricness, manage to write:

The time has come to pass the time.

I am not having good times here. I do not know many people who are here, and I have doubts about why they are here. Worse, I have doubts about why I am here. (Note the frequency of the word here. *The place I am is the salient characteristic of my situation.) It's possible that I'm here to be cool or to meet people or to meet girls (as distinct from people) or to get out of crew or to be arrested. Of course the possibility exists that I am here to precipitate some change at the University. I am willing to accept the latter as true or, rather, I am willing, even anxious, not to think about it any more. If you think too much on the second tier (think about why you are thinking what you think) you can be paralyzed.*

I really made the conflicting-imperative scene today. I have never let down the crew before, I think. Let down seven guys. I am one-eighth of the crew. I am one-fifth of this demonstration. And I am not even sure that this demonstration is right. But I multiplied these figures by an absolute importance constant. I hate to hamper the hobby of my friends (and maybe screw, probably screw, my own future in it), I am sorry about that,

but death is being done by this University and I would rather fight it than row a boat.

But then I may, they say, be causing a right-wing reaction and hurting the cause. Certainly it isn't conscionable to hold Dean Coleman captive. But attention is being gotten. Steps will be taken in one direction or another. The polls will fluctuate and the market quiver. Our being here is the cause of an effect. We're trying to make it good; I don't know what else to say or do. That is, I have no further statement to make at this time, gentlemen.

The news comes in that Avery Hall, the architecture school, has been liberated. We mark it as such on Grayson's map. At about 8 P.M. we break back into Kirk's inner office, which had been relocked by security when we gathered into one room when the cops came in the morning. The $450,000 Rembrandt and the TV have gone with the cops.

We explore. The temptation to loot is tremendous, middle-class morality notwithstanding, but there is no looting. I am particularly attracted by a framed diploma from American Airlines declaring Grayson Kirk a V.I.P., but I restrict myself to a few Grayson Kirk introduction cards. Someone finds a book on masochism behind a book on government. Someone else finds what he claims is Grayson's draft card and preparations are made to mail it back to the Selective Service. On his desk is an American Airlines jigsaw puzzle which has apparently been much played with.

We have a meeting to discuss politics and defense, but I sit at the door as a guard. A campus guard appears and, before I can do anything, surprises me by saying, "As long as you think you're right, fuck 'em." He hopes something good for him might come out of the whole thing. He makes eighty-six dollars a week after twenty years at the job.

I go down to the basement of Low, where the New York City Police have set up shop. There are approximately forty of them; there is precisely one of me. I ask one for the score of the Red Sox game. He seems stunned that a hippie faggot could be interested in such things, but he looks it up for me. Rained out.

I use the pay-phone to call a girl at Sarah

Lawrence. I tell her how isolated I feel and how lonely I am and hungry and tired and she says oh. I explain that I'll be busted any minute and she says she knows that.

I return upstairs. One of these people who knows how to do things has reconnected a phone, but he needs someone to hold the two wires together while he talks. I do it. I'll do anything to feel like I'm doing something.

THURSDAY, APRIL 25:   I get up and shave with Grayson Kirk's razor, use his toothpaste, splash on his after-shave, grooving on it all. I need something morale-building like this, because my revolutionary fervor takes about half an hour longer than the rest of me to wake up. . . .

SATURDAY, APRIL 27:   . . . I get back to Math around 4:30 and sit down on the public-relations ledge over Broadway. People from a peace demonstration downtown are depositing money and food in a bucket at the bottom of a rope. Each time we haul it up and re-lower it we include I.D.'s for people who want to get into the campus. A remarkable number of cars toot their support, and when a bus driver pulls over to wave us a victory sign, ten people nearly fall off the ledge.

In the evening I discover that the electricity to the kitchen is cut off. I run downstairs and almost call for "someone important" but somehow I am unwilling to accept that kind of status relation. I tell several of my peers and one of them finds the fuse box and sets things right.

I volunteer for shopping. We buy twenty dollars of food for eighteen dollars (the merchants earlier had contributed food outright) and on the way back meet a gentleman who seems to belong to Drunken Faculty to Forget the Whole Mess. Someone whom I think of as a friend threatens to punch me because I am carrying food.

As the evening wears on I feel less useful and more alienated, so I assign myself the task of keeping the mayonnaise covered. After covering it twelve times I give up and decide to write home. I wonder whether the Paris Commune was this boring.

In the letter I try to justify rebelling on my

father's money. I point out that one of the dangers of going to college is that you learn things, and that my present actions are much influenced by my Contemporary Civilization (C1001y) readings. After sealing the letter I realize that my conception of the philosophy of law comes not so much from Rousseau as from Fess Parker as Davy Crockett. I remember his saying that you should decide what you think is right and then go ahead and do it. Walt Disney really bagged that one; the old fascist inadvertently created a whole generation of radicals.

I discover a phone which has not been cut off and call my brother. As I am talking someone puts a piece of paper beside me and writes "This . . . phone . . . is . . . tapped." I address myself briefly to the third party and go on talking. It feels good to talk to someone on the outside, although it is disappointing to find out that the outside world is going on as usual.

SUNDAY, APRIL 28:   Four hours of meetings about tactical matters, politics, and reports from Strike Central. I begin to long for a benevolent dictator. It is announced that we are spending as much money on cigarettes as food. I wonder, as I look about me, whether Lenin was as concerned with the breast size of his revolutionary cohorts as I am. It is now daylight-saving time; under all the clocks are signs saying "It's later than you think."

I spend the day sunning and reading *Lord Jim* on the ledge. At 3 P.M. four fire trucks scream up and men go running onto the campus with axes. Some people think this is the bust, but it seems like the wrong public agency to me. It turns out to be a false alarm.

The neighborhood little kids are anxious and able to squeeze through the fences. I talk to some of them and they are all conversant with the issues and on our side. I conduct an informal class in peace graffiti and distribute chalk.

The older brothers of these same kids are in the middle of Broadway throwing eggs at us. This action—one of them tells me later—is completely apolitical.

We have red flags flying from the roof. I explain to a cop on the sidewalk below that these stand for revolution, not for communism. He says yes, he remembers reading something about that. I hope he is not referring to the *Daily News.* The *News* charges us with vandalism and alcoholism. (Actually we voted to bar both grass and liquor, and there was only one dissident, named Melvin.) One cartoon, titled "Dancing to the Red Tune," shows a beatnik and some sort of cave girl dancing as a band sings "Louse up the campuses, yeah, yeah, yeah."

In the evening I walk into a room where there is a poetry reading. I don't want to be rude so I stay. A med student who looks like Dr. Kildare reads a poem entitled "Ode to Mickey Mantle's Five-hundredth HR."

Mutiny on the Bounty (Gable) is on TV and I find it inspirational, or at least amusing.

The student radio station, WKCR, announces that a clergyman is wanted in Fayerweather; a couple wants to get married. This does not surprise me. Reverend Starr performs the ceremony and says, "I pronounce you children of the new age." Shortly after we hear it, we see a candlelight procession approaching. The bride is carrying roses. She hands them to me and I pass them inside. The demonstration peaks for me as I touch the roses—I am stoned on revolutionary zeal. The newlyweds call themselves Mr. and Mrs. Fayerweather.

I volunteer for jock-watch from 2:00 to 3:00 but do not wake up the next man and stay out on the entrance window ledge until five. I am to let no one in as we now have a population of 150 and we want a stable commune—no tourists. We even consider a Stalinist purge to reduce the mouths to feed. Only tonight does my roommate decide to occupy a building. I have about seven degrees of disdain and contempt for him, but he got in before my watch. I stamp "Rush" on the hand of anyone who leaves. This allows them to get back in.

During my watch five guys in black cowls come by dragging a coffin and murmuring in Latin.

MONDAY, APRIL 29:   The Majority Coalition (read: jocks) have cordoned off Low and are trying to starve the demonstrators out. We decide to break the blockade. We plan tactics on a blackboard and go, shaking hands with those staying behind as though we might not be back. There are thirty of us with three cartons of food. We march around Low, making our presence known. Spontaneously, and at the wrong tactical place, the blacks in front jump into the jock line. I go charging through the gap with my box of grapefruit and quickly become upon the ground or, more accurately, on top of two layers of people and beneath two. I manage to throw three grapefruit, two of which make it. Then I become back where I started. Some blood is visible on both sides. Back at Math, some of our people say that the jocks they were fighting had handcuffs on their belts. Band-Aided noses abound and are a mark of distinction. We discuss alternative plans for feeding Low and someone suggests blockading the jocks—"If they run out of beer they're through." In the meantime, we can see hundreds of green armbands (for amnesty) throwing food up to the Low windows. We decide on a rope-and-pulley system between a tree and the Low windows, but there is some question about how to get the line up to the people in Low without the jocks grabbing it. When one kid suggests tying an end to a broom handle and throwing it like a harpoon, John (Outside Agitator) suggests we train a bird. A helicopter has already been looked into by Strike Central, but the FAA won't allow it. Finally we agree on shooting in a leader line with a bow and arrow.

A girl and myself are dispatched to get a bow. We go to the roof of the Barnard Library where the phys. ed. archery range is. We are in the midst of discovering how incredibly locked the cabinet is when a guard comes out on the roof. We crouch. He walks right past us. It would be just like TV were I not so preoccupied with it being just like TV. After ten minutes he finds us. the girl laughs coyly and alleges that oh, we just came up to spend the night. I am rather taken with the idea, but the guard is unmoved and demands our I.D.'s. This is our first bust.

Our second bust, the real one, begins to take shape at 2:30 A.M. We hear over

WBAI that there are busloads of TPF (Tactical Police Force, Gestapo) at 156th and at 125th and that patrol cars are arriving from all precincts with four helmeted cops per auto. I am unimpressed. So many times now we've been going to be busted. It just doesn't touch me anymore. I assume that the cops are there to keep the Mau Maus out.

A girls comes up to me with some paper towels. Take these, she says, so you can wipe the vaseline (slows tear-gas penetration) off your face when you're in jail. I haven't got vaseline on my face. I am thinking that vaseline is a big petroleum interest, probably makes napalm, and anyway it's too greasy. I hear over the walky-talky that Hamilton has been busted and that the sundial people are moving to Low and Fayerweather to obstruct the police. I put vaseline on my face. I also put vaseline on my hands and arms and legs above the socks and a cigarette filter in each nostril and carefully refold my plastic-bag gas mask so I'll be able to put it on quickly with the holes at the back of my head so my hair will absorb the gas and I'll be able to breathe long enough to cool the canister with a CO_2 fire extinguisher and pick it up with my asbestos gloves and throw it back at the cops. Someone tells me that he can't get busted or he'll miss his shrink again.

I take my place with seven others at the front barricade. All along the stairs our people are lined up, ready to hole up in the many lockable-from-within rooms on the three floors above me. We sing "We Shall Not Be Moved" and realize that something is ending. The cops arrive. The officer bullhorns us: "On behalf of the Trustees of Columbia University and with the authority vested in me . . ." That's as far as he is able to get, as we answer his question and all others with our commune motto — "Up against the wall, motherfuckers." We can't hold the barricade because the doors open out and the cops simply pull the stuff out. They have to cut through ropes and hoses and it takes them fifteen minutes before they can come through. All the while they're not more than thirty feet from me, but all I can do is watch their green-helmeted

heads working. I shine a light in their eyes but Tom tells me not to and he's head of the defense committee so I stop.

At 4:00 A.M. the cops come in. The eight of us sit down on the stairs (which we've made slippery with green soap and water) and lock arms. The big cop says "Don't make it hard for us or you're gonna get hurt." We do not move. We want to make it clear that the police have to step over more than chairs to get our people out. They pull us apart and carry us out, stacking us like cord wood under a tree. The press is here so we are not beaten. As I sit under the tree I can see kids looking down at us from every window in the building. We exchange the "V" sign. The police will have to ax every door to get them out of those offices. They do. Tom Hayden is out now. He yells "Keep the radio on! Peking will instruct you!" When they have sixty of us out they take us to the paddy wagons at mid-campus. I want to make them carry us, but the consensus is that it's a long, dark walk and we'll be killed if we don't cooperate, so I walk. At the paddy wagons there are at least a thousand people cheering us and chanting "Strike! Strike! Strike!" We are loaded in a wagon and the doors shut. John tells a story about how a cop grabbed the cop that grabbed him and then said "Excuse me." We all laugh raucously to show an indomitable spirit and freak out the cops outside.

We are taken to the 24th precinct to be booked. "Up against the wall," we are told. I can't get over how they really do use the term. We turn and lean on the wall with our hands high, because that's what we've seen in the movies. We are told to can that shit and sit down. Booking takes two hours. Lieutenant Dave Bender is the plainclothesman in charge. He seems sternly unhappy that college turns out people like us. He asks John if he thinks he could be a policeman and John says no; he doesn't think he's cut out for it.

We are allowed three calls each. A fat officer makes them for us and he is a really funny and good man. He is only mildly displeased when he is duped into calling Dial-a-Demonstration. He expresses interest in meeting a girl named Janice when three of us give him her number, one as his sister, one as his girl friend, and one as his ex-wife.

We go downstairs to await transportation to court. A TPF man comes in escorting Angus Davis, who was on the sixth floor of Math and refused to walk down. He has been dragged down four flights of marble stairs and kicked and clubbed all the way. A two-inch square patch of his hair has been pulled out. Ben, Outside Agitator, yells, "You're pretty brave when you've got that club." The officer comes over and dares him to say that again. He says it again. The cop kicks for Ben's groin, but Ben knows karate and blocks it. John says to the cop, "Thank you, you have just proved Ben's point." This is sufficiently subtle not to further arouse the cop, and he leaves. A caged bus takes us all the way downtown to the tombs (the courthouse). The kid beside me keeps asking me what bridge is this and what building is that. Finally he recognizes something and declares that we are going to pass his grandmother's house. I am busy trying to work a cigarette butt through the window grate so that I can litter from a police bus. Arriving, we drive right into the building; a garage door clamps down behind us.

Our combs and keys are confiscated so that we won't be able to commit suicide. In the elevator to the cells a white cop tells us we look like a fine bunch of men — we ought to be put on the front lines in Vietnam. Someone says that Vietnam is here, now. As we get out I look at the black cop running the elevator for some sort of reaction. He says "Keep the faith."

He said "Keep the faith," I say, and everyone is pleased. We walk by five empty cells and then are jammed into one, thirty-four of us in a 12x15 room. We haven't slept in twenty-four hours and there isn't even space for all of us to sit down at one time.

Some of our cellmates are from Avery. They tell us how they were handcuffed and dragged downstairs on their stomachs. Their shirts are bloody.

After a couple of hours we start to perk up. We bang and shout until a guard comes, and then tell him that the door seems to be stuck. Someone screams "All right, all right, I'll talk." It is pointed out that you don't need tickets to get to policemen's balls. We sing folk songs and "The Star-Spangled Banner." They allowed one of us to bring in a recorder and he plays Israeli folk music.

A court officer comes and calls a name. "He left," we say. Finally he finds the right list.

We are arraigned before a judge. The Outsiders are afraid they will be held for bail, but they are released on their own recognizance, like the rest of us, except they have some form of loitering charge tacked on to the standard second-degree criminal trespassing.

Back at school I eat in a restaurant full of police. As audibly as possible I compose a poem entitled "Ode to the TPF." It extolls the beauty of rich wood billies, the sheen of handcuffs, the feel of a boot on your face.

Meeting a cellmate, I extend my hand to him and he slaps it. I have to remember that — handslaps, not shakes, in the Revolution.

1,000 Police Act To Oust Students From Five Buildings At Columbia; Move in at University's Request

MEDIATION FAILS

Proposal by Kirk to
End Dispute Spurned
by Faculty Group

A handpicked force of 1,000 policemen moved onto the Columbia University campus early today and began ordering student demonstrators out of five buildings the students have occupied in a tense, week-long protest.

The police moved with stunning suddenness at 2:30 A.M. while most of the city and much of the campus and its surrounding neighborhood slept.

As the hour for the police assault approached, tension mounted sharply on the campus as groups of students held informal meetings. At 1:45 A.M., when word reached the Mathematics Building that "a bust," or police raid, was imminent, student demonstrators began strengthening their barricades and girding themselves for the assault.

WKCR, the campus radio station, at 1:30 A.M. reported that a police move appeared close, and it urged students to remain in their dormitories.

Move Delayed

The raid originally had been scheduled for 1:30 A.M. It was postponed several times because of what police officials described as "tactical delays."

A high police official said later that the raid had been delayed to wait until Harlem was asleep.

Wearing helmets and carrying flashlights, they fanned through the darkened campus which they had divided for purposes of the assault into seven sectors that were designated "target areas."

These were Hamilton, Avery and Fayerweather Halls, the Low Memorial Library and the Mathematics Building—all occupied structures—and the areas of 115th Street and Morningside Drive and 116th Street and Amsterdam Avenue.

Target Gets Priority

Hamilton Hall, which Negro students and a scattering of off-campus black activists had occupied since the student uprising began last Tuesday afternoon, was the first police target.

As the police moved on Hamilton Hall, other policemen issued an ultimatum to the students occupying Low Library demanding they leave peacefully or be ejected.

Speaking over a bullhorn a white-helmeted policeman called to "the occupants" of Hamilton Hall, saying: "We want you to come out and come out now. We are authorized by the trustees of the university. This is it. Come out now. You made your point. Come out now."

It was understood to be the hope of the police commanders that they could remove the Negro students with a minimum of force, thus making it easier for them to evict the white students from the four other occupied campus buildings.

The police commanders, who led a force that included 200 men from each of five precincts, were said to be carrying written instructions from Police Commissioner Howard R. Leary to use necessary force but to show restraint in their handling of the students.

As the first move in their coordinated attack, the police at 2 A.M. severed all telephone service and water supplies to the five occupied buildings. The student protesters had depended heavily during the demonstration on telephone communication to keep in touch with the situation in each of the buildings they held.

Meanwhile, pockets of students, many huddled under blankets against the chill night air, moved from building to building trying to see what was going on. And outside the Low Library, where about 200 students gathered in a milling crowd, a "town crier" with a bullhorn issued minute-by-minute bulletins about events leading up to the raid.

Mr. Leary, accompanied by two representatives of the university administration, was directing the operation on the campus. Chief Inspector Sanford D. Garelik supervised the force, which included members of the Emergency Service Division, policewomen and detectives, as well as uniformed patrolmen.

University Made Request

The police acted in response to a request from the administration of the university it was understood. Under normal procedure, the police would take no action on the campus, which is private property, unless formally authorized to do so by university officials.

Fires Break Out In Two Buildings

Blood Flows on Campus Walk
— Barnard Girls Scream
Obscenities at Police

The second battle of Columbia University, in which policemen pummeled unresisting students and students smashed policemen with bricks early yesterday morning, only reaffirmed for many at Columbia what the first battle on April 30 had shown:

That several hundred student demonstrators could paralyze almost at will the operations of the 214-year-old university, and the university could exact a high price for that achievement.

It was a night of high emotion and frenzy, in which 51 students and 17 policemen were injured, fires were set in buildings, Barnard girls shouted obscenities that surprised men, and blood was splotched on College Walk.

When the violence had subsided at 5:30 A.M. on the rubble-strewn campus, the strains from the song "We Want a Revolution" from the play "Marat/Sade" drifted clearly from a student's window.

But for some, the words of Vice President David B. Truman, expressed publicly 16 hours earlier, were more keenly in mind. He said that the Vietnam War had created restlessness among students and that if the war did not end, "it is debatable if the university could continue."

Issues Fade in the Night

The many and varied issues that have roused feelings of contempt and even hatred between some students and university officials were as inconsequential during the night as who won the touch football game that had taken place in mid-campus at the outset of troubles Tuesday afternoon.

The serious sidewalk discussions among students and faculty in the afternoon sun also faded during the night,

to be replaced by obscene language, bullhorns that predicted peril and called for peace, and the anguished cries of those who felt and others who saw the violence.

It was not a night for moderates. Some faculty members sought to ease the positions of student leaders and administration officials as the likelihood of a student-police clash developed. But as one senior faculty member said:

"We have no credibility with the students, and the administration doesn't talk to us."

The night raised many questions:

Why did the students engage in more violence, even before the police clashes, than they had until now?

Why did the administration choose this period, when tension was high on the campus, which is virtually shut down, to suspend publicly four student leaders Tuesday and thereby create an issue for the demonstrators?

And why did the police use plainclothesmen on the campus when they had aroused such great opposition from students and engaged in the bitterest fighting during the first police-student clash on April 30?

None of the answers to these questions is entirely clear. Jacques Nevard, Deputy Police Commissioner for Press Relations, said yesterday that the plainclothes men "were pressed into service to aid policemen in uniform."

Newsmen saw hundreds of uniformed policemen standing in formation in center of the campus at one point when the plainclothes men, some with badges hidden, raced across South Field to chase students into dormitories. Many students were caught and beaten.

The student destruction of Columbia buildings and property was apparently spontaneous. At least 20 windows were broken by students who tossed rocks. Wooden fences surrounding shrubbery and flowers and a metal ramp on the steps leading to Low Library were

appropriated for barricades created by the students at the main campus gates at 116th Street and Broadway and Amsterdam Avenues.

The university's decision to suspend four student leaders who refused to appear by 5 P.M. Tuesday at the office of an assistant dean of Columbia College to answer charges of participating in the previous disturbance was the immediate cause of the troubles.

Students who had occupied Hamilton Hall, which contains the dean's office and classrooms, to protest the suspension decision were ordered out of the school at 7:30 P.M. Tuesday.

Most of the students refused to leave and the university asked the police to remove them. The doors to the building remained open during the night as almost 800 students gathered outside, divided into camps for and against the demonstrators.

Eggs were thrown by the antidemonstrators at the students in the building and the response was loud chants of "Strike, strike, strike." The students inside were led by Mark Rudd, chairman of the Columbia chapter of the Students for a Democratic Society, which is leading the student strike.

130 Are Arrested

At 2:20 A.M. yesterday, the police moved into the tunnels under Hamilton Hall and subsequently arrested about 130 students, including Mr. Rudd. No violence was reported.

Shortly after, fires broke out on a top floor of Hamilton and in Fayerweather Hall, across the campus. Fayerweather, which has classrooms and laboratories, was invaded by some students who had moved toward that end of the campus in search of the police vans that would take away the arrested students.

The students did not obstruct city firemen who put out the blazes. The cause of the fires is under investigation.

The first clash between students and the police

apparently occurred shortly before Hamilton Hall was evacuated. Two plainclothes men were spotted by a student with a bullhorn who urged students to "get them." The students gave chase, but the policemen eluded them.

Moments later, after students smashed several windows of Low Library, which contains the President's offices, a student worker for the campus radio station WKCR, reported he was struck by a plainclothes policeman with a blackjack.

With at least 700 students milling around, President Grayson Kirk asked the police to clear the campus of anyone who refused to leave or enter the dormitories.

At 3:50 A.M. about 50 helmeted police marched in formation through John Jay Hall, a dormitory and college cafeteria, and positioned themselves on the campus. More than 200 students then raced toward them shouting "Cops Must Go," and threw at least five rocks and several pieces of wood at the police, who retreated into John Jay.

By this time, newsmen had noticed that more than 130 bricks had been removed from the sidewalks in three different areas on the campus.

At about 4:30 A.M. more than 500 uniformed policemen with night sticks massed outside the Amsterdam Avenue-116th

Street gate and about 200 students massed behind their barricades, some climbing on top of the 15-foot high pile of wooden barriers and everything else that was movable on campus.

The police removed the barricade to the often obscene shouts of students. When the police broke through at 4:50 A.M. they were met by at least 100 students, arm-in-arm who walked toward the police and then began running away. The Associated Press reported that a brick thrown by a student struck a policeman on the head.

The front line of policemen began running after the students. Newsmen saw one policeman club a student to the ground. He was bleeding from the head when another patrolman struck him three times with his nightstick. At least four students who did not resist the police were beaten.

The police, using bullhorns, told the students to leave the campus or return to dormitories. Most did not. Groups of policemen with a commander moved toward three undergraduate dormitories, to Ferris Booth Hall, a social center, and to Furnald Hall, a dormitory.

There were some scuffles, some beatings and rock-throwing. But soon after the students went into the building they returned to the center of the

campus where the police had regrouped.

It was 5:10 A.M. and the worst violence now occurred, when the police sent about 50 plainclothes men charging toward students from John Jay and Livingston Halls, who were on the grass about 100 yards from the buildings.

The policemen, some shouting "Get 'em," caught several students, beat them to the ground, and on one occasion, kicked a student several times. The students were arrested.

The plainclothesmen then swept westward, racing after students who had come out of Furnald Hall. One student was clubbed several times as he jumped over a hedge five feet from the building.

The policemen charged into the building and fought with students. Four students came out with bloody heads; one policeman was helped away with a head wound. One newsman said a policeman briefly drew a pistol. The Police Department denied any guns were drawn.

Students showered the police with bricks, bottles and light bulbs. They screamed obscenities and a small group of uniformed policemen at the building door shouted obscenities back.

Why Those Students Are Protesting
FROM *TIME* MAGAZINE

One great educator became so infuriated with what he called the licentious, outrageous and disgraceful behavior of students at his college that he quit in disgust. The college was at Carthage, the year was A.D. 383, and the dismayed teacher, as he relates in *Confessions,* was St. Augustine. Sometimes students can try the patience of a saint.

One of those times is now. Seldom before have so many groups of students organized so militantly or seemed to try so hard to reorder their colleges, their countries or the world at large. It is the biggest year for students since 1848—a year of student-led revolution in Europe.

The rise of this obstreperous generation is a genuine phenomenon. It was unforeseen by educators, who scarcely a decade ago were overstating the case in criticizing what came to be called "the silent generation." Now the cry for student power is worldwide. It keeps growing and getting a lot of attention and quite a few results. For the first time in many years, students are marching and fighting and sitting-in not only in developing or unstable countries but also in the rich industrial democracies. In the U.S., the movement has spread from the traditionally active, alert and demonstrative student bodies of the elite schools to many usually quiescent campuses.

The protesting activists, still a very small minority, overlook the accomplishments of society but criticize its shortcomings. Possibly idealistic but skeptical of ideologies, they contend that governments have not performed up to their original promises. The student leftists disdain Soviet-style Communism as spiritually corrupt. The democrats fault the West's inequalities of wealth and race.

The activists demand change and want to determine its course. The university should not be the conserver of society, they argue, but the fountain of reform. They believe that students should be not merely preparing to enter the active world but a force within it. Many of them have a fashionable disaffection for organized religion, but they express the Judaeo-Christian belief that one man should act where he is, and that if he does so, he can help to change the world.

DEMONSTRATIONS & ISSUES

During the past three months, students have demonstrated for change in 20 countries. They have taken to the streets in such usual centers of student unrest as Brazil, Japan and The Netherlands and in such normally placid places as Denmark, Switzerland and West Germany. Student protests have led to the temporary closing of at least three dozen universities in the U.S., Italy, Spain, Tunisia, Mexico, Ethiopia and other countries. Belgian student demonstrations, fanning the old Flemish-v.-Walloon controversy, brought the government down. Egyptian students, marching in spontaneous protest against government inefficiency, obliged Gamal Abdel Nasser to rearrange his Cabinet. Communist Poland put down street demonstrations, but only after suspending more than 1,000 rebellious students. More successful were Czechoslovakia's students: their protests were a significant factor in pushing out the old Stalinists and shifting

the direction of government toward greater liberty.

In the U.S., a significant facet of the phenomenon is that more students are moving away from alienation and toward highly political activism. While the hippie movement is waning, student power has shifted from passive protest to specific action aimed at accomplishing practical goals. Some youngsters who had despaired of the whole political system, and doubted that they could ever accomplish real change by working inside it, were given a new sense of hope and power by the crusade for Eugene McCarthy in New Hampshire. Following a romantic cause to a remote state, a few thousand students used old-fashioned ward politics to help bring out the vote. The result brought Robert Kennedy into the presidential race. And that—plus student protests against the Administration's Viet Nam policies—had something to do with Lyndon Johnson dropping out.

The latest worldwide wave of student activism started in the U.S. several years ago, partly as a demand for more freedom and power of decision on campuses. It was stimulated by two larger emotional issues. The first was civil rights. In their demonstrations in the early 1960s, U.S. students discovered that they had the power to move legislators to action. And while they would be horrified at the thought, the students—says Harvard Professor Seymour Lipset—learned their tactics from the white Southerners who used civil disobedience to protest the 1954 Supreme Court decision for desegregation of schools. Out of this developed the pattern of sit-ins, lie-ins, marches and some violence. After civil rights, the second issue was Viet Nam. This was not merely a question of sticking up for somebody else; the draft made it a highly personal issue for many students. They did not like the prospect of getting shot at in a war that many of them considered to be unjust and immoral.

PRIVILEGE & PERMISSIVENESS

The U.S. protests have clearly had an international impact. In Berlin, Rio de Janeiro and Tokyo, student activists study the sit-in and seizure tactics that U.S. students used to protest the war, to desegregate Southern lunch counters and to immobilize the University of California in 1964. When television carries pictures of students demonstrating in London or Manhattan, students in Amsterdam and Prague start marching.

For all their differences of nationality, mood or cause, student activists around the world have many common traits and habits. They tend to read the same authors, particularly the U.S.'s C. Wright Mills, Norman Mailer and Paul Goodman. Their favorite is California Professor Herbert Marcuse, 69, who argues that individuals are dominated and manipulated by big institutions of government and business, and that man has the obligation to oppose them. And they tend to have the same heroes; among them are such disparate Americans as Martin Luther King, Stokely Carmichael and Robert Kennedy, who is now much more popular with students abroad than at home. The far-out radicals idolize not the old leaders of Eastern Europe but such revolutionaries as Ho Chi Minh, Régis Debray and, above all, Che Guevara, around whom grows the martyr's myth.

One reason that students are getting more attention is that there are so many of them—and larger student bodies make larger demonstrations. Since the mid-1950s, university enrollments have doubled and more: from 380,000 to 880,000 in Latin America, from 739,000 to 1,700,000 in Western Europe, from 2,600,000 to 7,000,000 in the U.S. Among these, the vast majority are not militant and are often repelled by and sometimes moved to protest against the extravagances of the extremists. The majority are not apathetic but are more concerned with courses than causes. By the best estimate of educators at home and abroad, 1% to 2% of the students in a university are highly committed leaders and agitators tending to extremism. Beyond them, roughly 5% to 10% are activists who take part in demonstrations, though the number can go much higher when a sensitive issue is raised.

The Young Democrats claim some 100,000 members on U.S. campuses;

the Young Republicans, 150,000. The conservative Young Americans for Freedom has 25,000; the radical leftist Students for a Democratic Society is much smaller—5,500 members—but more influential. What it lacks in size, the S.D.S. makes up in zeal and ability to play the press for headlines. Typically, the S.D.S. has only 60 active members among 4,700 students at Princeton, but it is the biggest partisan organization on campus, and one of its highly committed members was elected chairman of the undergraduate assembly last week. An underlying principle of S.D.S. activism is to make as much trouble as possible for the Establishment. Some of its members quite openly, if naively, espouse Marxism as their basic philosophy. Most activists seem to subscribe to the not unreasonable theory that in this era hardly anyone listens to a quiet man, so they make as much noise as possible.

There are many reasons—economic, social, educational—for the current activism of students. More than any prior generation, they are children of permissive parents, and the Spock marks are showing. Today's young are used to having their complaints acted on instantly. "They are the babies who were picked up," notes Harvard's David Riesman. They have less direction than previous generations, are challenged by their parents to think for themselves. For all the rather exaggerated talk of the generation gap, American student activists tend not so much to defy their parents as to emulate them. And their parents are inclined to approve of what they are doing.

The many studies of student activists show that the great majority of them come from families that are prosperous, politically active and liberal. Almost half of the protest-prone students are Jewish; few are Catholic. The most active students cluster in schools that have a tradition of dissent and a tolerance for it—universities such as California, Wisconsin, Columbia. Most of the activists are students of the arts and humanities; they are apt to be bright but dreamy, and not yet committed to careers. Few are in the professional schools—business, engineering or medicine. Since many universities no longer demand compulsory attendance at lectures, they have the time to ring doorbells for a candidate or march for civil rights. Some sympathetic professors spur the activists on, grant them long periods off, extend deadlines for tests and theses.

Activists are often economically liberated. They take their own prosperity for granted; affluence has become so common and scholarships so plentiful that few students have to work their way through. The youngsters may criticize their parents for devoting too much time to making money, but they like the freedom that money gives them. Describing student activists, the University of Michigan daily said: "They took their tactics from Gandhi, their idealism from philosophy class and their money from Daddy."

WANTED: RELEVANCE & INVOLVEMENT

Around the world, the first target of the student activists is the university. They feel, with some reason, that their education is not sufficiently existential, that it is not relevant to today's life. They want a larger voice in choosing professors and framing courses. Particularly in Europe and Latin America, student radicals view the university as a microcosm of society, with its lack of class mobility, its numerous bureaucracies, its concentration on material goals. Their aim is to transform the university from a personnel agency for the economy to a more vocal force for social protest and reform. They want it to take over the role once held by such recently tamed institutions as Britain's Labor Party, West Germany's Social Democrats, and U.S. trade unions.

In the U.S., this viewpoint has taken several directions: protests by Boston University students against acceptance of a $500,000 gift from a landlord who once had slum properties (he withdrew the gift); protests by Princeton students against the university's work for the Pentagon-allied Institute for Defense Analyses (trustees are considering disassociating from the institute). In the current uprising at Columbia, extremists forced the university to stop construction of a gymnasium on a location considered offensive to some people in neighboring Harlem.

Closely related to the student protests is the growing movement for black student power. From Yale to San Francisco State, Negro activists and some white supporters have sought to make the university become more active in uplift drives in the slum community, to introduce more courses in Afro-American history, and to recruit more Negro students, professors and administrators. In most cases, the administration has quickly acceded to the demands. Last week the trustees of California's 18 state colleges voted to increase, from 2% to 4% of the entering class, the number of Negro, Mexican-American and other minority-group students to be admitted under special standards — that is, not by grades alone.

NEEDED: TOLERANCE & PARTICIPATION

The students have taught the university administration two lessons: 1) some of the changes that they want are really improvements, and 2) the way to deal with student power is to anticipate it, to initiate changes before the students demand them. Administrators who have permitted students to participate in some policy areas applaud the results, say that it prevents protest and often raises standards. Students should be permitted to voice their opinions on dormitory rules, on the performance of professors, and on what courses should be added or dropped.

But there is an all-important difference between student advice and student control. If students could dictate the hiring and firing of professors, they would tend to select those with whom they agree — and fall into an echo chamber. Latin American students have considerable control over many universities, and the consequence is chaos and inferior education. A university is not a democracy and cannot become one without degenerating into anarchy. At a conference on "Students and Society" at California's Center for the Study of Democratic Institutions last year, the president of the student body of St. Louis' Washington University put it aptly: "Were Washington University to be turned over to the students and faculty, it would fold in about six months because nobody would know how to run it."

Both the students and the elders have

some other lessons to be learned. What is needed most of all is more mutual respect. The student activists are more critical than constructive. They often have no immediate, practical answers for the problems that they expose—but older people should not lightly dismiss them for that. Sometimes it is enough just to ask the right questions. Student protests have stirred authorities in Spain, Germany and other countries to some fitful steps toward modernization. And students have begun to move U.S. universities in some desirable directions—toward a more involved role in the local community, toward a rethinking of the relevance of education.

For their part, the students might recognize that they do not have a monopoly on idealism. After all, the drives against poverty and racism in the U.S. were energized not by them but by their elders. It would also profit the students to recognize the temporary nature of their power and the severe limits on it. Theirs is primarily the power to disrupt. They can interfere with the established authority, but they cannot change it without help from other powerful groups in the population—as Czech students learned in their successful protest and Polish students learned in their unsuccessful one. With that in mind, activist students might do more to court allies not only among their more moderate contemporaries but also among older people. In this, they are not helped at all by some of the retrogressive tendencies of the extremists: they are often intolerant of anyone who disagrees with them, all too willing to interfere with the rights of others, and sometimes ready to stoop to hoodlumism and fascist methods.

Student power can be beneficial; student tyranny never is. Student involvement in politics should be encouraged, but student abuse of the democratic process must always be resisted. Students might well bear in mind the fine distinctions between reasoned dissent and raw intolerance, between knowledge and wisdom, between compromise and copping out. Already 1968 has produced one supreme lesson: students have much more to gain by working actively for change within the existing system than by dropping out of it.

The "Paper of Record" mentioned in the following headline is the *New York Times;* this report on its reporting is from the *Village Voice.* Both papers obviously intended to tell the "truth," though neither agrees with the reports of students who were involved.

Pre-Fitting the News
At the Paper of Record

JACK NEWFIELD

It was 2 A.M. last Tuesday morning, outside Hamilton Hall, a few minutes before 1000 police and plainclothesmen began to charge the barricaded Columbia University student rebels. I turned to a tense and exhausted Human Rights Commissioner, William Booth, and asked, "What are your thoughts at this moment?"

"That the publisher of the New York Times and the District Attorney of Manhattan are trustees of Columbia," Booth replied.

It proved to be a prophetic comment in light of the way the Times reported the events at Columbia the next two days. Almost every story this planet's official "newspaper of record" published was inept, dishonest, and slanted against the student demonstrators. Police brutality was downplayed. President Kirk was remanticized into a Lincolnesque victim. The fact that the police department's display of force unified the students for the first time was ignored. The questions why plainclothesmen were used in the raid, and why no ambulances were present, were never asked.

But before analyzing the stories published by the Times, two background facts must be established. First, that there actually was brutality, and second, that the Times itself was unethically implicated in the planning of the police raid.

The fact of brutality seems self-evident. Almost 100 injured students treated at two hospitals. Bloody newsreel footage on television. The savage beating of one of the

Times's own reporters, Robert Thomas. The testimony of Dr. June Finer in the New York Post that the police sadism exceeded anything she had witnessed in Alabama or Mississippi.

Now to the mysterious complicity of the Times. On the day of the bust, the Times city editor Arthur Gelb had lunch with Police Commissioner Howard Leary. At lunch, or a few hours later, Leary gave Gelb a copy of a mimeographed memorandum detailing the logistics of the police department's plans for mass arrests that night. The memo included details down to the minute, like "At 1:30 A.M., mounted police to move on campus."

Later in the day, the memo was passed discreetly to several reporters who would be assigned to cover the police raid It was intentionally NOT shown to certain reporters, including Richard Reeves, who covers Mayor Lindsay, because the Times editors feared they would tip off the students about the timing of the bust. One cannot help but wonder at this point what the Times editors would have done if they were told the students planned to liberate other campus buildings. Would they not tip off the police and administration? But the more important question is why did the police department brief the Times so thoroughly about their plans? For protection? Because the Times's publisher is a Columbia trustee?

The police briefing was so complete that the Times's story of the raid was written several hours before it actually took place, and was in type by mid-night. Only a few facts had to be added when reporters called in with the actual details. The next day, A. M. Rosenthal was bragging how 500,000 copies of the Times's last edition contained the story of the 2 A.M. raid, while only 50,000 copies of the last edition of the News had the story. At 1 A.M., on the Columbia campus, Jules Feiffer and I accidentally saw Rosenthal emerge from a secret meeting of top police brass. Rosenthal, a

little embarrassed, claimed he did not know if a police raid on the students was imminent.

Now to analysis of Times coverage of the police raid, the only background necessary to recall that all the "think pieces" and editorials published by the Times since the revolt began at Columbia have been stridently anti-SDS. One editorial, in fact, on April 25, was titled, "Hoodlumism at Columbia."

The four-column lead story in most copies of the late city edition of the April 30 New York Times, written in advance by Sylvan Fox, a former New York City police department press officer, began: "A handpicked force of 1000 policemen moved onto the Columbia University campus early today and began ordering student demonstrators out of the five buildings the students have occupied in a tense week-long protest.

"The police moved with stunning suddenness at 2:30 A.M. . ."

The police did not "order" students out of the buildings; they dragged them out. And what "stunning suddenness"? The Times had the minute by minute details of the operation more than 12 hours in advance.

The next day, May 1, the Times printed one major lead story on Columbia and eight subsidiary stories. The afternoon before, the lead story in the New York Post was that the police brutality had created a new campus majority against the administration. That crucial insight was totally missing from the Times coverage the next day. And not until the 23rd paragraph of Sylvan Fox's lead story were "charges" of police brutality even mentioned.

The major side-bar story was by Rosenthal. It began on the front page and was intended as a mood piece about the campus. It focused on the anguish of President Kirk and the vandalism of the students who occupied his office. It did not describe a single act of police brutality. But Rosenthal, remember, was with Commissioner Leary while the raid was being planned.

(Student leaders who rifled the files in President Kirk's office say they have a memo indicating that on at least one occasion Columbia officials used Rosenthal when they wanted a friendly story in the Times.)

The subsidiary story, on page 35, that dealt with police brutality, was not written by Times reporter Thomas, who needed 12 stitches in his scalp, but by Martin Arnold.

Arnold is one of the brightest and fairest reporters on the Times, and his city room friends say the editors "changed" and "toned down" his copy. Nevertheless, he wrote a story worthy of textual analysis in all journalism schools.

In his third paragraph, Arnold wrote:

"To an experienced anti-war or civil rights demonstrator, yesterday morning's police action on the Columbia campus was, for the most part, relatively gentle."

Now there is some truth to that. The police were not quite as systematically brutal as they were during the anti-draft demonstrations last December, or even in Washington Square Park April 27. But the point is, on those occasions, the Times ALSO failed to report any police brutality. Times reporter John Kifner was a witness to the police brutality in Washington Square Park two weeks ago, and offered to write a lengthy story about it, but was rebuffed by his editors. (Four paragraphs of his copy was inserted into the main story, however.)

But after satisfying his desk by describing the police action as "relatively gentle," Arnold goes on to describe for persevering readers what actually went on in the darkness at Columbia:

"On a small green plot dividing Avery and Fayerweather Halls two uniformed policemen grabbed a young woman and as each officer held her by an arm they spun her about and flung her into a tree.

"Nearby two other officers were seen flinging a man to the ground. When he tried to get up, they grabbed him and threw him down again. A plainclothesman rushed up and stomped the fallen man.

"At one point, Prof. Sidney Morgenbesser was standing on the north steps of Fayerweather shouting loudly to about 125 students and 30 faculty members who had gathered, some in blankets against the chill, to block the two double door entrances. 'You ought to very carefully observe what transpires. Watch carefully.'

"Plainclothesmen and uniformed officers formed a wedge and, without any attempt to pick up or even push aside the people, charged through the faculty and student line, stomping on hands and feet and arms and flinging bodies to the ground. John F. Khanlian, an undergraduate, said, 'I was hit with a club in the head. I was punched in the nose.' He could hardly see because blood was running down the side of his face.

"In Avery Hall, Robert McG. Thomas Jr., a New York Times reporter, was struck on the head by a policeman using handcuffs as brass knuckles. He required 12 stitches to close the wound. Steve Shapiro, a Life magazine photographer, was punched in the eye by a policeman and one of his cameras was smashed after, he said, he had shown the officer his press identification."

Finally, there is the case of John Kifner. Kifner a first-rate investigative reporter, was the only daily journalist to be inside any of the "liberated" buildings when the police attacked; he had gotten into the Math Building at 11:30 P.M. Monday. But when Kifner volunteered to write an exclusive story for the Times on what it was like inside the beseiged Math Building in the hours before the bust, the desk inexplicably told him they weren't interested. Instead, the editors assigned Kifner to write a piece on the vandalism committed by the students. The fact that most of the property damage, especially in the Math Building, was caused by the police, did not appear in the printed version of Kifner's copy.

I saw police storm into the Math Building with crowbars and axes. At one point, an officer came out and exclaimed, "The creeps have burrowed into the walls. We need more axes." But Kifner's story only described the vandalism of the rebels, which was, in fact, merely piggyness and sloppiness, probably causing only a fraction of the actual property damage. The students did not break windows and chop up walls the way the police did.

Five years from now, when Newsweek, or CBS, or some curious author wants to research what really happened during the great bust at Columbia, these yellowed Times clippings will be their only resource. The distortions and slanting will be institutionalized as truth by then. That is the real tragedy, that the Times's reputation for objectivity will endure, despite any bitter words in The Village Voice.

According to Kunen (see above), Dean Deane was the author of the original "strawberry statement": "Whether students vote 'yes' or 'no' on an issue is like telling me they like strawberries."

FROM

Up Against the Ivy Wall
HERBERT A. DEANE

REFLECTIONS ON STUDENT RADICALISM

The occupation of University buildings, the holding hostage of the Acting Dean of Columbia College, and the looting of the files of the President which took place at Columbia during April and May of this year are the most recent and most widely publicized in a series of protest activities that have moved far beyond the bounds of peaceful assembly, picketing, and expression of opinion. The first major action of this kind occurred three years ago when a mass demonstration in front of Low Library forced the cancellation of the NROTC awards ceremony. In the same period similar demonstrations and "sit-ins," involving the use of coercion to prevent University activities to which the protesters object or to accomplish aims to which they are committed, have taken place at many other universities and in the larger society, both in this country and abroad. While the events at Columbia are thus part of a much more general pattern, the circumstances and the actions have their own special character to which attention must also be given.

No one can doubt that the continuation and escalation of the war in Vietnam during the past three years have been the major factors responsible for the mood of bitter dissent and frustration of many students and teachers in American universities. Students in constantly increasing numbers have become convinced that the course pursued by the United States government in Vietnam is morally and politically indefensible. More significantly, many of these students and their teachers have come to believe that our political leaders have been a good deal less than candid in their statements about the war, and, at least until Senator McCarthy's decision to launch his campaign for the Presidential nomination and President Johnson's decision not to seek re-election, many students were seriously questioning whether the ordinary democratic political process and the normal avenues of criticism and protest had any real capacity to influence the course of events and the directions of governmental policy. This growing sense of frustration and disillusion with normal political activities has been reflected in a sharp rise in the level and intensity of campus protests.

A second major factor in generating protest and disillusion on the campuses has been the urban and racial crisis in our country, culminating in the widespread riots of last summer and in the wave of destruction that followed the assassination of Dr. Martin Luther King, Jr., this April. Here again, many students and teachers, especially at urban universities located near ghetto areas, have become increasingly outraged by the miseries and injustices that mark the lives of slum-dwellers. Moreover, they have watched, with deepening frustration, the inability or unwillingness of government at every level to deal effectively with the problems. Despite the clear warnings and prescriptions in the Report of the Kerner Commission, most Congressmen and state and local legislators have been unwilling even to begin the massive and costly efforts required to deal with the economic ills of the slum areas that make up a large part of the central city. The principal lesson the legislative majorities seem to have learned from the riots is the need for more men and more sophisticated weapons to deal with the rioters.

One serious consequence of this highly charged campus mood and this deepening frustration with the ordinary processes of criticism and dissent has been that the more radical students have turned their energies to attacks on their universities and to efforts to interfere with university activities which

have (or are alleged to have) some connection with the military establishment and the prosecution of the war in Vietnam or with the racial crisis in our cities. It is no accident that two of the major issues in the Columbia demonstrations this spring involved the University's ties to the Institute for Defense Analyses and the building of the gymnasium in Morningside Park. These issues were selected and emphasized because they could when presented in highly simplified and stark terms, attract support from a much larger group of students who were opposed to the war in Vietnam and to racism. In the past year, the attacks of student radicals have been extended to the university itself and to its basic functions of teaching and research, even when these functions have little or no connection with the war or the urban crisis, on the ground that the university is deeply enmeshed in the ills of a corrupt social system since it is both an element in the "power-structure" of the society and the training-ground for the employees who man the middle and upper levels of the business, government, and military bureaucracies. To such attacks, when they pass from words to coercive and violent actions, the university is peculiarly vulnerable. It conducts its normal activities by peaceful means and rational discussion, and it has neither the ethos nor the instruments to deal effectively with violence or threats of violence. In our classrooms, libraries, and laboratories disciplinary problems have been virtually non-existent, and our lives together as teachers and students have been governed much more by unspoken conventions than by written rules.

It may be useful to explore some of the common assumptions and value-commitments that underlie the protest activities of radical students at Columbia and its sister institutions during the past three years. Again and again one is struck by the posture of complete self-righteousness and of unyielding moral absolutism in the attitudes and actions of the radical leaders. "I am totally right and completely moral, and you—if you disagree with me—are absolutely wrong and wicked. Therefore, there is no basis for any real discussion with you. You have no rights that I must respect, and you must agree to accept everything that I demand. If you fail to do so, I am justified in using any and all means to insure the triumph of right and justice, of which I am the embodiment and exponent." Faced with this complete moral certainty, one is tempted to cry out, in Cromwell's great phrase, "I beseech you, in the bowels of Christ, think it possible you may be mistaken." For, to the moral absolutist, force directed against the wicked and the unbelievers becomes, as Ortega warned us, the *prima* or *unica ratio* rather than the *ultima ratio.* Discussion, tolerance of difference, compromise, negotiation—all the methods by which civilized men seek to resolve or to sustain their differences so that they can go on living together and learning from one another despite their differences on many matters—have no part in the attitudes of the true believer. He is entranced by the Sorelian notion that politics—the civil and civilizing activity, *par excellence*—is inherently and irreparably a corrupt and corrupting business since it necessarily involves discussion and compromise with other individuals and groups. For him, as for Sorel, only "pure violence," commitment to myth and non-rational appeals, and "black ingratitude" towards all reformers and mediators are strong enough medicine to polarize society into the two hostile groups of savage repressors and advocates of heroic violence and so to save us all from the decadence that he sees as the inevitable end of compromise and rationality.

Closely associated with this moral absolutism is the assumption—as pernicious as it is ancient (and dear to the hearts of anti-radical crusaders like the first Senator McCarthy)—that the pursuit of ends that one regards as supremely good and desirable legitimates the use of all means, including coercion and violation of the rights and freedoms of others, which one believes to be necessary to accomplish his goals. Radical students, who, not so long ago, were among the strongest supporters of civil liberties and freedom of expression for all, and particularly for unpopular minorities, have on some recent occasions abandoned these libertarian

principles and resorted to the use of force to prevent those with whom they disagree from exercising their freedom to act and to speak. Because they feel strongly that NROTC has no right to exist on the Columbia campus, they have a "right" to disrupt its awards ceremony even though the NROTC students, their parents, and their friends wish this ceremony to take place. Because of their deep hostility to the war in Vietnam and, in some cases, to all wars except those of "national liberation," they have a "right" to prevent other students from being interviewed on the campus by representatives of the armed forces or of certain corporations and government agencies. They are unmoved by the fact that both the faculty and their fellow-students have overwhelmingly endorsed the principle of "open recruitment" on the campus.

Behind this assumption of a "right" to interfere forcibly with the exercise of the rights of others, even of the large majority, stands the more general postulate that freedom of expression for all members of the community is a "bourgeois" notion and that freedom belongs properly only to those whose views are "right" and "progressive." The ill-concealed elitism of this view is a clear echo of the Leninist doctrine that only the enlightened vanguard understands the historical situation and the mission of the proletariat, while the masses, corrupt and ignorant, must be led, manipulated, and coerced for thier own eventual good. And, curiously enough, the elitism of some of our contemporary radical students also echoes the claim that only the elite have a right to freedom found in the pseudo-doctrines of Fascism, supposedly the antithesis of Leninism. (Do we have here an example of the dialectical principle of the interpenetration of opposites?) This view that freedom rightly belongs only to the enlightened minority is clearly manifested when some of the leaders of SDS, for example, talk about the stupidity and political backwardness of their "unradicalized" fellow students and when they admit that they would not be influenced by a student referendum in which their views were decisively rejected.

These attitudes of moral rigidity and self-righteousness, unwillingness to engage in meaningful discussion, and contempt for the rights and liberties of others, including the large majority of faculty and students, were all obvious during the period from April 23 to April 30 when the Columbia buildings were being occupied. The student leaders of the demonstrations were never willing to engage in genuine discussion of their original "demands" and were even less willing to modify those demands or to seek for a compromise solution. The leader of SDS publicly dismissed, with contempt, the last in a series of mediation proposals set forth by the *ad hoc* Faculty Group. The record clearly indicates, on the other hand, that the administrative officers and the Trustees of the University made significant changes in their original positions and genuine efforts to accept in large measure the proposals set forth by the *ad hoc* group. The leaders of the demonstrations presented to the University — that is, to the large majority of the faculty and the students as well as to the administration and the Trustees — only a choice between two almost impossible alternatives: complete capitulation not only to their specific demands, including amnesty, but also to their continuing claims to "power," or calling in the police in order to respond with force to force. Every member of this University was unhappy with the latter alternative, but hardly a single voice was raised in the long hours of faculty discussion in favor of the first course, even by those who were to some degree sympathetic with one or another of the protesters' specific demands.

No one with any sense would argue that Columbia University on April 22, 1968, was a perfect institution which had no need of changes in its organizational patterns, in its means of communication among administrators, faculty, and students, in its relations with the surrounding community, or in its academic program and requirements. Many of its administrative officers and some members of its faculty had, for years, been aware of the need for revisions and reforms and had spent countless hours in discussing the necessary changes and in bringing some of them into being. But if Columbia was not perfect, if it had defects and required reforms, it was like every other human institution since the world began. And it is simply untrue to say that this University was so hopelessly corrupt that it needed to be destroyed or revolutionized. Any university, and especially one as large and complex as Columbia, is difficult to change rapidly, and this is due far more to the resistance to novelty and to the capacity for long-continued discussion which are natural to most academics than to callousness or insensitivity to problems. (In 1908, the noted English classicist, F. M. Cornford, in his delightful book *Microcosmographia Academica,* warned young academic politicians about the inherent conservatism of scholarly communities; so little has the situation changed that the book is still well worth reading sixty years later in its sixth edition.)

In conclusion, a few words should be said about the likely political consequences of the attitudes and activities of "revolutionary" student activists. It is obvious that nothing approaching the classic revolutionary situation exists in the United States today. The working-class, especially the organized working-class, is deeply committed to the *status quo* and has achieved substantial gains during the last thirty-five years; as a consequence, organized labor is a strongly anti-revolutionary force in the society. They and the middle-class (and the line separating them is often difficult to draw) have no desire to blow up the existing social system; indeed, if they confront efforts to bring about a revolution, they are likely to respond in a sharply negative fashion. The most serious trouble-spot in the society is found in the urban slums, and particularly among the inhabitants of the ghetto. Their frustration and misery, however, are much more likely to take the form of riots and violent protests than that of organized revolution to replace the social and political system. The most likely consequences of violent protests by the left, such as the demonstrations led by student "revolutionaries," are, therefore, a resurgence in ultra-right-wing movements and an even more widespread swing towards conservatism in this country. We already see ominous signs of these developments, such as the sharp rise in former Governor Wallace's standing in the national polls between April and August 1968, and the surprising strength of the pro-Reagan forces across the nation before and during the Republican convention of 1968. It should be remembered that even in France, where student radicals received some support and encouragement from the workers and their unions, the major result of their violent demonstrations was the resounding victory won by General De Gaulle. Some of our young revolutionaries may tell us that they welcome a "temporary" strengthening of reaction, since the far right will eliminate or weaken the social-democrats, liberals, and conservatives and thus sharply polarize society into two completely hostile segments, the forces of revolution and those of reaction, and that they will emerge victorious from this confrontation. Our response can only be that right-wing repression would destroy all that we value in American society, and that the ultimate victory of revolution over reaction in this country is just as unlikely as it was in Germany before Hitler, when the Communist Party defended its tactical alliances with the Nazis by the unrealistic argument that Fascism, having eliminated all the enemies of Communism, would prove unable to deal with the objective social problems, and that its collapse would permit the German Communist Party to emerge as the "residual legatee."

FROM
Up Against the Ivy Wall
MARK RUDD

SYMBOLS OF THE REVOLUTION

During the course of the Columbia strike a whole set of symbols and slogans inevitably emerged. It is difficult for someone who wasn't there, or more accurately, for someone who's not part of the New Left to understand these symbols and their significance. Red flags, red armbands, "Up against the wall, motherfucker," communes, all became integral parts of the strike, helped to define the strike.

UP AGAINST THE WALL,
MOTHERFUCKER!

Perhaps nothing upset our enemies more than this slogan. To them it seemed to show the extent to which we had broken with their norms, how far we had sunk to brutality, hatred, and obscenity. Great! *The New York Times* put forward three interpretations of the slogan, the only one of which I remember is the one which had to do with putting the administration up against the wall before a firing squad — apparently our fascistic "final solution." The truth is almost as bad: the slogan defined Grayson Kirk, David Truman, the Trustees, many of the faculty, the cops as our enemies. Liberal solutions, "restructuring," partial understandings, compromise are not allowed anymore. The essence of the matter is that we are out for social and political revolution, nothing less. This, of course, puts the administration of Columbia University in somewhat of a bind: if they accede to any of our demands they will be the first representatives of the ruling class to have fallen under to a motley mob of student rebels. Secondly, they will only be whetting our insatiable appetites. Better to beat us down: 1,100 busted, hundreds to be thrown out of school.

"Up against the wall, motherfucker" defines the terms. It puts the administration and the interests they represent on one side, leftist students and the interests of humanity on the other. Those undecided in the middle are forced to choose sides. The great victory of the strike was that so many joined our side and so few supported the administration (the few hundred or so in the "Majority Coalition" were the most isolated and pathetic people on campus). The "organized" left on campus had been small — perhaps 150 were active in SDS, if that — but the number who identified with the left, with opposition to the war and to racism and now, the whole structure of capitalism, grew to immense proportions.

"Up against the wall, motherfucker" has

had a long odyssey. It originated in the ghetto, with the cops using it when they stop and search or bust people. Columbia strikers, to their mixed reaction, found the cops really do use it. LeRoi Jones got two years in jail for using it in a poem:

The magic words are
Up against the wall, motherfucker,
This is a stick-up.

(Of course, when quoted in *The New York Times,* the poem contained the word "mother-blank.") An SDS chapter on the lower East side, a group organizing hippies, winos, drop-outs, neighborhood people with a program of revolutionary politics and life-style, adopted the slogan as its name. We picked it up in our chapter, using it for the title of one edition of our newspaper, the edition which appeared on April 22, 1968, the day before the demonstrations began. In that paper appeared an open letter to Grayson Kirk in which I defined our goal as socialism, and Kirk and the ruling class as our enemies. The letter ended with the quote from LeRoi Jones. From there, the slogan became a natural for the strike, ranging in use from graffiti to shouts of the entire Math commune against the police.

We co-opted the word "motherfucker" from the ghetto much as we adopted the struggle of blacks and the other oppressed as our own. When young people start calling those in power, the people whose places we're being trained to fill, "Motherfucker" you know the structure of authority is breaking down. We recognize that our own quest for freedom puts us against "the man" just as black people and Vietnamese fight him. The war comes home.

The obscenity, too, helped define our struggle. Finally, we could say in public what we had been saying among ourselves. We could use our own language, much more expressive than the repressed language of Grayson Kirk. When I told a meeting of the Ad Hoc Faculty Group that the talks we were having with them were bullshit, I expressed myself thoroughly, naturally. The reaction to the style was stronger than the reaction to the content. All forms of authority, traditional "respect" (you show respect, obviously, by not using your own language), had broken down. The norms of repression and domination, maintaining the hierarchical structure of the classroom and the society, were swept aside. The revolution frightened some, broke others, freed many.

ROCK

Few people under thirty-five—or is it forty?—are unaware of rock music as a popular art form and as a viable life style as well. Since Elvis Presley warmed the dull winter weekend evenings of 1955-1956 on the television variety shows of Jimmy Dorsey and Ed Sullivan (no camera shots below the belt), neither American music nor the boy or girl next door has been the same. Elvis's ducktail haircut, tight black trousers, and pelvic gyrations—however bland in the 1970s—marked the beginning of overt, visible protest by the young against convention in America.

Not that Elvis started it all. He was merely the first to be *seen* by all.

The two strains, Negro rhythm-and-blues and white hillbilly music, based on their antecedents, spiritual-blues-jazz and Scots-Irish folk, which fused into what Bill Haley and then Alan Freed popularized as "rock n' roll," were certainly well established in the years immediately following World War II. But they still were accessible only to specialized ethnic and regional audiences. Joe Turner's original "Shake, Rattle, and Roll," or the Ray Charles of "It Should've Been Me," and, on the other hand, the whiskey-sad ballads of Hank Williams illustrate these two genres in the pre-Presley period.

To oversimplify: rhythm and blues was tough, gutsy, suggestive ("Ya wearin' those dresses, the sun come shinin' through / I can't believe my eyes all that mess belongs to you"), and not without a sense of self-irony ("I'm like a one-eyed cat peepin' in a seafood store"); country music was sentimental, idealized, occasionally bathetic—even the superior work of an artist like Hank Williams (You'll walk the floor the way I do / Your cheatin' heart will tell on you"). Appropriately, the former utilized a heavy regular beat and the backing of piano and sax; the latter, like its "traditional" forerunner, ran heavily to strings. In the meantime, jazz had become "bop"—abstracted, introverted, certainly not "popular" music. The rest, as they say, is history.

This volume presents a sampling of black rhythm-and-blues as rendered by Holliday, Charles, Berry; and white rock and "folk-rock": Dylan, the Beatles, Steppenwolf. In this section we have concentrated on the Stones because they represent, to us, the most successful synthesis of these various elements. They are capable, as no other white group (and a British one, at that) of sounding American black ("Under the Boardwalk"), or hillbilly ("Country Honk"), while their interpretations remain uniquely their own. Finally, their public life style (drug busts, acted-out hostility, suicides), on-stage attitudes, and songs themselves, seem designed to say "fuck you" to all society holds sacred. Thus, musically and personally, they stand most directly in the line of Presley (not to mention the hero-villains of "Blackboard Jungle"). As one pundit has remarked (and we paraphrase): Jagger and the Stones are most frightening to parents not only because they threaten to seduce their daughters, but their sons as well.

PART FIVE

This is part of an essay about "Baby Jane" Holzer, a model and actress who was one of New York's "beautiful people" and whose taste and habits were closely watched by the In press. Here Tom Wolfe reports her reactions to her first live concert by the Rolling Stones in New York.

FROM

The Kandy-Kolored Tangerine-Flake Streamlined Baby
TOM WOLFE

THE GIRL OF THE YEAR

Bangs manes bouffants beehives Beatle caps butter faces brush-on lashes decal eyes puffy sweaters French thrust bras flailing leather blue jeans stretch pants stretch jeans honey-dew bottoms eclair shanks elf boots ballerinas Knight slippers, hundreds of them, these flaming little buds, bobbing and screaming, rocketing around inside the Academy of Music Theater underneath that vast old mouldering cherub dome up there—aren't they super-marvelous!

"Aren't they super-marvelous!" says Baby Jane, and then: "Hi, Isabel! Isabel! You want to sit backstage—with the Stones!"

The show hasn't even started yet, the Rolling Stones aren't even on the stage, the place is full of a great shabby mouldering dimness, and these flaming little buds.

Girls are reeling this way and that way in the aisle and through their huge black decal eyes, sagging with Tiger Tongue Lick Me brush-on eyelashes and black appliqués, sagging like display window Christmas trees, they keep staring at—her—Baby Jane—on the aisle. What the hell is this? She is gorgeous in the most outrageous way. Her hair rises up from her head in a huge hairy corona, a huge tan mane around a narrow face and two eyes opened—swock!—like umbrellas, with all that hair flowing down over a coat made of . . . zebra! Those motherless stripes! Oh, damn! Here she is with her friends, looking like some kind of queen bee for all flaming little buds everywhere. She twists around to shout to one of her friends and that incredible mane swings around on her shoulders, over the zebra coat.

"Isabel!" says Baby Jane, "Isabel, hi! I just saw the Stones! They look super-divine!"

That girl on the aisle, Baby Jane, is a fabulous girl. She comprehends what the Rolling Stones *mean.* Any columnist in New York could tell them who she is . . . a celebrity of New York's new era of Wog Hip . . . Baby Jane Holzer. Jane Holzer in *Vogue,* Jane Holzer in *Life,* Jane Holzer in Andy Warhol's underground movies, Jane Holtzer in the world of High Camp, Jane Holzer at the rock and roll, Jane Holzer is—well, how can one put it into words? Jane Holzer is This Year's Girl, at least, the New Celebrity, none of your old idea of sexpots, prima donnas, romantic tragediennes, she is the girl who knows . . . The Stones, East End vitality . . .

"Isabel!" says Jane Holzer in the small, high, excited voice of hers, her Baby Jane voice, "Hi, Isabel! Hi!"

Down the row, Isabel, Isabel Eberstadt, the beautiful socialite who is Ogden Nash's daughter, has just come in. She doesn't seem to hear Jane. But she is down the row a ways. Next to Jane is some fellow in a chocolate-colored Borsalino hat, and next there is Andy Warhol, the famous pop artist.

"Isabel!" says Jane.

"What?" says Isabel.

"Hi, Isabel!" says Jane.

"Hello, Jane," says Isabel.

"You want to go backstage?" says Jane, who has to speak across everybody.

"Backstage?" says Isabel.

"With the Stones!" says Jane. "I was backstage with the Stones. They look *divine!* You know what Mick said to me? He said, 'Koom on, love, give us a kiss!' "

But Isabel has turned away to say something to somebody.

"Isabel!" says Jane.

And all around, the little buds are batting around in the rococo gloom of the Academy of Music Theater, trying to crash into good seats or just sit in the aisle near

Photograph by DeFrancis.

the stage, shrieking. And in the rear the Voice of Fifteen-year-old America cries out in a post-pubertal contralto, apropos of nothing, into the mouldering void: "Yaaaagh! Yuh dirty fag!"

Well, so what; Jane laughs. Then she leans over and says to the fellow in the Borsalino hat:

"Wait'll you see the Stones! They're so sexy! They're pure sex. They're *divine!* The Beatles, well, you know, Paul McCartney —*sweet* Paul McCartney. You know what I mean. He's such a *sweet person.* I mean, the Stones are *bitter—* "the words seem to spring from her lungs like some kind of wonderful lavender-yellow Charles Kingsley bubbles"— they're all from the working class, you know? the East End. Mick Jagger—well, it's all Mick. You know what they say about his lips? They say his lips are *diabolical.* That was in one of the magazines.

"When Mick comes into the Ad Lib in London—I mean, there's nothing like the Ad Lib in New York. You can go into the Ad Lib and everybody is there. They're all young, and they're taking over, it's like a whole revolution. I mean, it's *exciting,* they're all from the lower classes, East End-sort-of-thing. There's nobody exciting from the upper classes anymore, except for Nicole and Alec Londonderry, Alec is a British marquis, the Marquis of Londonderry, and, O.K., Nicole has to put in an appearance at this country fair or something, well, O.K., she does it, but that doesn't mean—you know what I mean? Alec is so—you should see the way he walks, I could just watch him walk— *Undoes-one-ship!* They're *young.* They're all young, it's a whole new thing. It's not the Beatles. Bailey says the Beatles are *passé,* because now everybody's mum pats the Beatles on the head. The Beatles are getting fat. The Beatles—well, John Lennon's still thin, but Paul McCartney is getting a big bottom. That's all right, but I don't particularly care for that. The Stones are thin. I mean, that's why they're beautiful, they're so thin. Mick Jagger— wait'll you see Mick."

Then the show begins. An electronic blast begins, electric guitars, electric bass, enormous speakers up there on a vast

yellow-gray stage. Murray the K, the D.J. and M. C., O. K.?, comes out from the wings, doing a kind of twist soft shoe, wiggling around, a stocky chap, thirty-eight years old, wearing Italian pants and a Sun Valley snow lodge sweater and a Stingy Brim straw hat. Murray the K! Girls throw balls of paper at him, and as they arc onto the stage, the stage lights explode off them and they look like falling balls of flame.

And, finally, the Stones, now—how can one express it? the Stones come on stage—

"Oh, God, Andy, aren't they *divine!*"

—and spread out over the stage, the five Rolling Stones, from England, who are modeled after the Beatles, only more lower-class-deformed. One, Brian Jones, has an enormous blonde Beatle bouffant.

"Oh, Andy, look at Mick! Isn't he *beautiful!* Mick! Mick!"

In the center of the stage a short thin boy with a sweat shirt on, the neck of the sweat shirt almost falling over his shoulders, they are so narrow, all surmounted by this . . . enormous head . . . with the hair puffing down over the forehead and ears, this boy has exceptional lips. He has two peculiarly gross and extraordinary red lips. They hang off his face like giblets. Slowly his eyes pour over the flaming bud horde soft as Karo syrup and then close and then the lips start spreading into the most languid, most confidential, the wettest, most labial, most concupiscent grin imaginable. Nirvana! The buds start shrieking, pawning toward the stage.

The girls have Their Experience. They stand up on their seats. They begin to ululate, even between songs. The looks on their faces! Rapturous agony! There, right up there, under the sulphur lights, that is *them.* God, they're right there! Mick Jagger takes the microphone with his tabescent hands and puts his huge head against it, opens his giblet lips and begins to sing . . . with the voice of a bull Negro. Bo Diddley. You movung boo meb bee-uhtul, bah-bee, oh vona breemb you' honey snurks oh crim pulzy yo' min down, and, camping again, then turning toward the shrieking girls with his wet giblet lips dissolving . . .

And, occasionally, breaking through the ululation:

"Get off the stage, you finks!"
"Maybe we ought to scream," says Jane.
Then she says to the fellow in the hat: "Tell
me when it's five o'clock, will you, pussycat?
I have to get dressed and go see Sam
Spiegel." And then Baby Jane goes:
"Eeeeeeeeeeeeeeeeeeeee

The session at which "Sympathy" was recorded is featured
in the movie "One Plus One" by the avant-garde French
director Jean-Luc Godard; he uses it as an example of
revolutionary art.

Sympathy for the Devil

MICK JAGGER AND KEITH RICHARDS

Please allow me to introduce myself,
I'm a man of wealth and taste.
I've been around for many a long, long year,
I've stolen many a man's soul and faith.
I was around when Jesus Christ had his moment of doubt and
pain;
I made damn sure that Pilate washed his hands and sold his faith.

Pleased to meet you,
Hope you guess my name,
But what's puzzling you,
Is the nature of my game.

I stuck around St. Petersburg,
When I saw it was time for a change.
I killed the Tsar and his ministers —
Anastasia screamed in vain.
I rode a tank, held a general's rank,
When the blitzkrieg raged and the bodies stank.

Pleased to meet you,
Hope you guess my name.
But what's puzzling you,
Is the nature of my game.

I watched with glee while your kings and queens
Fought for ten decades for the gods they made.
I shouted out, "Who killed the Kennedys?"
When after all it was you and me.

So let me introduce myself,

I am a man of wealth and taste,
And I lay traps for troubadours
Who get killed before they reach Bombay.

Pleased to meet you,
Hope you guess my name.
But what's puzzling you,
Is the nature of my game.

Pleased to meet you,
Hope you guess my name.
But what's puzzling you,
Is the nature of my game.

Just as every cop is a criminal,
And all the sinners, saints.
As heads is tails, just call me Lucifer
Cos, I'm in need of some restraint.
So if you meet me, have some courtesy,
Have some sympathy and some taste.
Use all your well-learned politesse,
Or I'll lay your soul to waste.

Pleased to meet you.
Hope you guess my name.
But what's puzzling you,
Is the nature of my game.

The Rolling Stones' Grand Finale*

FROM ROLLING STONE

I didn't know his name or anything, but he was standing along side of me. You know, we were both watching Mick Jagger, and a Hell's Angel's, the fat one. I don't know his name or anything, he reached over—he didn't like us being so close or something, you know, we were seeing Mick Jagger too well, or something. He was just being up tight. He reached over and grabbed the guy beside me by the ear and hair, and yanked on it, thinking it was funny, you know, kind of laughing. And so, this guy shook loose; he yanked away from him.

Now this guy that you're talking about, is this the black guy that got killed?

Yeah, right. He shook loose,

* Altamont.

and the Hell's Angel hit him in the mouth and he fell back into the crowd and he jumped off stage and jumped at him. And he tried to scramble, you know, through the crowd, to run from the Hell's Angel, and four other Hell's Angels jumped on him. They started mugging him and,

This is when they claim he had the gun?

No, no, he didn't pull out the gun yet. See, and they started, they were mugging him, and then he started running . . . and he was running straight into the crowd, you know, pushing people away, you know, to run from the Hell's Angels.

What was this guy's condition? Had he been smoking, had he been drinking, or do you know?

He was really straight, he was really . . . Feeling really weird about being pushed around and stuff, but he was really pretty straight.

When the cat started grabbing him, what did he say? What did this black guy say?

He just gave him a weird look, kind of a mean look, and yanked away, he didn't give him any verbal provocation or anything. So they're chasing through the crowd. And they hitting him and one Hell's Angel pulled out a knife and stabbed him in the back.

What kind of knife? ·

I couldn't tell. I just saw the flash of the blade. Everything was happening too fast. And he hit him in the back and he pulled out a gun and held it up in the air you know . . . like that was kind of his last resort, you know . . . and . . .

Could you tell what kind of a gun?

It was a long . . . long barrel, really long. Looked like a six shooter or something . . . I've never seen . . it was really . . . like the barrel was about six inches or so . . .

Like a service revolver or something?

Yeah . . . it was really a fancy gun . . . really shiny . . . He had it in the air, and he was still running, and people were telling him—I remember this chick screaming "Don't shoot anyone." And he was too scared to shoot because he could have shot anyone in the crowd or anything. So he didn't shoot.

And one of the Hell's Angels grabbed the gun from him . . . and then stabbed him again in the back.

They grabbed the gun from him, and then stabbed him again in the back?

Yeah, yeah.

What did the cat who stabbed him look like?

I think there was two people that stabbed him. One had his hair straight. It was straight and thick, and it was straight back, combed straight back. The front of his . . . you know . . . he combed it back so much that the front of his head was kind of bald . . . getting thin. I know what he looks like but, I can't describe him.

But you'd know him if you saw him, right?

Yeah, yeah. I've seen him before.

Would you be willing to testify?

No. I don't want to get killed. They hit him . . . I couldn't tell whether it was a knife or not . . . but on the side of the head. And then he kind of stumbled and he fell down on his knees. He came running toward me. I grabbed onto the scaffold, held onto the scaffold, you know, and then he came running kind of toward me and then he fell down on his knees, and then the Hell's Angel, the same one I was talking about, grabbed onto both of his shoulders and started kicking him in the face about five times or so and then he fell down on his face, you know. He let go and he fell down on his face. And then one of them kicked him on the side and he rolled over, and he muttered some words. He said "I wasn't going to shoot you." That was the last words he muttered.

How close were you to all of this?

About three feet away.

You kept right up with them. You could have gotten hurt.

I just stayed as close . . . like,

I wanted to jump into it but I couldn't so I stayed close so that as soon as they were done mugging him I could help him.

That's a real question there: why 300,000—well 299,000—people would allow themselves to be dominated by a hundred Angels?

Yeah, well I couldn't see it either. If some people had jumped in I would have jumped in. But nobody jumped in and after he said "I wasn't going to shoot you," one of the Hell's Angels said, "Why did you have a gun?" He didn't give him time to say anything. He grabbed one of those garbage cans, you know, one of those cardboard garbage cans with the metal rimming, and he smashed him over the head with it, and then he kicked the garbage can out of the way and starting kicking his head in. Five of them started kicking his head in. Kicked him all over the place. And then the guy that started the whole thing, the fat guy, stood on his head for a minute or so and then walked off. And then the ones I was talking about, described to you, he wouldn't let us touch him for about two or three minutes. Like, "Don't touch him, he's going to die anyway, let him die, he's going to die."

So what did everybody do? Did anybody say anything?

Chicks were just screaming. It was all confusion. I jumped down anyway to grab him and some other dude jumped down and grabbed him, and then the Hell's Angel just stood over him for a little bit and then walked away. We turned him over and ripped off his shirt.

You turned him over so he was face up?

No, so he was face down.

So you could see his back?

We rubbed his back up and down to get the blood off so we could see, and there was a big hole on his spine and a big hole on the side and there was a big hole in his temple. A big open slice. You could see all the way in. You could see inside. You could see at least an inch down and stuff, you know. And then there was a big hole right where there's no ribs on his back . . . and then the side of his head

was just sliced open . . . you couldn't see so far in . . . it was bleeding quite heavy . . . but his back wasn't bleeding too heavy after that . . . there . . . all of us were drenched in blood.

Did you stick with him after that?

Yeah. I picked up his legs and someone else . . . this guy said he was a doctor or something . . . I don't know who he was . . . he picked up his arms and he said, "Got to get him some help because he's going to die. We've got 15 or 20 minutes, if we can get him some help . . ." And so we tried to carry him on the stage. Tell Mick Jagger to stop playing so we could get him on the stage and get some attention for him.

Who told Jagger that?

No one told Jagger that, but someone was trying to tell him to stop and he kept leaning over and looking out at the crowd like he was paying attention and trying to figure out what was happening.

This is while he's singing?

Yeah. He kept leaning over with his ear trying to hear what somebody was telling him, but he couldn't hear. So they kept on playing and the Hell's Angels wouldn't let us through . . . get on the stage . . . They kept blocking us saying go around . . . go through some other way. They wouldn't let us through. They knew he was going to die in a matter of minutes. They wanted him to die probably so he wouldn't talk or something, you know. And so we carried . . . we turned around and went the other way. It took about 15 minutes to get him behind the stage. We went around that whole thing and got behind where there was a Red Cross truck . . . something like that. And someone brought out a metal stretcher and laid him on that. Well first we laid him on the ground. And then we felt his pulse and it was just barely doing it . . .

Real slow or real fast or what?

Real slow and real weak. His whole mouth and stuff is bashed up into his nose and stuff and he couldn't breathe out of his nose. He was trying to breathe out of his mouth. There really wasn't anything you could do. We carried him over to some station wagon and then whoever owned the car hopped in and some other people hopped in and I stayed there. I went over and they had this thing of coffee and I had it . . . poured it all over to wipe off all the blood.

Hot coffee?

Yeah, because there was nothing else. Then I walked away feeling, wanting to do something, wanting to tell somebody what happened so they could get the Hell's Angels. It scared me so much I couldn't do anything . . . it really put me on such a big bummer . . . really, for days. For the last couple of days I've been really brought down about it.

Do you intend to go to anymore of these mass concerts?

If there's no Hell's Angels there. No violence. I don't know, I enjoyed it until that happened. I did get bummed out . . . I got a little depressed about . . . the way I was feeling from being pushed around and stuff by the crowd. But the Hell's Angels were responsible. They're really the whole thing.

Robert Hiatt, a medical resident at the Public Health Hospital in San Francisco, was the first doctor to reach 18-year-old Meredith Hunter after the fatal wounds. He was behind the stage and responded to Jagger's call from the stage for a doctor. When Hiatt got to the scene, people were trying to get Hunter up on the stage, apparently in the hope that the Stones would stop playing and help could get through quicker.

"I carried him myself back to the first aid area," Hiatt said. "He was limp in my hands and unconscious. He was still breathing then, though quite shallowly, and he had a very weak pulse. It was obvious he wasn't going to make it, but if anything could be done, he would have to be get to a hospital quickly.

"He had very serious wounds. He had a wound in the lower back which could have gone into the lungs, a wound in the

back near the spine which could have severed a major vessel, and a fairly large wound in the left temple. You couldn't tell how deep the wounds were, but each was about three-fourths of an inch long, so they would have been fairly deep.

"It was just obvious he wasn't going to make it. There was no equipment there to treat him. He needed to be operated on immediately, to have a couple of large vessels repaired. Treatment immediately would have been intravenous fluids, none of which were available."

Dr. Richard Baldwin, the general practitioner from Point Reyes who supervised and coordinated the various medical units, agreed: "He got a bad injury in that they got him in the back and it went in between the ribs and the side of the spine, and there's nothing but big arteries in there, the aorta, the main artery in the body, and a couple kidney arteries. And if you hit one of those you're dead. You're dead in less than a minute and there's nothing anyone can do. In other words, if you're standing in front of the hospital, or even if he was stabbed in an operating room, there's nothing they could have done to save him. That's one of those injuries that's just irreparable."

Roland W. Prahl, senior coroner's investigator for Alameda County, said Hunter's official cause of death was "shock and hemmorhage due to multiple wounds in the back, a wound on the left side of the forehead, and another on the right side of the neck."

Prahl said that as far as he knew, Hunter was taken from the scene on a stretcher to the racetrack offices area. Fearing further mutilation to the body, sheriff's deputies then apparently transported him to another location on the grounds in their van. He was brought by deputies to the coroner's office at 10:50 that night, and an autopsy was performed Sunday.

"I don't know if doctors treated him at any time at the site," Prahl added, "But I do know he was never in a hospital. They

pronounced him dead at the site; if anyone had thought he was alive, they'd have helped him." Prahl, however, didn't know who "they" were.

Three others had died (two in a hit-and-run accident, another by drowning), countless more were injured and wounded, during the course of this day-long "free" concert. It was such a bad trip that it was almost perfect. All it lacked was mass rioting and the murder of one or more *musicians*. These things *could* have happened, with just a little more (bad) luck. It was as if Altamont's organizers had worked out a blueprint for disaster. Like:

1 – Promise a free concert by a popular rock group which rarely appears in this country. Announce the site only four days in advance.

2 – Change the location 20 hours before the concert.

3 – The new concert site should be as close as possible to a giant freeway.

4 – Make sure the grounds are barren, treeless, desolate.

5 – Don't warn neighboring landowners that hundreds of thousands of people are expected. Be unaware of their out-front hostility toward long hair and rock music.

6 – Provide one-sixtieth the required toilet facilities to insure that people will use nearby fields, the sides of cars, etc.

7 – The stage should be located in an area likely to be completely surrounded by people and their vehicles.

8 – Build the stage low enough to be easily hurdled. Don't secure a clear area between stage and audience.

9 – Provide an unreliable barely audible low fidelity sound system.

10 – Ask the Hell's Angels to act as "security" guards.

All these things happened, and worse. Altamont was the product of diabolical egotism, hype, ineptitude, money manipulation, and, at base, a fundamental lack of concern for humanity.

"Jagger was very, very shattered," according to an associate who was with the

Stones post-Altamont. "I cannot overemphasize how depressed and down he was with the way it turned out. They'd like to just be able to blink and make it go away. When they knew about the murder — it shook them."

Jagger had been so eager to do the gig that when he learned, in Muscle Shoals, that his San Francisco advance people were having trouble coming up with a site, he kept saying: "Well, man, we'll play in the streets if we have to." He was almost prepared to pick a street corner in downtown Market Street in San Francisco and play there.

But then, after Altamont had been set up and all the people were there, and the violence had begun, and Angels were menacing everybody in sight, the reports started coming in to the Huntington Hotel, and the Stones did *not* want to complete the gig. Well, they couldn't do that . . . So they thought about going straight out there, playing immediately, and closing the concert down as quick as possible. In the end, they decided to play it according to the original plan.

But they knew early in the day that it was grim and getting grimmer.

Mick Taylor, the newest Rolling Stone, was still aghast at what had happened when contacted in London shortly after his return home from Altamont.

"I was really scared," he said. I was frightened for all of us, particularly for Mick because he had to be very careful what he said all the time, very careful. He had to pick and choose his words. When you read about a thing this size — like 300,000 people, four people born, four people killed — you don't think of it as a violent thing. But that's all I saw; violence all the time. I've always heard about the incredible violence in America, but I'd never actually seen it. They're so used to it over there, it's a commonplace thing. They find it easier to accept. I've just never seen anything like that before.

"It was just completely barbaric, like there was so much violence there it completely took the enjoyment out of it for me . . . it was impossible . . . to enjoy the music, or anything, because most of the violence was going on right in front of the stage, right in front of our eyes, and like I've never seen anything like it before. I just couldn't believe it.

"About five minutes after we arrived, just after we got out of the helicopter, I was with Mick and there were a couple of security guards with us, and a guy broke through and punched Mick in the face. That put me off a bit, but even after that had happened I didn't expect all those other things.

"It got so bad at one point that we just had to stop playing, we had to keep stopping in the middle of numbers. Mick did his best to cool the people out. He was doing everything in his power to cool them out. We were speechless for a little while afterwards . . . We didn't enjoy it.

"I think at one point we might have walked off stage, but that would have been a disaster. We just had to carry on and play the best we could. We played longer than we would have done because we had to keep stopping all the time. We still did a complete show. We must have been on stage for about an hour-and-a-half. It seemed like ages.

"The Hell's Angels had a lot to do with it. The people that were working with us getting the concert together thought it would be a good idea to have them as a security force. But I got the impression that because they were a security force they were using it as an excuse. They're just very, very violent people.

"I think we expected probably something like the Hell's Angels that were our security force at Hyde Park, but of course they're not the real Hell's Angels, they're completely phony. These guys in California are the real thing — they're very violent.

"I had expected a nice sort or peaceful concert. I didn't expect anything like that in San Francisco because they are so used to having nice things there. That's where free concerts started, and I thought a society like San Francisco could have done much better.

"We were on the road when it was being organized, we weren't involved at all. We would have liked to have been. Perhaps the only thing we needed security for was the Hell's Angels.

"I really don't know what caused it but it just depressed me because it could have been so beautiful that day."

According to Keith Richard, it *did* go pretty well. On his arrival in London, he told a United Press reporter that Altamont "was basically well-handled, but lots of people were tired and a few tempers got frayed."

It is impossible to speak of the music that went down without placing it in the context of the violence, the fear and the anxiety, which, during the course of the day, peaked to higher and higher points of refinement and climax.

As Santana was setting up a chick toward the front of the stage was telling her old man: "It's weird. They consulted the astrologers before setting the dates for Woodstock, but they couldn't have consulted an astrologer about today. Anyone can see that with the moon in Scorpio, today's an *awful* day to do this concert. There's a strong possibility of violence and chaos and any astrologer could have told them so. Oh well, maybe the Stones know something I don't know."

The violence was not long to follow. (It had already begun earlier, of course, but to have it going on while the bands were playing was a new twist.) Between the first song and the second, one young-looking fellow tried to pass nearby to get on stage. He was wearing a blue and yellow sports shirt, jeans and had long straight blond hair over his ears. As he tried to get by some Hell's Angels he was kicked in the face by an Angel's booted feet and pulverized with punches and lay spread out on the ground unable to move or be moved, there were so many people jammed up to the stage.

A lot of photographers kept right on taking their photos through the worst of it, right up close, without getting hassled. So did the movie crews — but then they had Angels for bodyguards.

Not every photographer was so lucky, though. John Young, 24, who moved in with his Leica to capture some of the bashing, wound up with 13 stiches in his head. The Angels were beating a couple of naked people to the ground during Santana's set. In moments, the nudies were up again, and Young started taking pictures, when the Angels resumed bashing them.

An Angel spotted him — out of some ten or twelve photogs immediately surrounding him — and demanded: "I want your film or you get hit." Young kept shooting, and the Angel leapt at him, smashing the camera into Young's face. Down he went. When several Angels began pounding him, Young rolled into a protective ball. "It felt like they were hitting me with a hammer and a broken bottle," Yound said later. Observers said it was pool cues.

The Angels, many of them, were carrying — and applying to a lot of non-Angel heads — loaded pool cues, saw-offed (usually) to a length somewhat longer than a billy club. About the length, in fact, of the cattle prods that we've all seen in photographs of red-neck brutality against black people in the South.

Eventually they got around to removing the film from his camera. Drenched in blood — hair, face, neck, shirt back and front — Young ran 50 yards into the crowd, then sort of collapsed until the Red Cross took him to their tent, where they cleaned him up, administered novocaine, and stitched him up.

"I'd never seen a Hell's Angel before," explained Young, who's from a small town in Maine, "and I didn't really know they could *do* that." After the patchwork, he was able to watch the rest of the concert. He took no more photos.

Santana began their next song, but were interrupted by the Angels' running across stage to the right to beat someone up. Santana finished their set amidst very uptight vibes around the stage.

The next group up was the Airplane and by the time they came on it was standing room only for about seventy-five yards from the stage but everyone slowly sat down when the people seventy-six yards from the stage yelled.

Sam Cutler announced that a woman had given birth and clean sheets and diapers were needed and within minutes the stage was beseiged with them. Then Cutler introduced the Jefferson Airplane and they began their set with "We Can Be Together" and ended the set with "Volunteers of America." In between there was a disturbance with some Hell's Angels and members of the audience and Marty Balin was knocked out by a punch from one of the Angels when he tried to intercede in the disturbance. Paul Kantner began to make a speech about the event and was challenged by a Hell's Angel who grabbed a microphone and the people began to boo. Another Hell's Angel came up to Kantner and a fight almost broke out between them but was cooled down before any punches were thrown on stage and they went into a song. When it ended, Grace Slick was rapping softly into the microphone about what was going down with the Hell's Angels and everyone else. It was almost too much to take in. An Instant Re-Play would have been useful, the action was so thick and heavy. Consider the symbolism alone:

With all the grandeur of Bert Parks inviting last year's Miss America to step forward, the Airplane had asked, "Will the Hell's Angels please take the stage."

Then came that "up against the wall motherfucker" song, with its soaring (old-fashioned) harmonies, Marty Balin's voice riding high and clear over the ensemble, the Jefferson Airplane celebrating the forces of chaos and anarchy, proud to be part of that trip. Very, very proud.

Then Marty saw a black man getting swallowed up by the forces of chaos and anarchy — in the form of the angels, half a dozen of whom were thumping the shit out of him. At some point near the start of "Somebody to Love," Balin jumped in to break it up. He at least laid a hand on an Angel. It is said he threw a punch, and maybe said, "Fuck you!"

During the second half of "Somebody to Love," Marty Balin lay unconscious, having gotten himself blasted by an Angel. The rest of the band played on, Balin's absence, in musical terms, scarcely mattered. The sound was so bad you couldn't tell the difference.

It was at just about this point that the Angels' position became clear. They were in charge of the stage. They had taken it that morning. It was *theirs,* musicians or no musicians. What the fuck, wasn't nobody tough enough to *take* it from them, was there? The Stones? Not likely. It had become, to a disturbing degree, a Hell's Angels Festival.

Nothing profound happened musically, during the Flying Burrito Brothers set. It seldom does. But somehow the simple verities of their contrified electric music soothed the warriors. There were no fights. As luck would have it, Mick Jagger and Keith Richard chose to emerge from the backstage trailer where they'd been holed up to have a look at the stage and the audience during this period of calm. They strolled about, wound up onstage, smiling, for a bit. Then back to the trailer, where, in true super-star fashion, Jagger was signing autographs (on album jackets, and even draft cards). Whenever they ventured any distance from the smallish white trailer, it was behind three or four burly Angels.

The hill on the concert side of the west fence was packed almost as tight with people as center stage area. People tended to fade into one another after awhile — unless there was something especially strange or loud about them that made you remember they were real and not just part of a huge movie set.

There was the young mother in the blue blouse with Peter Pan collar and pleated skirt, looking like she'd just stepped out of a Hayward model home, who pushed ahead of her husband. In one hand she carried a baby only a few months old. She'd nudge the person ahead of her with the baby, smile and look wide-eyed at them as they turned to see who was pushing — and then she'd push right through.

Then about a dozen Angels, mostly officers, some carrying double, ploughed through the crowd on their bikes. An admirer in the crowd offered a shaggy Angel a swig from his wine bottle. The Angel, sporting clean new colors, stopped, dismounted, grabbed the gallon in both hands and put it to his lips for just a moment, handed it back and putted on off — a lotta show for a little sip of wine.

"We come down on our bikes," said Sonny Barger later, "because we were told we were supposed to park in front of the stage, and so like when we started coming down through the crowd everybody was outa sight got up and moved and we come down in low gear and didn't try to run into anybody or do any of that kind of thing. Everybody got up really nice, some people offered us drinks on the way down and like . . . we must have come into approximate contact with at least a thousand people and outa them thousand people we had trouble with one person . . . one broad jumped up and said something that pertained to a four letter word and then Angels and one of [the] Angels stopped his bike and he had his old lady on the back and he said, 'Are you gonna let them talk about Angels like that?' and she jumped off the bike and slapped the other broad that said that that was in the crowd

and got back on the bike and we proceeded down with no problem. We pulled up in front of the stage and parked where we were told we were supposed to park."

The flaw in this story, according to Sam Cutler and Rock Scully, is no one told the Angels to put their bikes down in front of the stage.

It got cold. Then it got colder. Time passed. More time. The Stones were waiting, like they always wait. Tuning up, they said. But really, there was something else going on, and it tied in with the whole super-star sensibility in which the Stones increasingly enwrap themselves. They were waiting for it to get really dark out, so the banks of spotlights would set them off to the most dramatic effect possible.

The scene back there was dense with groupies (most dazzling: Miss Mercy behind her racoon-ring eye makeup), and celebrities (a toss-up between Tim Leary, who went forth, gamely flashing smiles and peace signs in the direction of violence; and manager/promoter/entrepreneur Steve Paul, gloomy in his blue bathrobe, muttering dire presentiments), not to mention writers and phtotgraphers.

Out front, the battle was rejoined during Crosby, Stills, Nash and Young's desultory performance (the rest of the band had played only after David Crosby had urged them to in the strongest terms). The Angels, at one point, amassed a fairly spectacular charge, pool cues flailing whoever got in their way. At the end of their set, several stretchers were sent into the audience and bodies were passed overhead and across the stage to the Red Cross area. Those who were carried out and those who departed under their own steam were quickly replaced, as it became obvious that the next set was going to be the Stones.

Despite balloons and pennants and a few other picturesque touches (like the big polyethylene walk-in bubble/dome some co-freaks had set up); the physical

atmosphere at Altamont was singularly ominous and depressing. The more people arrived, the more clear it was that this was nowhere in particular; just a patch of land, covered with bleached-out long grass and sticker burrs. Nothing had been done to make it the least bit festive. And the later it got, the worse the air became — filled with a rancid combination of fog, dust, smoke and glare. A squinty grey light made everything hard to look at.

The 300,000 anonymous bodies huddled together on the little dirt hills were indeed an instant city — a decaying urban slum complete with its own air pollution. By the time the Stones finally came on, dozens of garbage fires had been set all over the place. Flickering silhouettes of people trying to find warmth around the blazing trash reminded one of the medieval paintings of tortured souls in the Dance of Death. The stench of the smoke from tens of thousands of potato chip packages and half-eaten sandwiches brought vomiting to many. It was in this atmosphere that Mick sang his song about how groovy it is to be Satan. Never has it been sung in a more appropriate setting.

Suddenly, the lights glowed on, a cold-fire red gleaming on the Stones, as they wedged between the Angels onstage to their places. Jagger's demonic orange and black satin cape/robe gleamed wickedly. Into "Jumpin' Jack Flash," rather haltingly. To open up a little dancing room for himself, Jagger had to ask the Angels to step back a few paces. There must have been a hundred people — who knows? maybe 200 — on that stage, and Jagger was performing in a small pocket at center stage, like it or not.

"Carol" was a little better, but stiff.

"Sympathy for the Devil." They stopped in the middle. A skirmish had broken out at stage left. This was the knifing/stomping of Meredith Hunter, perhaps 25 feet from where Jagger pranced and sang, then stopped. To one observer 20 feet to Jagger's rear, the glint of the long knives was clearly visible. So, if the Stones were looking, they saw it too. The same observer spoke with several others who were on-stage (as did ROLLING STONE), and none, except for the onstage Angels, claim to have seen a gun.

One Angel later told it this way to KSAN-FM: This black guy had come toward the stage and been pushed off by Angels. "He flipped over and he's got this revolver—it looked like a cannon. It was pointed right at me. I hit the deck and this gun was pointed right at Jagger." And then, according to this account, "everybody was on him and that was the last I seen of him . . . When it was all over, man, Jagger looks at me and says, 'why?' I says: 'I dunno, man, that's just the way people are.'"

Whether Jagger had time for this game of eye contact is dubious. He was busy telling the audience—"brothers and sisters, come on now! That means everybody just cool out! We can cool out, everybody! Everybody be cool, now. Come on."

Turning toward side of stage: "How are we doing over there? Everybody all right? Can we still collect ourselves? I don't know what happened, I couldn't see, I hope you're all right. Are you all right? Okay, let's just give ourselves another half a minute before we get our breath back. Everyone just cool down. Is there anyone who's hurt? Okay, I think we're cool, we can groove. We always have something very funny happen when we start that number."

"Sympathy" started again, but not too convincingly. Somebody tried to climb onstage. Angels tossed him back.

Jagger: "Why are we fighting? Why are we fighting? We don't want to fight at all. Who wants to fight, who is it? Every other scene has been cool. We gotta stop right now. You know, if we can't there's no point . . ."

The fight scene got worse.

Long silence at the mike. Dense uncertainty crowded the night chill. Amazingly, Jagger seemed to lose control of his audience. A rare moment.

Keith Richard stepped forward: "Either those cats cool it, man, or we don't play . . ."

Pause. More nastiness in the audience immediately in front of the stage. Of 300,000 people, only a few thousand can see the trouble.

Jagger, with something like a sob: "If he doesn't stop it, man . . ."

Richard: "Keep it cool! Hey, if you don't cool it, you ain't gonna hear no music!"

An Angel commandeered the mike to shout: "Fuck you!"

The goring had ended by now, and Jagger took the mike again to say, "We need a doctor here, now! Look, can you let the doctor get through, please. We're trying to get to someone who's hurt."

People who were trying to help Meredith Hunter were raising bloody hands to show Mick how bad it was.

A doctor got through, the man was carried off, eventually.

Next a blues, an instrumental to ease the tension. When it's over, Jagger says: "That's to cool out with."

Then, "Stray Cat Blues."

"Love in Vain." Jagger again urges the crowd to sit down. They do, as he watches. "Now, boys and girls, are you sitting comfortably? When we get to the end and we all want to go absolutely crazy and jump on each other, well, then we'll stand up again. I mean, we can't seem to keep together standing up."

"Under My Thumb." A bad fight this time: a body sails across the stage. "We're splitting; we're splitting if those cats don't stop," Jagger shouts! "I want them out of the way! I don't like doing it to them . . ." The onstage crowd in to surround him. An extremely menacing moment.

What an enormous thrill it would be for an Angel to kick Mick Jagger's teeth down his throat. They have been watching his dancing and wild gesticulations with disgusted

scowls, derisive laughter, elbows in each other's ribs. The looks on their faces read: "So easy—I could stomp shit outa this fuckin' sissy *so easy* —I could snuff this motherfucker!" Several of the Angels who have parked their bikes in front of the stage gun their engines defiantly.

From the stage, it is difficult to hear the shouts from the middle and outer reaches of the huge crowd, which extends a quarter of a mile out into the night. Some are shouting: "Music, music, music . . ." Other chanting: "Get off the fucking stage, get off the fucking stage . . ."

Jagger follows the long onstage silence with: "Please relax and sit down. If you move back and sit down, we *can* continue and we *will* continue. We need a doctor as soon as possible, please."

Stones road manager Sam Cutler, who had MC'd all day long, takes the mike to try to clear the stage. "First of all, everyone is going to get to the side of the stage who's on it now, aside from the Stones, Please, everyone. We need a doctor and ambulance, right away. Just sit down and keep calm and relax. We can get it together."

They finish "Under My Thumb." Then get into a new song they've never performed in public before: "Brown Sugar." It goes well. Beautifully, in fact. The Stones are making miraculous music, despite everything.

"Midnight Rambler," comes next, and, oooh, it is funky; but too late. The damage has been done. It's later and later by the minute. Many are leaving.

Jagger takes a hit of Jack Daniels bourbon and makes a toast of it. "One more drink to you all."

"Live With Me," is driving, vibrant.

It's just amazing. There could be no worse circumstance for making music, and the Stones are playing their asses off. Jagger is incredible. They all look like they'd rather be *anyplace* else. But it's getting better and better. Driving, powerhouse waves of rhythm roll on and on. Jagger is opening up. At first, when he really was trying to cool everybody out, his performance was the epitomy of cool: restrained, distanced, but still—even with fear welling in his throat— deeply *inside* each song, laying it on us.

Now, as he feels himself taking command again, the passion is building song by song. It is hard to imagine that "Gimmie Shelter" ever got a more burning treatment. "Queenie" is a bitch. During "Satisfaction," long-stem roses shower off him from the audience (and where did *they* get them? Must have been laid on them by Stones' management). He changes the line in "Honky Tonky Woman" to say "I laid a divorcee right here in Frisco . . ." (some think he said "in Tracy . . ." which is the small town off the highway from Altamont; same difference, really) and gets a big laugh from everybody.

It ends with "Street Fighting Man," a great performance of it, an unfortunate selection, considering what kind of day it's been.

It has been an awful day. One of the worst in memory. The tendency was to blame it on the Angels, and, fundamentally, on the Stones, since they had paid the Angels to come and act as security. Sam Cutler, acting on behalf of the band, had paid the Hell's Angels $500 worth of beer to come and act as a security force. . . .

People were comparing the Angels with regular cops in confrontation situations, and nobody said they liked Angels better. Said one person who'd been on the streets during the People's Park demonstrations in Berkeley: "Not one of those policemen conducted themselves in a manner that even could be compared with what the Angels were doing. It was just impossible—imposing their will with over three hundred thousand people!" Said another: "They acted just like pigs."

A photographer who'd taken part in the Chicago demonstrations during the

Democratic Party Convention felt the Chicago cops had been both more together when it came to applying force, and more reasonable.

During the worst of the Angels' outrages, a few of the braver non-Angels had suggested (quietly) to the friends that with enough men they could put the Angels down, and maybe they ought to. But cats like Marty Balin, who actually leapt into the fight the Angels were exceedingly rare. They usually got bloody fast. . . .

To all complaints that they had been over-zealous—too rough—in keeping the stage clear, the Angels simply replied that they was just doin' their thing. Which is violence.

"Rough?" said Frisco Pete. "What I feel the roughness is if we say we're gonna do somethin', we do it. Do you understand that? That's our whole thing. Now if these people asked us to do this thing, we did it. What are we supposed to do? We ain't cops. We're not info that thing. When we decide to do somethin', it's done, no matter how far we have to go to do it." . . .

The night before it started, Altamont felt great. There were campfires all over the place (many of them the product of the race track's fence, which is now being replaced), and people were engaged in a range of worthy activities, like smoking dope or sharing it, drinking beer or sharing it, playing tapes of the Stones, or playing guitars and singing their own, playing touch football under the stage lights Chip Monck's work crews were using to set up a stage.

Monck had gotten all the necessary goods—lumber and wiring and speakers and tools and scaffolding—to the Altamont site at Friday afternoon. By 9 o'clock, he had erected a thoroughly serviceable stage, and well before midnight it would be basically set.

Two diesel generators, already raging to supply power for the lights, were the only noise. Huge derricks lifted scaffolds, then speakers and lights into place in the island of light. Everyone

was remarking how much it was like a Fellini movie. To heighten the effect, there were three dozen or so wrecked cars from the raceway's normal activity: destruction derbies. As the hour grew later, freaks were to be seen sleeping in their front seats. At least one couple balled in the back seat of a crunched old Plymouth.

Down the service road, gleaming by the floodlight glare came eight ancient trucks, each loaded with about a dozen porta-toilets. A weird sight. They were applauded all along the way. . . .

Dealers were among the first to show—spacey madmen with their dazzling raps. "Our goal," one was saying, "is to smuggle five tons of dope to London, but you don't print shit like that, man, it's like a war. Twice been in Mexico in drag, to make buys. Oh, man, the way hash gets smuggled into this country . . . Most smack smugglers are in it for the bucks. I mean, I'm in·it for the bucks, but it's a trip, too, and it makes things like *this* happen, and it helps the trip . . ." etc.

The dealers were more than mildly disconcerted to see so much shit being given away on Friday night. Maybe there'd be nobody buying come Saturday. But they had nothing to fear: it got a lot greedier when there were 300,000 instead of 30,000, and finally when it got really bad, when the music was on and the Angels were wailing, all deals were cash on the line. Merchants and consumers. . . .

By 7:30, Saturday morning, the hills were solidly packed with people, and it was clear that those who expected only 100,000 or so had miscalculated. For as far as you could see in any direction, the army of rock freaks was advancing over rises and hillocks, through valleys, along the road and the railroad tracks, converging on Altamont. Whatever else it would be, it would be *big*.

From the air, it was an incredible scene. From six to eight miles from the site, cars lined the highway like the traffic jam in *Weekend*. Nothing on wheels except motorcycles could move, so people just left their cars and started the long hot trek to the racetrack. The air was alive with aircraft.

As the helicopter nears the site, the pilot says, "See that big brown spot off to the right? Those are people."

He's right, The huge, brown mass now appears to be moving. It no longer just looks like a burnt out field. From every direction, people are converging on the scene. It looks like the peons following Marlon Brando to the town where he's killed in *Viva Zapata!*

We circle the area once for pictures and swoop toward the asphalt racetrack where another copter is hovering to land. Faces become distinct now and we set down, causing a whirlwind. Bystanders look interested momentarily until they see we aren't from a band and then turn away.

Jan Vinson, who piloted the Stones helicopter, swore he would never work a rock festival again, because of the "mass confusion and because I was put in a position which was dangerous to both me and the machine and the crowd. Those people were messed up on everything—dope, wine, needles. They were higher than any altitude I've ever flown at. I wasn't about to get out of the chopper and talk to any of them. If the Hell's Angels hadn't been there, it would have been worse. They did a good job of keeping the way cleared when crowds surged around us, and didn't bother me at all."

Some people—mainly news crews and film crews, but also some civilians—paid up to $250 an hour to be airlifted to the concert site by helicopter, 45 minutes each way. Traffic congestion on the roads was bad enough that helicopter was the only way to be certain that all the bands and equipment would get there on time.

Crosby, Stills, Nash and Young, who were to fly in and out in time to be in Los Angeles for a gig at UCLA that evening, had arranged to go out on a 9-passenger chopper leaving from Marin Heliport in Sausalito.

David Crosby, first to arrive with the band's road crew, was enthusiastic, hopeful about the day. A broad smile creased his face, even after he heard the helicopter pilot had refused to land because of fog and they would have to drive 20 miles through and beyond San Francisco to catch another helicopter at International. . . . . . . Airport.

"We'll make it," he said. But be back in time for the gig?

He smiled again. "We've got till 8 o'clock."

It was nearly noon already.

It was quarter to three on Saturday when the first helicopter carrying the Stones and their entourage touched down on the asphalt pit area of the Altamont racetrack. Immediately, a minor mob scene formed as about 500 people jumped off the nearby fence they were sitting on or. . . . . rushed from the hill toward the copter, almost crushing a smiling Stone and his escorts.

"Who is it? Who is it?' rasped a blonde chick to her black-garbed girlfriend.

"It's Mick Jagger! It's Mick Jagger!" And, mouth wide with joy, she bent over slightly, arms pressed tightly to her sides, her hands clenched as if in religious fervor—the way only 16-year-old chicks can do to show just how excited they are.

They were both soon lost in the sea that seemed to swallow the Stones.

Shortly thereafter, a crazed freak broke through shouting, "I hate you, I hate you!" and punched Mick smack in the chops. It was a foretaste of delights to come.

Mid-morning on Saturday, Berkeley people laid what looked like a thousand tabs of sunshine acid on the Angels—not good sunshine: it had a lot of speed in it—and this was being dispersed both at the Angels' bus thirty yards uphill and on the stage. At one point, 500 reds were scattered on the front portion of the stage. The Angels were downing tabs of acid/speed and reds in huge gulps of Red Mountain wine. The more they took, the more fighting there was. The usual thing was

to pick off non-Angels, but they were seen to turn on their own prospects (non-members who were trying to gain full status into the club). One prospect was soundly kicked—they were jumping on him—after Santana's set. He took a terrible beating, and, amazingly, was back on his feet ten minutes later, telling the full-fledged Angels he was their brother and everything was cool.

Meredith Hunter wasn't the only one who never made it home from Altamont. Three others died that day, two in a hit-and-run auto case, one by jumping into an irrigation canal where the fast-moving waters overpowered him. . . .

One thing is most certain: Even the most incomplete medical reports show that this was a festival dominated by violence. The volunteer medics treated more than just the usual bad trips and cut feet. They also treated dozens of lacerations and skull fractures. On top of those, they had an extraordinary number of bad trips—so many that they ran out of thorazine even though they didn't start using it until late in the day. They came to the four medical tents in waves after each escalation by the Angels, many of them having bad trips on good acid—bad trips seemingly induced by the violence going on around them. People sitting near the stage said they could feel the wave of paranoia spreading through the stoned crowd with each beating. Acid plus muggings equalled terror and revulsion.

Understandably, there was a bad aftertaste in the mouths of medical volunteers along with just about everybody else at the festival. Richard Fine, chairman of the Medical Committee for Human Rights, labeled the concert promoters "morally irresponsible" for the manner in which the festival was staged.

"We had one day to mobilize medical personnel and supplies. We got shitty support from the people running the thing who didn't realize what was crucial from a medical standpoint, and wouldn't give us the authority to do such things as set up a workable evacuation procedure. And we had no time to mobilize community people for help with bad trips. It was just piss-poor planning. A lot of the bad trips were violent because there was so much violence in the air. There were a lot of beatings. Girls were beaten—I sewed up a lot of girls. It was like the fucking [police] Tac[tical] Squad ran around. We feel that we as well as everyone else in the crowd was exploited by the promoters," Fine fumed.

According to Fine, the medical people had been promised telephone communications. It never happened. They'd been promised a helicopter. None materialized. And when it turned dark—during the hour and a quarter wait for the Stones— and dozens of people lay injured in the medical area, Stones representatives refused to turn on the backstage lights so the medics could tend to them. The lights would just damn well have to wait until the Stones came out to play. (To turn them on before might rob some impact from the Stones' entry. People were injured? Well . . . tough shit . . . the Stones were more important.)

The MCHR is an all-volunteer group which provides medical aid at almost all Bay Area demonstrations and festivals. They're an irreplaceable part of the scene. They were assisted at Altamont by four Red Cross chapters, Langley Porter Neuropsychiatric Institute staff members, and dozens of volunteers. The medical aid was coordinated primarily by Dr. Richard Baldwin of Point Reyes, who said the main problem was "all those freak-outs."

"With all our units, we treated probably about 700 freak-outs," he guessed, "plus all those we never saw, that were handled by friends in the crowd. That's a lot. They came in waves. We got one big wave early in the morning, and then another when the violence broke out with the Airplane. Then it was back to 'normal' again. The biggest wave we got was near the end, when the Angels started picking up again. They were leading each other in twos and threes, totally confused and totally freaked-out by it," Baldwin said.

The standard procedure for dealing with bum trips was to assign a person experienced in drug crises to each person who came in. They would try to "talk down" anyone in trouble on a one-to-one personal basis. But as the day wore on, and the violence increased, personnel were unable to keep up with the massive numbers seeking help, and doctors had to start relying solely on thorazine. Although none had any idea how much thorazine was finally used, doctors had to have an emergency supply flown in later in the day as bad trips increased. Aside from thorazine, though, first aid tents were well stocked with everything they needed.

Some of the bad trips were the result of yellow pills given away in the crowd and said to be organic acid. "It was very crude stuff," according to Baldwin. Most of the dope being sold at the festival, though, was of about standard street quality. Several bummed out when they drank wine without knowing it had acid in it. Only two drug cases had to be evacuated, though, both because of too many reds. The extraordinary amount of wine consumed posed another problem for Baldwin's crews.

Aside from the bad trips, doctors treated a large number of victims of the Angel rampages. The number of violence-induced injuries was "unusually high," according to Fine. Doctors at one tent said they treated 12—one skull fracture, one fractured facial bones, and 10 skull lacerations. And that wasn't even the tent behind the stage, which was the first aid station closest to the danger zone and thus presumably the one most of the injured would go to.

Both doctors seemed certain that, despite reports, there were no births at the festival. First reports had four babies being born, two before, two during the music. There were cases of false labor, but none of the medical staff at the site delivered a baby, and no one showed up at any of the medical tents with a new-born child. The same was true of local hospitals. "I think somebody just picked up on that story because it sounded groovy and the promoters could use the story about births to try to balance out the deaths," Fine charged. . . .

David Crosby put most of the blame for the whole sordid mess on sloppy planning due to a lack of time, but had some scathing remarks for the Stones as well.

"You can't have that big a gathering that sloppily, and it wasn't sloppy for lack of effort, but for lack of time," he said. "The people made a heroic effort. But doing it that sloppily, we could have paid much heavier dues. We could have dumped a helicopter full of two or three good rock bands into a crowd of about a thousand people and killed them all; we could have paid *much* heavier dues.

"There were several big mistakes. They weren't necessarily mistakes of intent, but people just didn't really know certain things. The Rolling Stones are still a little bit in 1965. They didn't really know that security isn't a part of anybody's concert anywhere anymore. I mean, our road managers could have covered it. Nobody would have gotten on that stage, nobody would have hassled anybody. We didn't need the Angels. I'm not downgrading the Angels, because it's not healthy and because they only did what they were expected to do. I don't know why anyone would expect them to do anything other than exactly what they did. The mistake that was made was in thinking security was needed, and that the Angels should do it. The Stones don't know about Angels. To them an Angel is something in between Peter Fonda and Dennis Hopper. That's not real, and they just found out the reality of it. Unfortunately, we all had to pay some dues for that.

"Another level of this is that I don't think gatherings that big is where it's at. I don't think it's conducive to making magic. The Airplane and the Dead have done this kind of thing right before. They've taken a sunny afternoon and a beautiful field and put a few thousand people on the best possible state of consciousness that a few thousand people can reach on this planet that I know of. Full-out brotherhood and a full-out really happy feeling. That kind of trip you can probably do and you can probably control how many people come to it and what kind of people by how you disseminate the information. Our own band is kind of like that, and this big trip thing is not for me, since this one went down. I've talked to my friends in the Airplane and they're kind of the same way, and the Dead, too, and we're three of the bands you'd call if you want to do that kind of hugeness, and we won't go now. We won't play this kind any more," Crosby stated emphatically.

The rest of his own band feels pretty much the same way, he noted. "They were all bummed out by this; they did it mostly for me, because I asked them to. When you're trying to do something that's as fragile as making music, to have a couple cats pick some dude off, fire on him with blows that are out of his order of magnitude entirely, lay him out cold and then kick him for 15 minutes right in front of you, you just can't do it." . . .

And, finally, some harsh words for the Stones themselves. "I think the major mistakes were taking what was essentially a party and turning it into an ego game and a star trip. An ego trip of 'look how many of us there are' and a star trip of the Rolling Stones, who are on a star trip, and who qualify in my book as snobs. I've talked with them many times and I still think they're snobs. I didn't want to talk to them at all Saturday, once I saw what was going on. I'm sure they don't understand what they did, and I'm sure they won't understand my thinking they're snobs, but they are in my book. I don't like them. I think they have an exaggerated view of their own importance; I think

they're on a grotesque ego trip. I think they're out of touch with the people to whom they're trying to speak. I think they are on negative trips intensely, especially the two leaders." . . .

Asked for his comments on the festival, Marty Balin declined. Paul Kantner was the lone member of the Airplane willing to speak, and his basic point was to make clear the fact that the Angels would not be asked to provide security at any more concerts involving the Airplane. Members of the Grateful Dead refused to discuss it at all, at least not for the record.

The Dead were scheduled to play just before—and then, as the day wore on, just after—the Stones. But by the time the Stones had finished their set, the scene was too tense to risk stretching the day out any longer. That's the way things went at Altamont—so badly that the Grateful Dead, prime organizers and movers of the festival, didn't even get to play. . . .

A full week after the event, the legal hassles still hadn't been straightened out. The murder investigation was continuing, several lawsuits were being prepared, and the only thing that was certain was that someone is responsible for something, and eventually will have to pay the price.

The Stones' New York management apparently felt pressed to say *something*. But they were unable to get it together. A press conference planned for Friday following the concert (which attorney Melvin Belli was scheduled to attend, having booked a San Francisco-New York flight) was cancelled.

Belli, who represented Jack Ruby during his trial for offing Lee Harvey Oswald, and is one of the nation's gaudier torts lawyers—also one of the best —was representing just about everybody who'd been involved in organizing the concert—the Stones and all their management and retinue, the Dead, even the race track. This may explain why he was playing his cards so close to the vest.

He acknowledged on one

hand, that it was "like a hurricane went through Altamont." He said, on the other hand, that "you've got to anticipate, with this number of people, that this would happen." Basically, Belli thought it had gone pretty smoothly—though lots of questions "remained unresolved," and if he'd "had more time to arrange things, it could have gone smooth as clockwork."

Asked who was responsible for the deaths and the damage, Belli said it was a "foolish" question.

Ron Schneider had told Ralph Gleason that the event was covered by a $5 million Lloyd's of London insurance policy.

Asked about the amount of the Stones insurance for the event—reports ranged from a $100,000 to Schneider's $5 million—Belli called it "ample." What did that mean? "I mean *ample,*" he said. Might it include some recompense for the family of the young man who had been murdered?

The question summoned forth Belli's most contemptuous voice. "I think," he declared, "that you're over your head in a legal story like this, when you're asking whether there's going to be recompense for the man that died when it hasn't been established whether he was at fault."

Is it possible, then, that everybody who'd been at Altamont might *somehow* have been at fault, and therefore the Stones (et al.) bore no responsibility for the injured, the wounded and the maimed? That was a question Belli had no time to hear. . . .

A full nine days later, the Altamont Raceway area looked more than anything else like a picture of Hiroshima the day after—not a person to be seen, the whole area still piled high with the litter and refuse that were the last remnants of what had been. A couple fences in the area had been mended, but the fence around the racetrack was still down. The thousands of wine bottles and tons of litter were stacked in piles around the grounds, but none of it had been removed. A lone man walked about the huge field, stooping over occasionally to pick up a scrap of paper.

Cutler had made an appeal over the radio the day after the concert for the "beautiful people of San Francisco" to come back and help clean up the some tons of litter which they had left there "by their very presence." Also to help dismantle the stage, the scaffolding, and the other construction which had a lifetime of one day.

Oh, there was a little help. Ralph Haley, 23, of Washington, and his wife Sandy (they had been married December 4th) were in San Jose visiting friends Thursday when they heard about the festival. They went Friday to help set things up, and Sunday started heading the clean-up detail. They got some help from George Cooper of Spokane, fresh out of the service, Steve Mercier of San Francisco, and Mike and Susan Metcalf of Berkeley, members of Ecology Action. And 30, maybe 40, others of the original 300,000. They figured they had

at least another week of work ahead of them.

"The land itself is OK," said Haley, "It's mostly just debris. There must be a million Red Mountain bottles here, and about half of them are broken. Spirits are really good; we're doing it because we want to. There's pretty good vibrations here while we're working, but it gets pretty cold at night." They planned to clean the land of the neighboring ranchers when they finished around the speedway, "if the ranchers will let us." Fat chance the ranchers will let them. They're pretty leery about longhairs these days. Remember what happened to Sharon Tate. One local rancher went so far as to quite seriously and quite openly propose genocide as the solution to the whole concert problem. Try to tell that man you want to mend his fence.

That lesson was learned by program director Tom Swift and the staff of KMPX-FM in San Francisco. The jocks there had started a project to help clean the place up. They got

several hundred volunteers, plus the support of the CHP, the San Francisco police, and Mayor Joseph Alioto. The Livermore Herald News was going to co-sponsor the project. Then, when the dust was starting to settle, Swift got this letter from Herald News managing editor Fred Dickey:

"After talking with several ranchers, we discovered they're too skittish to even think about importing San Francisco kids for clean-up.

"So after hearing that and weighing other factors, Mr. Sparks decided the risk is too great for the possible gains in such a joint venture.

"Accordingly, I must withdraw from the project we discussed.

"Thank you for your interest."

Meanwhile, scavengers are combing over the grounds for pop bottles they can turn in for deposit, and several have taken geiger counters out to the raceway to find change and valuables that were left behind.

Who knows, maybe for them the festival will have been worth it.

Street Fighting Man
MICK JAGGER AND KEITH RICHARD

Everywhere I hear the sound of marching, charging feet, boy.
Comes summer here and the time is right for fighting
In the street, boy.

But what can a poor boy do
Except to sing for a rock 'n' roll band.
Guess in sleepy London town,
There's no place for a street fighting man.

Hey, think the time is right for a palace revolution,
But where I live the game to play is compromise solution.
But what can a poor boy do
Except to sing for a rock 'n' roll band.
Guess in sleepy London town,
There's just no place for a street fighting man.

Hey, said my name is called Disturbance.
I'll shout and scream,
I'll kill the king.
I'll rail at all his servants.

But what can a poor boy do
Except to sing for a rock 'n' roll band.
Guess in sleepy London town,
There's no place for a street fighting man.

The two pieces which follow record some
of the controversy which surrounded
the Rolling Stones; in addition, both
writers show us how much the Stones'
style influenced contemporary taste.
It is interesting to compare the point of
view of these writers with the point of
view of Baby Jane Holzer, who saw the
Stones several years earlier—before they
had become so important.

On And On
Mick's Orgy Rolls
ALBERT GOLDMAN

"Don't expect them to scream!"
That was the tight-lipped
warning passed to Mick Jagger
on the now-legendary night,
Nov. 8, 1969, when the Rolling
Stones took the stage to bring
back the good old days of
rock 'n' roll to America. The place
was the Los Angeles Forum, an
18,000-seat, color-coded,
deep-freeze tank with the
acoustics of an undampened
bowling alley. The bill was
black-heavy with people like
B. B. King, the regnant blues
belter, and Ike and Tina Turner,
the belle and beau of the ball-
'n'-socket circuit. Two hours of
diathermy by these deep-fat
fryers had put the packed house
into a sweaty, happy mood,
when suddenly the Forum's
zeppelin searchlights switched
off and through the murmurous
hush of 18,000 craning minds,
there sliced the hysterical cry,
"THE ROLLING STONES!!!"
    Wham! The stage explodes
in blue-white incandescence.
Out firks the manic form of Mick
Jagger, a black forked radish,
cinched with a wickedly studded

belt and topped off with a
towering red, white and blue
Uncle Sam hat. After him chases
Keith Richard, flame-colored,
sequin-spangled, ear-ringed,
brandishing a plastic see-
through guitar. Then the other
Stones: Bill Wyman, a red-clad
executioner, Charlie Watts, a
T-shirted construction worker,
and the new guy, Mick Taylor,
with his bright cotton shirt puffed
at the sleeves in enormous
mutton chops.
    Boomeranging the Uncle
Sam with one hand while
collaring the mike with the
other, Jagger screams "Hello!,"
springs into the air and slams
down in a split, as the Stones
start bashing out "Jumpin'
Jack Flash." The audience,
recoiling in audiovisual shock,
not only screeeeeeeeeeams,
but starts climbing the furniture,
dancing in the aisles and
charging the unguarded stage.
Tasting the crowd's warm, salty
blood, Mick the Jagger goes
mad, tears off his belt, flogs
the stage floor, incites the mob
to riot and offers himself as their
superhuman sacrifice.
    Up and up the fever chart
zigzags, on and on the orgy
rolls, until after two shows,
eight hours, a couple of buckets

of sweat and a million killing
watts of electro-encephalic
energy, apocalypse is attained.
It's 5:30 in the morning—the
Woodstock hour—and Jagger
is jigging on the ruins of Western
Civilization. He's into his final
medley, with a dozen powerful
amps screaming, "I Can't Get
No Satisfaction." Suddenly, the
Stones turn the corner into
"Street Fighting Man," and the
whole audience levitates. Every
man, woman and love-child
mounts his chair, raises his
right arm over his head and
makes his biggest, blackest,
hardest fist! What a climax!
What a gesture! What pure
Nuremberg!

*Held a general's rank, rode a
    tank*
*When the Blitzkrieg raged and
    the bodies stank!*
            —The Rolling Stones,
        "Sympathy for the Devil"

Ja wohl! Mein friends, dot's
right! Dot good ole rock 'n' role
could warm the cockles of a
storm trooper's heart. O.K.
They don't give you a torch
and an armband, like in the
real old days, and send you
down the Rhine to swing with
the summer solstice. But you

can still squeeze in hip by haunch with thousands of good kamerads; still fatten eyes, ears, soul on the Leader, still plotz out while he socks it to you in stop-time, and, best of all, boys and girls, you can get your rocks off, no, with that good old arm action that means—well, you know what it means.

No question about it, Der Führer would have been gassed out of his kugel by the scene at the Forum. The ultimate performer, Mario's Magician, the prophet who wrote in "Mein Kampf" about the little guy's desire to step out of his day job, where he feels he's a nothing, and become part of "a body of thousands and thousands of people with a like conviction." There, that shows you, Der Führer was so far ahead of his time that only now are the kids catching up with him and showing their fondness for the old freak by digging him under the sneaky guises of comedy and camp.

Still, young people today don't know half enough about Hitler. They've been brainwashed by those shrecky Hollywood movies made during the war years, when one Jewish actor after another took off the Hit as a lunatic and a murderer. (They say he even took dope! It wasn't dope, just a few pain killers.) Young people should only know that Der Führer was a self-proclaimed revolutionary and a youth leader. He was the first great tribal shaman and magical minstrel. He was the first to mix the primitive with the futuristic, the first to get it all together, the lights, the sounds, the great clothes and gladiatorial salutes. Why, the guy even wore a maxi coat! O.K. He wasn't much to look at—though he was a terrific dancer! Still who ever offered a beauty prize to Peter Townshend, with that nose of his—or John Lennon with *his* thing? Energy is beauty, baby. Great dictators are transfigured by zap!

Actually, the idea that rock is Fascism spelled Fashion is as familiar as the fact that

smoking causes cancer. The political parallel has been exploited in films like "Privilege" and "Wild in the Streets," sermonized upon by Sunday journalists and, most recently, the Rock-Berlin Axis has been explored by the current generation's greatest masterpiece, The Who's rock opera, "Tommy." When the opera's deaf, dumb and blind hero, martyr of the older generation and messiah of the younger, throws off the shackles of his afflictions, he instantly becomes a teen tyrant who fetters his disciples with the same manacles of mind and sense once locked on him. True, the kids rebel finally and go hymning off into the rosy revolutionary dawn. But they leave behind them "Tommy's minatory message: "Beware the victims and the martyrs; they shall become oppressors in their generations."

What no one has the courage to confess these days is the irresistible attractiveness of the Fascist ceremonial. Denied any real control over his political destiny, filled with hatred and rebelliousness against an old order that strikes him as cruel and corrupt, unrelieved by the satisfactions of work or religion, how else, one wonders, is modern man to right his psychic balance or satisfy the urgencies of his soul? The ethic of love, love, love, give, give, give, good, good, good is beautiful. When, however, has it justified itself as the rule of life? Everything we have learned from the masters of the modern mind testifies to the vanity of being better than you are. The current generation seems like an army of doppelgängers, chanting love and peace as they march to the most militant strains ever blared from the horns of war.

To take the Rolling Stones— in many senses the archetypal rock group—as instance: what a record they have compiled as impersonators of the Devil! Granted there is more evil in one tuning peg of Jimi Hendrix's guitar than in a million copies of "Their Satanic Majesties";

still, the fact remains that the Stones owe much of their success to what might be called the "will to evil." Commencing with such callow misdemeanors as "Let's Spend the Night Together" and escalating through the graver sins of "She Comes in Colors," "Street Fighting Man" and "Sympathy for the Devil," the boys have sneered and fleered and ground their heel into the face of middle-class respectability. They have testified, to the tune of millions of dollars, to the great contemporary longing to be bad.

What has emerged from their triumphal progress—which includes some notable drug busts and the sorry death of Brian Jones—is a public image of sado-homosexual-junkie-diabolic-sarcastic-nigger-evil unprecedented in the annals of pop culture. If the youth public that is so into peace and beatitude were not titillated out of its tepees by this specter of Sodom and gonorrhea, how could they possibly promote the Stones to their present position as the laureates of rock 'n' riot?

The irony—perhaps the vindication—of this strange history is that, in pursuing their evil courses, the Stones have attained to beauty. In their early years, they were little better than facsimile stampers, Xeroxing the work of their black betters, like Chuck Berry and Bo Diddley. In their naughty middle years, they achieved a not-so-fine art of caricature, becoming the musical equivalents of the cartoonist Crumb, reducing a plethora of pop images to a fistful of jeering grotesques. Commencing with their closest communion with sin, "Sympathy for the Devil," they suddenly shifted from a head music of ideas about other people's ideas to a genuine musical life flow: The rolling, rolling *moto perpetuo* of "Sympathy" showed that the Stones had a real musical body that answered to the rhythm of Mick Jagger's body, shaking and soliciting from the stage. Now, in their forthcoming album, "Let it

Bleed," this movement toward musical and sensuous beauty reaches its culmination in a remarkable track that blazes a new trail for English rock.

The beauty part of the new record is not the expanded version of "You Can't Always Get What You Want," featuring a 60-voice boy's choir, or the new country version of "Honky Tonk Woman"—though those are good cuts for everyday consumption. The real Thanksgiving sound is offered on the first band, titled "Gimmie Shelter." An obsessively lovely specimen of tribal rock, this richly textured chant is rainmaking music. It dissolves the hardness of the Stones and transforms them into spirit voices singing high above the mazey figures on the dancing ground. The music takes no course, assumes no shape, reaches no climax; it simply repeats over an endless drone until it has soaked its way through your soul.

Half blue grass and half green gage, "Gimmie Shelter" is music to get stoned by. Taken as a counterpoint to the ranting rave-ups the Stones have been staging this past week as they roll toward Madison Square Garden, this cool, impersonal, self-absorbed incantation suggests the schizzy split dividing every contemporary head. It suggests what is actually the fact: that the same kids who are Sieg Heiling one night at some diabolic rally in Pandemonium may be lying the next night in their tents and sleeping bags passing the peace pipe from hand to hand as they watch the tribal fires flicker and go out.

Pop: No, The Rolling Stones Are Not Fascists

DON HECKMAN

Suddenly, it's almost 1970, and the realization that rock music has been with us in force for a decade and a half comes as a distinct shock. Has any other stylistic movement in American popular music—Swing, New Orleans / Dixieland, Ragtime, you name it—been so powerful for so long?

The answer is no. And what makes it all the more significant, rock shows little sign of deterioration. To the contrary, in fact, because it appears to be seeping into, and blending with, musical styles (jazz and concert music, to name the two most noticeable examples) that long have maintained artistic autonomy.

Given the zephyr-quick success/failure trip so typical of the popular arts, rock music must possess something more than momentary fashion to warrant such longevity. (Consider how men's hair styles have lengthened, from crew-cut to shoulder length, and women's shirt lengths have shortened, from below the knee to near the hip, in the Rock Decade-And-A-Half). But if not fashion, then what? Several weeks ago Albert Goldman
* See page 132.

offered another explanation, writing in The Sunday Times that "The current generation seems like an army of doppelgängers, chanting love and peace as they march to the most militant strains ever blared from the horns of war." Using the Rolling Stones as his archetypical example, Goldman suggested that ". . . rock is Fascism spelled Fashion. . . ."

Strong words. And words that receive confirmation, in many people's minds, from the extraordinarily ritualistic behavior of the audiences at the past year's huge rock festivals. But Fascism? The picture of Mick Jagger as a shadowy reincarnation of The Leader is, I'm afraid, a little too stark for me to buy. No, rock music is neither momentary fad nor "Fascism spelled Fashion."

That it is the clarion voice of an exceedingly vocal generation is obvious enough. Less obvious is the reason why such a clarion voice was needed. Oppression is almost as strong a word as fascism, but I wonder if it doesn't provide a more relevant clue to the staying power of rock.

Oppression of the spirit is a less visible—and a less sensationalistic—phenomenon than fascism, but it is a phenomenon that is not unfamiliar to young people in the America of the sixties. Since it is an oppression which is subtle, covert, and, worst of all, self-righteous, it may be a little difficult for over-30's to perceive. But it is there, nonetheless, and it is a humbling force. Because of it, many young people see themselves disconnected from organized society and subject to the same kind of attempted spiritual—if not physical—emasculation as has been wreaked for centuries upon the black man.

Until the sixties, no one cared much about what young people thought or felt one way or the other; teen-agers were expected to be seen and not heard. Oh sure, they could sow wild oats and dip into freaky life styles, the older folks smiled tolerantly, knowing that the "kids" would soon get all the nonsense out of their systems and assume their rightful roles in the mature, secure, responsibility-focused adult society.

When an enormous bunch of war babies reached their mid-teens in the early sixties, however, all bets were off. The "kids" had numbers on their side; to make things worse, surging prosperity had given them a purchasing power that clearly represented too much of a commercial clout to overlook.

An impasse was inevitable, and as a result of it, the adult view changed. Teenagers were no longer seen as immature but basically decent young people who were struggling toward personal identity. All those fun-filled, special qualities of youth suddenly began to give off a reflection as distorted as a mirror in a horror house. Young people's sometimes fitful attempts at independence, their intense hatred of a war for which they served (and serve) as cannon-fodder, their search for personal relationships free of the encrustation of traditional social hypocrisy, their experiments with their own kind of drugs and stimulants, were transformed into visible projections of the hot, urgent —and largely repressed— currents of adult America's troubled unconscious. Call it voyeurism if you like. Again, the role was similar to that which had been assigned in the past to the black man. What was new was its association not with a racially different subculture, but with an entire generation, and often with the younger members of one's own family.

Laurens van der Post has described that repressed image in "The Dark Eye in Africa": ". . . the rational, calculating, acutely reasoning and determined human being that Western man has made of himself has increasingly considered [the dark side] of himself not as a brother but as an enemy, capable, with his upsurges of rich emotion and colorful impulses, of wrecking conscious man's carefully planned and closely reasoned way of existence." Van der Post, of course, is speaking of the big black bugaboo that Western man has created through the assigning of his own hidden impulses toward sexuality and violence onto the cultural identities of black people. But the principle is beginning to apply almost equally well to the older generation's attitude toward what it views as the excesses—and worse—of youth. Thus, when Albert Goldman describes the Rolling Stones as ". . . a public image of sado-homosexual-junkie-diabolic-sarcastic-nigger-evil unprecedented in the annals of pop culture," he is telling us less about the Stones than he is

about his own point of view, and the point of view of uptight, emotionally repressive, "mature" America.

Young people are quite aware of both the intensity and the extensiveness of these feelings. And, as with the blacks before them, isolation from the sources of power—in addition to identification as a freakish, oversexed, misled, irresponsible minority—has aroused a cynical attitude toward the values of the organized Establishment. instead of accepting the familiar symbols of social achievement— political position, mass media exposure, upward social mobility—young people have turned toward values which are more firmly rooted in the subgroup, rather than the mass society.

Black culture again provides a stimulus. The history of its influence upon the entertainment arts is an old story. Few people are unaware of the recurring thrusts of vitality that have been provided to popular music, for example, by African-rooted hard rhythms and wailing melodies. But the growth of the kind of black-influenced blues / rock played by the Stones, along with the alienation of a generation of youth, points to a deeper influence. Instead of simply modifying and adapting elements of black music to a familiar popular dilution, white performers such as Mick Jagger have dipped their souls into the visceral gutsiness of the blues, and come up with a music and a manner that closely follow the black conception of the performer as something more than an entertainer.

As Charles Keil explains in "Urban Blues": ". . . certain Negro performers, called 'entertaining' by Negroes and whites alike, have an added but usually unconscious ritual significance for Negroes. The ritualists . . . are singers, musicians, preachers, comedians. . . . These entertainers are the ablest representatives of a long cultural tradition—and they are all

identity experts, so to speak, specialists in changing the joke and slipping the yoke."

Thus, even though white musicians always have found varying degrees of inspiration in black music, it was not until young people became a feared and suspected subgroup themselves that their culture heroes not only imitated the musical qualities of black performers, but followed their lead as culture images, as well.

The Stones, more than any other white group, have personified the deepest emotional projections. When the Beatles spoke of needing only love, the Stones suggested spending the night together (and, in this new release, "Live With Me"). When other performers insisted upon artistic separation, the Stones reveled in physical contact with their audiences, with Mick Jagger continually provoking —as he did in the group's recent American tour—the kind of passionate physical response that is rarely seen this side of a James Brown concert.

The appeal Jagger makes is fundamentally similar to what happens between Brown and *his* audiences. Essential in both cases is the feeling of community, of shared ideals, emotions, and a common language. The very separateness of the community (or subgroup) —blacks in one case, young people in the other—helps provide a special "blitz" togetherness. And when Jagger sings, in "Let It Bleed," "Don't you think there's a place for you, in between the sheets" or "Take my arm, take my leg, oh baby won't you take my head" or "I'm going to shove my dagger down your throat," he is using metaphor in the same overtly sexual fashion that has always been traditional to black blues. He does so with the assurance that his audience is completely conversant with the subtleties of those metaphors. Far from urging his listeners toward mass, mindless conformity Jagger is calling for the open, uncluttered expression of feelings that young whites have been asked to repress for most of their lives.

"Let It Bleed" presents the Stones in their strongest suit — heavy, black-tinged, passionately erotic hard rock/blues. Two remakes of previously recorded songs, "Country Honk" ("Honky Tonk Woman," with a country beat)

and "You Can't Always Get What You Want" (here performed with a boys chorale), are fascinating alternatives to the originals.

The Stones will never make the kind of impact upon the mass market that the Beatles have. It is their fate, I suspect, to remain outside the corridors of middle-class preference precisely because their music

and their manners represent such an affront to the shibboleths of white respectability. But it is probably also true that the rock revolution they helped create had made a profound, and as yet not fully realized, change in the cultural and emotional attitudes of the generation that will come to power in the 1970's.

The Grateful Dead are one of the earliest of the San Francisco rock groups. In this essay from *Rat,* Arlene Brown reviews one of the Dead's concerts from the Women's Liberation point of view.

The Grateful Dead and Male Chauvinism
ARLENE BROWN

After our performance on Sat. night, a few Pageant Players went up to Portchester to catch the Grateful Dead doing a late show at Howard Stein's Capitol Theater. We got in free since someone in the group knew someone on the inside. The Grateful Dead are generally considered to be one of the grooviest rock groups, in terms of the cultural revolution: the most political, most freaky, doing free shows whenever they can, supporting communes, doing a more relaxed kind of jamming show, rather than a slick series of arranged numbers. And they're really great musicians. They were my favorite American group. I hadn't seen them perform for over a year, and was looking forward to it when we went up there. But in the back of my head, i was wondering how i would respond to them now that i have a much more complete consciousness of women's liberation, and a strong awareness of how Male the whole rock scene is.

We came in just as a busby berkeley film was ending. The Grateful Dead were to go on next. And the crowd was

hollering for them. I thought i was imagining things, but the atmosphere seemed hysterical, more than i've ever seen at a rock concert. I found out later that the Dead the night before had given the audience free acid, and this crowd wanted the same. The Dead came on, and opened up with a few fast numbers. The audience, or a large part of it anyway was up on its feet shouting, dancing, screaming, waving. That was beautiful. It was a nice change from the usual stoned stupor of rock concerts. But the audience was so high strung and crazy that they couldn't wait for the Dead to tune their instruments in between numbers. They would start hooting and screaming. Then someone from the Dead gave the finger to the audience, and this started the playful hostility which continued all evening between the audience and the Grateful Dead, and between the audience members themselves. It reminded me a bit of a nightclub, with the hostile drunks yelling comments at the performers. I did feel that the energy of the audience had nowhere to go in that theater, with all the seats. It was very frustrating to try to dance, and let loose, and you began to feel like a caged animal.

I felt sorry for the Grateful Dead at different moments,

having to contend with a bunch of nuts everytime they tried to tune up. But, then i thought, they agree to play at those theaters, they agree to play for those prices, they agree to play under those blue lights, that go off completely in between each number. And the audience is in darkness the whole time, so you can't possibly relate to anyone near you, only the STARS on stage.

Jerry Garcia and Phil Lesh did some beautiful blues, spiritual numbers on acoustic guitar. I was digging it. Then on comes Pigpen, and in his mellow lyrical voice sings about cala may, who some people say is built like a cadillac, but i know she's just a model T, by her shape, and she can't take the weight, etc., etc. Something inside me went boom. There i was digging this beautiful voice, beautiful guitar, but with words about some women's box. And i knew it would happen. I felt pretty sullen for the rest of the concert. I was also getting turned off by the fact that the audience just seemed to be waiting for the hits, like they didn't come to hear great music, great jamming, just the hits, which they were screaming for in between each number. The Grateful Dead just seemed like another commodity.

Everyone flipped out when Pigpen launched into "Turn on

454322332212224522222223

Your Love Light." It was what they were waiting for Pigpen's riffs for that night included a little story about how his baby calls him when she wants him, first softly daddy, then he says yeah, real cool, then louder Daddy, him still cool yeah baby, then she screaming DADDY, and he's still real cool, says yeah baby. yuk. yuk. The predominantly male audience naturally flipped out over this. I flipped out inside.

The men in the Pageant Players who went, said they felt funny themselves about the concert, the songs, etc. In fact, it was my boyfriend, who pointed out to me that the audience was mainly men, and they seemed to be flipping out over the Dead more than the women. Weird atmosphere. I thought about it all the next day, and realized the whole concert seemed like a hippie stag party.

We all know that the rock scene is male dominated, as are most other areas of creative work. But no other area is so totally male, as music. Has anyone reading this article ever met a woman bass player, a woman electric guitarist, woman drummer? I doubt it. And if you have, it's one or two, and maybe you had to think about it for a few minutes. Women write, paint, do theatre, etc. But men make music, and this goes for classical, jazz, rock.

When i was in Brooklyn College majoring in music, i spent many hours around musicians, jazz and classical.

And in the last few years, to some extent around rock musicians. And i tell you that musicians incorporate the hangups of straight society regarding men and women, more than men in the other fields. I know there are exceptions. But i found that in general guys who were poets, painters, were much more willing to see women as intellectual creative people, than were musicians, who thrive on a male ego, subservient "chick" relationship, which the whole hippie rock culture reinforces. And the fact that musicians spend so much time together playing music and that they are all men, makes their relationships with women purely sexual. It's exactly like the straight world where the man has his work outside the home, his main interests, outside the home, away from his woman. But he comes home to get fed, get laid, and maybe dig his kids.

I think that rock music has changed a lot of things, released a lot of energy, created some good images for young people, emphasized enjoyment, sensual pleasure, relaxation, freaking out, looking weird, turning on. But i also think as far as the male-female relationship goes, as far as women's liberation goes, and the image a woman should have of herself, it is totally reactionary, and must be changed. A woman can relate to rock music now only if she is a groupie, if not literally, then figuratively. As the drooling

sex hungry little girl dying for IT from Pigpen, Jim Morrison, or Peter Townshend. I can't relate to that bullshit.

I don't think music should be asexual either. I think music is communication on a very emotional, sexual level. That's why i've always dug it so much. But sexual not in a male chauvinist context nor narcissistic display. Women and men should be playing in groups together, women in groups together. Women playing the instruments, writing the material. And not just having a "chick" sex object singer, in a male group. There's nothing new about that. But women playing drums, or electric guitar is somehow very threatening to our images of what is feminine and masculine.

To me the whole image of the rock scene is an image of a mod, "pretty" long-haired, mini-skirted, or bell bottomed passive, sweet chick, nice enough to be at the side of any strong manly rock musician or business man. Or an image of a braless, long-skirted, sweet, mother earth commune hippie chick. Both of those are distortions. And accepted roles. Just as the aggressive, dominant, creative genius is the role that men play, and what women LOOK UP to. And that's not my revolution, nor any of my sisters'. Women unite. Let's start making music. Revolutionary music.

The association of West Coast LSD pioneers with rock music—which led to acid rock, the San Francisco Sound, and the apotheosis of the Haight-Ashbury district of that city as the Elysian Fields of hippiedom (remember the Summer of Love! Flowers in your hair!)—represents one development of rock as life style. The Hell's Angels thing, which was to culminate in the Altamont disaster (see above) is another. In the piece on the following page, Tom Wolfe

describes the meeting of the two at the house of Ken Kesey, wrestler, novelist *(One Flew Over the Cuckoo's Nest, Sometimes A Great Notion),* and the leader of the Merry Pranksters, first of the hallucinogenic communes, in appropriately psychedelic prose. On page 144, Ginsberg does the same in his way.

FROM
The Electric Kool-Aid Acid Test
TOM WOLFE

HELL'S ANGELS

Kesey met the Hell's Angels one afternoon in San Francisco through Hunter Thompson, who was writing a book about them. It turned out to be a remarkable book, as a matter of fact, called *Hell's Angels, a Strange and Terrible Saga.* Anyway, Kesey and Thompson were having a few beers and Thompson said he had to go over to a garage called the Box Shop to see a few of the Angels, and Kesey went along. A Hell's Angel named Frenchy and four or five others were over there working on their motorcycles and they took to Kesey right away. Kesey was a stud who was just as tough as they were. He had just been busted for marijuana, which certified him as Good People in the Angels' eyes. They told him you can't trust a man who hasn't done time, and Kesey was on the way to doing time, in any case. Kesey said later that the marijuana bust impressed them but they couldn't have cared less that he was a novelist. But they knew about that, too, and here was a big name who was friendly and interested in them, even though he wasn't a queer or a reporter or any of those other creep suck-ups who were coming around that summer.

And a great many were coming around in the summer of 1965. The summer of 1965 had made the Hell's Angels infamous celebrities in California. Their reputation was at its absolutely most notorious all-time highest. A series of incidents — followed by an amazing series of newspaper and magazine articles, *Life* and the *Saturday Evening Post* among them — had the people of the Far West looking to each weekend in the Angels' life as an invasion by baby-raping Huns. Intellectuals around San Francisco, particularly at Berkeley, at the University of California, were beginning to romanticize about the Angels in terms of "alienation" and "a generation in revolt," that kind of thing. People were beginning to get in touch with Thompson to see if he couldn't arrange

for them to meet the Angels — not the whole bunch, Hunter, maybe one or two at a time. Well, Kesey didn't need any one or two at a time. He and the boys took a few tokes on a joint, and the Hell's Angels were on the bus.

The next thing the citizens of La Honda knew, there was a huge sign at the Kesey place — 15 feet long, three feet high, in red white and blue.

THE MERRY PRANKSTERS
WELCOME THE HELL'S ANGELS

Saturday, August 7, 1965, was a bright clear radiant limelit summer day amid God's handiwork in La Honda, California. The citizens were getting ready for the day by nailing shut their doors. The cops were getting ready by revving up a squad of ten patrol cars with flashing lights and ammunition. The Pranksters were getting ready by getting bombed. They were down in the greeny gorge, in the cabin and around it, under the redwoods, getting bombed out of their gourds. They had some good heavy surges of God-given adrenaline going for them, too. Nobody ever came right out front and said it, but this happened to be the real-life Hell's Angels coming, about forty of them, on a full-fledged Angels' "run," the sort of outing on which the Angels did their thing, their whole freaking thing, *en* mangy raunchy head-breaking fire-pissing rough-goddamn-housing *masse.* The Pranksters had a lot of company for the occasion. It was practically like an audience, all waiting for the stars to appear. A lot of the old Perry Lane crowd was there, Vic Lovell, Ed McClanahan, and the others. Allen Ginsberg was there and so was Richard Alpert and a lot of San Francisco and Berkeley intellectuals. *Tachycardia,* you all — but Kesey was calm and even laughing a little, looking strong as an ox in his buckskin shirt, the Mountain Man, and he made it all seem right and inevitable, an inevitable part of the flow and right now in this moment. Hell, if the straight world of San Mateo County, California, had decided to declare them all outlaws over an innocuous thing like marijuana, then they could freaking well go with the flow and show them what the saga called Outlaw was really like. The Angels brought a lot of things into synch. Outlaws, by definition, were people who had moved off of dead center and were out in some kind of Edge City. The beauty of it was, the Angels had done it like the Pranksters, by choice. They had become outlaws first — to *explore,* muvva — and then got busted for it. The Angels' trip was the motorcycle and the Pranksters' was LSD, but both were in an incredible entry into an orgasmic moment, *now,* and within forty-eight hours the Angels would be taking acid on board, too. The Pranksters would be taking on . . . Ahor, the ancient horror, the middle-class boy fear of Hell's Angels, *Hell's Angels,* in the dirty flesh, and if they could bring that dark deep-down thing into their orbit —

Kesey! What in the freaking — tachycardia, you all . . .

Bob Dylan's voice is raunching and rheuming in the old jacklegged chants in huge volume from out the speakers up in the redwood tops up on the dirt cliff across the highway — *He-e-e-ey Mis-ter Tam-bou-rine Man* — as part of Sandy Lehmann-Haupt's Non-Station KLSD program, the indomitable disco-freak-jockey Lord Byron Styrofoam himself, Sandy, broadcasting over a microphone in a cabin and spinning them for you — Cassady revved up so tight it's like mechanical speed man sprocket — Mountain Girl ready — *Hey, Kesey!* — Hermit grin — Page ablaze — men, women, children, painted and in costume — ricochet around the limelit dell — *Argggggghhhhh* — about 3 P.M. they started hearing it.

It was like a locomotive about ten miles away. It was the Hell's Angels in "running formation" coming over the mountain on Harley-Davidson 74s. The Angels were up there somewhere weaving down the curves on Route 84, gearing down — *thragggggggggh* — and winding up, and the locomotive sound got louder and louder until you couldn't hear yourself talk any more or Bob Dylan rheumy and — *thraaaaaaaggggggghh* — here they came around the last curve, the Hell's Angels, with the bikes, the beards, the long hair, the sleeveless denim jackets with the death's head insignia and all the rest, looking their most royal rotten, and then one by one they came barreling in over the wooden bridge up to the front of the

house, skidding to a stop in explosions of dust, and it was like a movie or something — each one of the outlaws bouncing and gunning across the bridge with his arms spread out in a tough curve to the handlebars and then skidding to a stop, one after another after another.

The Angels, for their part, didn't know what to expect. Nobody had ever invited them anywhere before, at least not as a gang. They weren't on many people's invitation lists. They figured they would see what was there and what it was all about, and they would probably get in a hell of a fight before it was all over, and heads would break, but that was about par for the course anyway. The Angels always came into alien situations black and wary, sniffing out the adversary, but that didn't even register at this place. So many people were already so high, on something, it practically dissolved you on the spot. The Pranksters had what looked like about a million doses of the Angels' favorite drug — beer — and LSD for all who wanted to try it. The beer made the Angels very happy and the LSD made them strangely peaceful and sometimes catatonic, in contrast to the Pranksters and other intellectuals around, who soared on the stuff.

June the Goon gave a Hell's Angel named Freewheeling Frank some LSD, which he thought was some kind of souped-up speed or something — and he had the most wondrous experience of his life. By nightfall he had climbed a redwood and was nestled up against a loudspeaker in a tree grooving off the sounds and vibrations of Bob Dylan singing "The Subterranean Homesick Blues."

Pete, the drag racer, from the San Francisco Hell's Angels, grinned and rummaged through a beer tub and said, "Man, this is nothing but a goddamn wonderful scene. We didn't know what to expect when we came, but it turned out just fine. This time it's all ha-ha, not thump-thump." Soon the gorge was booming with the Angels' distinctive good-time lots-a-beer belly laugh, which goes: Haw! — Haw! — Haw! — Haw! — Haw! — Haw!

Sandy Lehmann-Haupt, Lord Byron Styrofoam, had hold of the microphone and his disco-freak-jockey rapping blared out of the redwoods and back across the highway: "This is Non-Station KLSD, 800 micrograms in your head, the station designed to blow your mind and undo your bind, from up here atop the redwoods on Venus!" The he went into a long talking blues song about the Hell's Angels, about fifty stanzas worth, some of it obscure acid talk, some of it wild legends, about squashing turtles on the highway, nutty stuff like that, and every stanza ending with the refrain:

Oh, but it's great to be an Angel,
And be dirty all the time!

What the hell—here was some wild-looking kid with the temerity to broadcast out over the highways of California that Angels were dirty all the time—but how the hell could you resist, it was too freaking madly manic— and pretty soon the Angels and everybody else were joining in the chorus:

Oh, but it's great to be an Angel,
And be dirty all the time!

Then Allen Ginsberg was in front of the microphone with finger cymbals on each hand, dancing around with a beard down to his belly and chanting Hindu chants into the microphone booming out over California, U.S.A., *Hare krishna hare krishna hare krishna hare krishna—* what the mollyfock is hairy krishma—who is this hairy freak—but you can't help yourself, you got to groove with this cat in spite of yourself. Ginsberg really bowled the Angels over. He was a lot of things the Angels hated, a Jew, an intellectual, a New Yorker, but he was too much, the greatest straightest unstraight guy they ever met.

And be dirty all the time!

The filthy kooks—by nightfall the cops were lined up along the highway, car after car, just across the creek, outside the gate, wondering what the fock. The scene was really getting weird. The Pranksters had everything in their electronic arsenal going, rock 'n' roll blazing through the treetops, light projections streaming through the gorge, Station KLSD blazing and

screaming over the cops' heads, people in Day-Glo regalia blazing and lurching in the gloom, the Angels going *Haw—Haw—Haw—Haw,* Cassady down to just his hell of a build, nothing else, just his hell of a build, jerking his arms out and sprocketing around under a spotlight on the porch of the log manse, flailing a beer bottle around in one hand and shaking his other one at the cops:

"You sneaky motherfuckers! What the fuck's wrong with you! Come on over here and see what you get . . . goddamn your shit-filled souls anyway!"—laughing and jerking and sprocketing—"Don't fuck with me, you sons of shit-lovers. Come on over. You'll get every fucking thing you deserve."

The hell of it, men, is here is a huge obscene clot of degradation, depradation and derogation proceeding loose and crazed on the hoof before our very eyes, complete with the very Hell's Angels, and there is nothing we can do but contain it. Technically, they might have been able to move in on the grounds of Cassady's exposing himself or something of the sort, but no real laws were being broken, except every law of God and man—but sheer containment was looking like the best policy. Moving in on those crazies even with ten carloads of armed cops for a misdemeanor like lewd display—the explosion was too grotesque to think of. And the cops' turret lights revolved and splashed against the dirt cliff in a red strobe light effect and their car-to-headquarters radios were wide open and cracking out with sulphurous 220-volt electric thorn baritones and staticky sibilants—*He-e-e-ey Mis-ter Tam-bou-rine Man*—just to render the La Honda gorge totally delirious.

Meanwhile, the Angels were discovering the goddamnedest thing. Usually, most places they headed into on their runs, they tested people's cool. What are *you* looking at, mother. As soon as the shock or naked terror registered, they would be happy. Or if there was no shock and terror but instead somebody tried some brave little shove back, then it was time to break heads and tear everybody a new asshole. But these mollyfocking Pranksters were test-proof. The Angels didn't know what permissive was until they got to Kesey's.

Go with the flow! The biggest baddest toughest most awfulest-looking Hell's Angel of them all was a big monster named Tiny. The second biggest baddest toughest most-awfulest-looking Hell's Angel was a big raw-boned guy named Buzzard, dark-looking, with all this dark hair and a beard, all shaggy and matted and his nose came out like a beak and his Adam's apple hung down about a foot, and he was just like an enormous buzzard. Tiny and Buzzard had a thing of coming up to each other when they were around non-Angels and sticking out their tongues and then licking each other's tongues, a big sloppy lap it up, just to shake up the squares, it really jolted them—so they came up right in front of this tall broad of Kesey's, Mountain Girl, and la-a-a-a-a-ap —and they couldn't believe it. She just looked right at them and grinned and exploded sunballs out of her eyes and started laughing at them, *Haw—Haw—Haw,* as if to say in plain language: What a bullshit thing. It was freaking incredible. Then some of them passed a joint around and they passed it to Mountain Girl and she boomed out:

"Hell, no! What the hell you doing putting your dirty mouth on this clean joint for! This is a clean joint and you're putting your dirty mouths on it!" Nobody in living memory had ever refused a toke from a joint passed by Angels, at least not on grounds of sanitation, except this crazy girl who was just bullshitting them blind, and they loved it.

It even got to the point where Mountain Girl saw Tiny heading into the mad bathroom with a couple of beer cans like he is going to hole up in there and drink a couple of cans in peace, but this is the bathroom all the girls around here are using, and Mountain Girl yells out to Sonny Barger, the maximum leader of the Hell's Angels, "Hey, Sonny! Tell this big piece of trash to stay out of our clean bathroom!"—in a bullshit tone, of course— and Sonny picks it up, "Yea, you big piece of trash! Stay out of the clean bathroom! They don't want you in there!"—and Tiny slinks out the door, outside, in a bullshit slink, but he does it—

And that's it! It's happening. The Hell's Angels are in our movie, we've got 'em in. Mountain Girl and a lot of the Pranksters had hit on the perfect combination with the Angels. They were friendly toward them, maybe friendlier than anybody had been in their lives, but they weren't craven about it, and they took no shit. It was the perfect combination, but the Pranksters didn't even have to think of it as a combination. They just did their thing and that was the way it worked out. All these principles they had been working on and talking about in the isolation of La Honda—they freaking well *worked.*

Go with the flow—and what a flow— these cats, these Pranksters—at big routs like this the Angels often had a second feature going entitled *Who Gets Fucked?—* and it hadn't even gotten to that before some blonde from out of town, one of the guests from way out there, just one nice soft honey hormone squash, she made it clear to three Angels that she was ready to go, so they all trooped out to the backhouse and they had a happy round out there. Pretty soon all the Angels knew about the "new mamma" out in the backhouse and a lot of them piled in there, hooking down beers, laughing, taking their turns, making various critiques. The girl had her red and white dress pushed up around her chest, and two or three would be on her at once, between her legs, sitting on her face in the sick ochre light of the shack with much lapping and leering and bubbling and gulping through furzes of pubic hair while sweat and semen glistened on the highlights of her belly and thighs and she twitched and moaned, not in protest, however, in a kind of drunken bout of God knew what and men with no pants on were standing around, cheering, chiding, waiting for their turn, or their second turn, or the third until she had been fenestrated in various places at least fifty times. Some of the Angels went out and got her ex-husband. He was weaving and veering around, bombed, they led him in there under glare and leer and lust musk suffocate the rut hut they told him to go to it. All silent—shit, this is going too far—but the girl rises up in a blear and asks him to kiss her, which he does, glistening secretions, then he lurches and mounts her and slides it in, and the Angels cheer Haw Haw —

— but that is her movie, it truly is, and we have gone with the flow.

So much beer — which is like an exotic binge for the Pranksters, beer. Mountain Girl and Kesey are up in the limelit bower and the full moon comes down through the treetop silhouettes. They are just rapping in the moonlight, and then Sandy wanders on up there and sits with them, high on acid, and he looks down and the floor of the forest is rippling with moonlight, the ground shimmers and rolls like a stream in the magic bower and they just sit there — a *buzzard!* Buzzard is wandering up the slope toward them and there in the moonlight in the dark in the magic bower he . . . *is* a buzzard, the biggest ever made, the beak, the deathly black, the dopply glottal neck, the shelled back and dangling wings, stringy nodule legs — Kaaawwwwwww! — and Kesey jumps up and starts throwing his arms up at him, like the way you would scare away a buzzard, and says,

"Aaaaagh! a buzzard! Hey! Get away, you're a buzzard! Get this buzzard out of here!"

It's a bullshit gesture, of course — and Buzzard laughs — *Haw! Haw! Haw!* — it is not real, but it is . . . *real,* real buzzard, you can see the whole thing with two minds — Kaw Kaw Kaaawwwww — and Buzzard jumps and flaps his arms — and the whole . . . connection, the *synch,* between the name, the man, the bird, flows together right there, and it doesn't matter whether he is buzzard or man because it has all come together, and they all see it . . .

They all see so much. Buzzard goes, and Sandy goes, and Kesey and Mountain Girl are in the moonlight ripply bower. By and by — where? — Kesey and Mountain Girl — and so much flows together from the lights and the delirium and the staticky sibilants down below, so much is clear, so much flows in rightness, that night, under the full moon, up above the flails and bellows down below —

The Hell's Angels party went on for two days and the cops never moved in. Everybody, Angels and Pranksters, had

a righteous time and no heads were broken. There had been one gang-bang, but the girl was a volunteer. It was her movie. In fact, for the next six or seven weeks, it was one long party with the Angels. The news spread around intellectual-hip circles in the San Francisco-Berkeley area like a legend. In these circles, anyway, it once and for all put Kesey and the Pranksters up above the category of just another weirdo intellectual group. They had broken through the worst hangup that intellectuals know — the *real-life* hangup. Intellectuals were always hung up with the feeling that they weren't coming to grips with real life. Real life belonged to all those funky spades and prize fighters and bullfighters and dock workers and grape pickers and wetbacks. *Nostalgie de la boue.* Well, the Hell's Angels were real life. It didn't get any realer than that, and Kesey had pulled it off. People from San Francisco and Berkeley started coming by La Honda more than ever. It was practically like an intellectual tourist attraction. Kesey would talk about the Angels.

"I asked Sonny Barger how he picks new members, new Angels, and he told me, 'We don't pick 'em. We *rec*ognize 'em.'"

And everybody grokked over that.

Likely as not, people would find Hell's Angels on the place. The Angels were adding LSD to the already elaborate list of highs and lows they liked, beer, wine, marijuana, benzedrine, Seconal, Amytal, Nembutal, Tuinal. Some of them had terrible bummers — bummers was the Angels' term for a bad trip on a motorcycle and very quickly it became the hip world's term for a bad trip on LSD. The only bad moment at Kesey's came one day when an Angel went berserk during the first rush of the drug and tried to strangle his old lady on Kesey's front steps. But he was too wasted at that point to really do much.

So it was wonderful and marvelous, an unholy alliance, the Merry Pranksters and the Hell's Angels, and all hours of the day or night you could hear the Hell's Angels gearing and winding down Route 84 to Kesey's, and the people of La Honda felt like the plague had come, and wasn't there anything that could be done. More than one of the Pranksters had his reservations, too. The Angels were like a time bomb. So far, so good—one day the Angels even swept and cleaned up the place—but they were capable of busting loose into carnage at any moment. It brought the adrenaline into your throat. The potential was there, too, because if the truth were known, there were just a few of the Pranksters who could really talk to the Angels—chiefly Kesey and Mountain Girl. Mainly it was Kesey. Kesey was the magnet and the strength, the man in both worlds. The Angels respected him and they weren't about to screw him around. He was one of the coolest guys they had ever come across. One day, finally, Kesey's cool came to the test with the Angels and it was a strange moment.

Kesey and the Pranksters and the Angels had taken to going out to the backhouse and sitting in a big circle and doing the Prankster thing, a lot of rapping back and forth and singing, high on grass, and you never knew where it was going to go. Usually it went great. The Angels took to the Prankster thing right away. They seemed to have an immediate intuitive grasp of where it was going, and one time Kesey started playing a regular guitar and Babbs started playing a four-string amplified guitar and Kesey got into a song, off the top of his head, about "the vibrations," a bluesy song, and the Angels joined in, and it got downright religious in there for a while, with everybody singing, "Oh, the vi-bra-tions . . . Oh, the vi-bra-tions . . . "

And then Kesey and a few of the Pranksters and a lot of the Angels, including Sonny Barger of the Oakland Chapter, the maximum leader of all the Angels, were sitting around in the backhouse passing around joints and rapping. The subject was "people who are bullshit."

There are certain people who are bullshit and you can always recognize them, Kesey was saying, and the Angels were nodding yeah, that certainly is right.

"Now you take _____," said Kesey, mentioning one of the Angels who was not present. "He's a bullshit person."

A bullshit person—and man—

"Listen, Kesey," says Barger, 100 percent Hell's Angel, "_____ is an Angel, and

nobody—*nobody*—calls an Angel a bullshit person."

—the freaking gauntlet is down. It's like forever and every eye in the place pins on Kesey's face and you can hear the blood squirt in your veins. But Kesey doesn't even blink and his voice doesn't even change one half tone, just the old Oregon drawl:

"But I *know* him, Sonny. If I didn't *know* him, I wouldn't call him a bullshit person."

Yeah—we-e-e-elll—everybody, Angels and Pranksters—well—Kesey *knows* him—there is nothing to do but grok over this statement, and everybody sits there, still, trying to grok over it, and after a second, the moment where heads get broken and fire gets pissed is over—*We-e-ell, ye-ah*—

Two or three days later it occurs to some of the Pranksters that they *still* don't know what the hell Kesey meant when he said that. He *knows* the guy. It doesn't make any sense. It's a concept with no bottom to it—but so what! At the moment he said it, it was the one perfect thing he could have said. Kesey was so totally into the moment, he could come up with it, he could break up that old historic push me, shove you, yeah-sez-who sequence and in an instant the moment, that badass moment, was over.

The Pranksters got pretty close to several of the Angels as individuals. Particularly Gut and Freewheeling Frank and Terry the Tramp. Every now and then somebody would take one or another of the Angels up into the tree house and give them a real initiation into psychedelics. They had a huge supply of DMT. As somebody once put it, LSD is a long strange journey; DMT is like being shot out of a cannon. There in the tree house, amid the winking googaws, they would give the Angels DMT, and Mountain Girl saw some of them, like Freewheeling Frank, after they came down. They would walk around in no particular direction, listing slightly, the eyes bugged wide open, glazed.

"They were as naked as an Angel is ever gonna git," she told Kesey.

First Party at Ken Kesey's With Hell's Angels
ALLEN GINSBERG

Cool black night thru the redwoods
cars parked outside in shade
behind the gate, stars dim above
the ravine, a fire burning by the side
porch and a few tired souls hunched over
in black leather jackets. In the huge
wooden house, a yellow chandelier
at 3AM the blast of loudspeakers
hi-fi Rolling Stones Ray Charles Beatles
Jumping Joe Jackson and twenty youths
dancing to the vibration thru the floor,
a little weed in the bathroom, girls in scarlet
tights, one muscular smooth skinned man
sweating dancing for hours, beer cans
bent littering the yard, a hanged man
sculpture dangling from a high creek branch,
children sleeping softly in bedroom bunks,
And 4 police cars parked outside the painted
gate, red lights revolving in the leaves.

DRUGS

The college graduate of 1960 who had
"experimented" with marijuana was the
uncommon one. The graduate of 1970
has just as probably not failed to try it,
to say nothing of an occasional foray into
the exotic and dangerous forests of the
hallucinogens: LSD, psylocybin,
mescaline, peyote, STP; amphetamines
and barbiturates; cocaine, the society
drug; and even—to the shock of experts,
casual trippers, and confirmed "heads"—
killer heroin.

Beyond the bald and obvious statement
that drugs are a problem, little can be
said that is definitive. At this very moment,
while people are turning on, becoming
harmlessly and pleasantly euphoric, being
arrested, killing themselves, and taking
other lives as well, the heads of the
experts trying to sort out the problems—
legalization, prosecution, "hard" versus
"soft," detoxification—are rolling as new
men with new ideas follow them to the
block.

The following section attempts, within
obvious limits, to present some prominent
points of view on the subject, while
sampling the styles—both of literature
and of life—in which is carried the tenor of
the user's existence.

PART
SIX

FROM

Marihuana: Myths and Realities

A NOTE FROM THE UNDERGROUND

There's another society underneath, above, and all around the edges of the straight American society you know and live in. It's inside your society geographically, legally, politically, even economically, but it's outside in feeling and soul, shunned and feared by more traditional elements, degraded by your mass-media, hounded by your police, but growing all the time now because it is more human and more fun than what you have to offer.

Let's not call it the "dope world" because dope implies narcotics and actual narcotics like heroin, morphine, Demerol, and cocaine, are not part of our world. Most of us turn on regularly with pot and use acid and, when they are available, we will also take our chances with hashish, DMT, peyote buttons, mescaline and psilocybin. Some of us also use speed sometimes, but the true meth freak is in no culture at all, not even ours. His world is his own, demoniacally strange or mutteringly content, far away and wrapped in isolation.

If you must label my world (and it seems you must), call it psychedelic. It's like a parallel dimension where thoughts and values are different but it coexists with and overlaps your world. We might pass each other on the street sometimes but we go in different directions. It stresses learning through personal experience rather than machinelike transmission of knowledge. It stresses sharing experience rather than passive entertainment. Living is in the eternal now rather than by the calendar. Turn on, tune in, and drop out; you keep asking what does it mean. It isn't a slogan, its's a telegram-description of the way we live.

All of my friends turn on. It's probably the only thing they all have in common. Rich kids from Beverly Hills, waitresses who love to go dancing at the Cheetah, politicos from the underground press, college students and professors, free-loving Keristans, spade beach-drummers, provos, utopian dreamers in their mountain shacks, liberal lawyers, artists, mailmen, mechanics, surfers, schoolgirls, ex-convicts, and bike-outlaws. I should know, I've sold grass to all of them and more. There is no "type" that I can see.

Turn on—to an ever-enlarging slice of reality. Reality includes everything that happens; every thought, feeling and sensation of every person; every motion and every movement; every occurrence, every event; every action, reaction and interaction, physical, personal, or social. Your personal reality is whatever you realize out of this, whatever you incorporate, whatever affects you. Psychedelic adventurers are expanding the scope of their personal realities. See more, hear more, feel more, know more, interact more—it sounds like a circus barker's spiel. Break down the defensive walls that "protect" the individual ego, let it mingle freely with the flowing event stream of reality. Destroy the old personality that grasps the world, exploits others, controls itself; build a new personality that enjoys the world, loves others, respects itself. Turning on is as simple as dropping the cap of acid, as complex as the universe itself.

Tune in—to this new and larger personal reality! Incorporate the fresh perceptions, the novel sensations; contemplate the disturbing ideas, face the feared memories. The doors of perception swing both ways; as there is an infinite external universe, so is there an infinite internal universe. The external infinity is shared by all, the internal infinity is inviolately private. Both are real, each is fascinating.

Drop out—of the socially sanctioned and economically based mainstream of American Life! This is a natural consequence of turning on and tuning in. Christ, Buddha and Ghandi all dropped out to live alone, growing spiritually in the peacefulness necessary to assimilate new concepts. The drop out period might be years long, but is rarely permanent.

Turn on and tune in are not separate events, they are variant aspects of the same process. It's not mysterious, not mystical; you turn on and tune in your radio. Turning it on opens the door to its potential and

Photograph by DeFrancis.

taps its source of power. Tuning it in selects its actuality and utilizes its power. The individual consciousness, like a two-way radio, is a communication channel between self and non-self. Like the radio, it can be turned on and tuned in.

All of you were turned on and tuned in during childhood — the socialization process of transmitting from old generation to new. Trouble is that it was done for you (or to you). AFC — Automatic Frequency Control. We prefer to do our own, believing in individual responsibility. Jefferson would have understood it; Emerson could have explained it; Thoreau would have dug it. Think before you label it un-American.

The learning process in Zen leads the monk through a series of subtle personality shocks that disrupt and disturb his originally normal and complacent world-view. The paradoxical koans defy logic, ignore convention. Ultimately he realizes

that both the unity and the flux are real and accepts reality.

The re-socialization process in our mental hospitals is more direct type of personality shock; electro-shock therapy. It's perhaps unfortunate that the knowledgeable machines called psychiatrists have no more regard for schizophrenics than they do for laboratory rats, but this primitive level of learning through pain and shake-up does change the patient's world-view.

Electricity compels change, paradox suggests it. Somewhere in between these two levels, psychedelics offer change. They push toward it but can be successfully resisted — hence there is no compulsion. They lead toward it, hence there is more than suggestion. The first few trips are severe personality shocks, later trips are more subtle, more varied.

Pot is much milder, a riffling breeze rather than a buffeting storm. A lot of good grass quietly smoked, or some hash (pot flower extract) can also lead to the flashing field of home. However, pot is more an everyday thing, a social occurrence.

My personal experiences along this line encompass three years of steady smoking and about 150 heavy trips. This has been augmented by discussions ("rapping," we call it) and by my support and guidance of others. As a dealer, it was easy to become a witch doctor, soul counselor, elder brother. I am not Leary, I am not the Magic Owl, I do not preach or push. Demonstration is my chief tool; compassion my chief guide. People are beautiful, dazzling, splendid creatures, no two alike, each precious.

Bird is a machinist by day, a doper by night. Pot relaxes him, eases the city life tensions so painful to his gentle soul. He gets high with his wife Windy and listens to jazz records. Whenever I go to see them, I'm invited to dinner. They enjoy my stories, tales of turmoil and excitement from the marketplace, but want no part of the actual events. They're just a happy, peaceful family, complete with baby laughter and car payments.

Lex is a creek-bottom renegade from East Texas, a one-percenter (outlaw bike rider) who is hot with numbers (ID changes for stolen bikes), used to ride with the Angels in Alameda. I hire him occasionally as an enforcer on questionable deals. He'll act tough all night for half a jar of reds (500 Seconals, a popular barbiturate). Excitement always surrounds him, he's that kind of guy.

Palo is an ex-English major from San Francisco State, now a bearded bell-ringing hippie who haunts Golden Gate Park; he's a scout for several big dealers. While you're waiting, he'll throw an I Ching for you or theorize on the daily life of the ancient Tibetan monks responsible for the Book of the Dead.

There are countless others, each is a trip. In our world few are afraid to follow their individual destinies.

Police call me a dope pusher; they consider me an evil public enemy and are often personally antagonistic over and above their normal anti-crime level. My customers, friends, cohorts, enthusiasts,

and beneficiaries appreciate the wares and the skill and knowledge necessary to procure, transport, and safeguard them. One popular song even blesses the pot sellers. It is a dangerous and exciting game with real perils and varied rewards. I have been selling pot and acid for three years now, in San Francisco and Berkeley, in Venice, Hollywood, the San Fernando Valley, and in many smaller towns throughout California and Arizona; on college campuses and city streets, on beaches and mountain tops, in parked cars and vacant apartments; by the joint, the lid, the kilo, the multi-kilo lot; by the cap, the hundreds of caps, the half-gram, and the gram.

Many of my friends are also dealers, successful dealers. We measure success, not by amount of profit but by length of operation. Ours is a semi-sacred mission; we believe in what we do. Being human, some of us become greedy at times or power hungry or personally vindictive. It is interesting to note, however, that these are usually the ones who get busted.

Most of us don't get busted. We are cool and cautious. We are aware enough on the emotional and personal vibration planes to spot phonies, informers, and undercover agents. We utilize our constitutional rights and our lawyers' abilities when necessary. We lack the moral weaknesses of the organized crime rings that push "hard stuff" (narcotics). Our ranks are growing daily. I don't mean to sound ominous or threatening. Space has been called the last frontier, but the mind is a frontier too, and a closer one.

The big hang-up in dealing is waiting around to score. Contacts are never permanent and seldom reliable as far as time-schedules are concerned. Like Burroughs* points out, business in the dope pyramid is a waiting game. The last gram of acid I scored was in Long Beach. I can remember us sitting around the pad, a one-room apartment, trying to relax. It got harder with each passing hour. Happy and his girl were lying on the bed gossiping nervously about her job, their friends, their recent eviction. I was pushing

---

* Wm. Burroughs, author of Naked Lunch.

the rocking chair past its endurance tolerances. Kelly rolled one joint after another and we passed them around. I had been waiting there for two days to cap this gram, the connection was supposedly flying down from the City (San Francisco) "immediately" with my 4,000 lovely lavender tabs. I had thirty-two one-hundred dollar bills in my pocket and was hoping I wouldn't need them all. If these had been strangers instead of old friends I'd also have had my .32 there; it's a big city and I'm paranoid.

Meanwhile, we're getting high. I take a deep hit of the acrid smoke, close my eyes and imagine the patterns made by the vapors swirling through my lungs. The first hit usually sears a little, but the anesthetic properties of the pot soon soothes your throat. I pass the joint to the timid teenaged girl on my left who smiles shyly at the warm touch of my hand. Physical contact is both a joy and a comfort. With subsequent hits I can feel the individual muscles of my body unwinding like a relaxing rattler; warm waves flow inside me, erasing away fatigue. The body feels detached, suspended; it no longer demands attention. Mind and spirit play a game of tag, ideas flash against the dark velvet backdrop of restfulness. The little girl next to me has become enhaloed with bright incandescent cloud; a flowered forest nymph whose spell cannot be avoided. The rest of the evening is spent in her arms and I forget what I'm waiting for. This might be debauchery on your moral scale, but on mine it's human, loving, joyous. Try it yourself—open mindedly and unashamed. Join the psychedelic world where no one can hide and so no one wants to.

How many of you citizens realize that many police officers turn on? One friend of mine was busted recently with thirteen lids; in court only three were produced as evidence, the rest had "disappeared." When two Southern California officers were prosecuted for possession last year, the papers never mentioned the arrest, investigation, or trial. Finally, after one was convicted, a tiny article was printed on a back page. The name of the co-defendant (who was acquitted) was not printed at all. I dislike publicity and abhor

sensationalism. I would commend this type of news coverage if it were not for the disparity between this case and the normal busts that headline the dailies. Lawyers, judges, doctors, psychologists, college professors, government officials, and many other Establishment figures also turn on. The times, they're a'changing, Bob Dylan sang, and that too is true.

White Rabbit
GRACE SLICK

One pill makes you larger
And one pill makes you small
And the ones that mother gives you
Don't do anything at all
Go ask Alice
When she's ten feet tall.
And if you go chasing rabbits
And you know you're going to fall,
Tell them a hookah-smoking caterpiller
Has given you the call
Poor Alice when she was just as small.
When the men on the chessboard
Get up and tell you where to go
And you just had some kind of mushroom
And your mind is movin slow
Ask Alice
I think she'll know
When logic and proportion
Have fallen slowly dead
And the white knight's talking backward
And the red queen's off in her head
Remember what the dormouse said:
Feed your head
Feed your head.

FROM
The Doors of Perception
ALDOUS HUXLEY

One bright May morning, I swallowed four-tenths of a gram of mescalin dissolved in half a glass of water and sat down to wait for the results.

We live together, we act on, and react to, one another; but always and in all circumstances we are by ourselves. The martyrs go hand in hand into the arena; they are crucified alone. Embraced, the lovers desperately try to fuse their insulated ecstasies into a single self-transcendence; in vain. By its very nature every embodied spirit is doomed to suffer and enjoy in solitude. Sensations, feelings, insights, fancies—all these are private and, except through symbols and at second hand, incommunicable. We can pool information about experiences, but never the experiences themselves. From family to nation, every human group is a society of island universes.

Most island universes are sufficiently like one another to permit of inferential understanding or even of mutual empathy or "feeling into." Thus, remembering our own bereavements and humiliations, we can condole with others in analogous circumstances, can put ourselves (always, of course, in a slightly Pickwickian sense) in their places. But in certain cases communication between universes is incomplete or even nonexistent. The mind is its own place, and the places inhabited by the insane and the exceptionally gifted are so different from the places where ordinary men and women live, that there is little or no common ground of memory to serve as a basis for understanding or fellow feeling. Words are uttered, but fail to enlighten. The things and events to which the symbols refer belong to mutually exclusive realms of experience.

To see ourselves as others see us is a most salutary gift. Hardly less important is the capacity to see others as they see themselves. But what if these others belong to a different species and inhabit a radically alien universe? For example, how can the sane get to know what it actually feels like to be mad? Or, short of being born again as a visionary, a medium, or a musical genius, how can we ever visit the worlds which, to Blake, to Swedenborg, to Johann Sebastian Bach, were home? And how can a man at the extreme limits of ectomorphy and cerebrotonia ever put himself in the place of one at the limits of endomorphy and viscerotonia, or, except

within certain circumscribed areas, share the feelings of one who stands at the limits of mesomorphy and somatotonia? To the unmitigated behaviorist such questions, I suppose, are meaningless. But for those who theoretically believe what in practice they know to be true—namely, that there is an inside to experience as well as an outside—the problems posed are real problems, all the more grave for being, some completely insoluble, some soluble only in exceptional circumstances and by methods not available to everyone. Thus, it seems virtually certain that I shall never know what it feels like to be Sir John Falstaff or Joe Louis. On the other hand, it had always seemed to me possible that, through hypnosis, for example or autohypnosis, by means of systematic meditation, or else by taking the appropriate drug, I might so change my ordinary mode of consciousness as to be able to know, from the inside, what the visionary, the medium, even the mystic were talking about.

From what I had read of the mescalin experience I was convinced in advance that the drug would admit me, at least for a few hours, into the kind of inner world described by Blake and Æ. But what I had expected did not happen. I had expected to lie with my eyes shut, looking at visions of many-colored geometries, of animated architectures, rich with gems and fabulously lovely, of landscapes with heroic figures, of symbolic dramas trembling perpetually on the verge of the ultimate revelation. But I had not reckoned, it was evident, with the idiosyncrasies of my mental make-up, the facts of my temperament, training and habits.

I am and, for as long as I can remember, I have always been a poor visualizer. Words, even the pregnant words of poets, do not evoke pictures in my mind. No hypnagogic visions greet me on the verge of sleep. When I recall something, the memory does not present itself to me as a vividly seen event or object. By an effort of the will, I can evoke a not very vivid image of what happened yesterday afternoon, of how the Lungarno used to look before the bridges were destroyed, of the Bayswater Road when the only buses were green and tiny and drawn by aged horses at three and a half miles an hour. But such images have little substance and absolutely no autonomous life of their own. They stand to real, perceived objects in the same relation as Homer's ghosts stood to the men of flesh and blood, who came to visit them in the shades. Only when I have a high temperature do my mental images come to independent life. To those in whom the faculty of visualization is strong my inner world must seem curiously drab, limited and uninteresting. This was the world — a poor thing but my own — which I expected to see transformed into something completely unlike itself.

The change which actually took place in that world was in no sense revolutionary. Half an hour after swallowing the drug I became aware of a slow dance of golden lights. A little later there were sumptuous red surfaces swelling and expanding from bright nodes of energy that vibrated with a continuously changing, patterned life. At another time the closing of my eyes revealed a complex of gray structures, within which pale bluish spheres kept emerging into intense solidity and, having emerged, would slide noiselessly upwards, out of sight. But at no time were there faces or forms of men or animals. I saw no landscapes, no enormous spaces, no magical growth and metamorphosis of buildings, nothing remotely like a drama or a parable. The other world to which mescalin admitted me was not the world of visions; it existed out there, in what I could see with my eyes open. The great change was in the realm of objective fact. What had happened to my subjective universe was relatively unimportant.

I took my pill at eleven. An hour and a half later, I was sitting in my study, looking intently at a small glass vase. The vase contained only three flowers — a full-blown Belle of Portugal rose, shell pink with a hint at every petal's base of a hotter, flamier hue; a large magenta and cream-colored carnation; and, pale purple at the end of its broken stalk, the bold heraldic blossom of an iris. Fortuitous and provisional, the little nosegay broke all the rules of traditional good taste. At breakfast that morning I had been struck by the lively dissonance of its colors. But that was no longer the point. I was not looking now at an unusual flower arrangement. I was seeing what Adam had seen on the morning of his creation — the miracle, moment by moment, of naked existence.

"Is it agreeable?" somebody asked. (During this part of the experiment, all conversations were recorded on a dictating machine, and it has been possible for me to refresh my memory of what was said.)

"Neither agreeable nor disagreeable," I answered. "It just *is*."

Istigkeit — wasn't that the word Meister Eckhart liked to use? "Is-ness." The Being of Platonic philosophy — except that Plato seems to have made the enormous, the grotesque mistake of separating Being from becoming and identifying it with the mathematical abstraction of the Idea. He could never, poor fellow, have seen a bunch of flowers shining with their own inner light and all but quivering under the pressure of the significance with which they were charged; could never have perceived that what rose and iris and carnation so intensely signified was nothing more, and nothing less, than what they were — a transience that was yet eternal life, a perpetual perishing that was at the same time pure Being, a bundle of minute, unique particulars in which, by some unspeakable and yet self-evident paradox, was to be seen the divine source of all existence.

I continued to look at the flowers, and in their living light I seemed to detect the qualitative equivalent of breathing — but of a breathing without returns to a starting point, with no recurrent ebbs but only a repeated flow from beauty to heightened beauty, from deeper to ever deeper meaning. Words like "grace" and "transfiguration" came to my mind, and this, of course, was what, among other things, they stood for. My eyes traveled from the rose to the carnation, and from that feathery incandescence to the smooth scrolls of sentient amethyst which were the iris. The Beatific Vision, *Sat Chit Ananda,* Being-Awareness-Bliss — for the first time I understood, not on the verbal level, not by inchoate hints or at a distance, but precisely and completely what those prodigious syllables referred to. And then

I remembered a passage I had read in one of Suzuki's essays. "What is the Dharma-Body of the Buddha?" ("The Dharma-Body of the Buddha" is another way of saying Mind, Suchness, the Void, the Godhead.) The question is asked in a Zen monastery by an earnest and bewildered novice. And with the prompt irrelevance of one of the Marx Brothers, the Master answers, "The hedge at the bottom of the garden." "And the man who realizes this truth," the novice dubiously inquires, "what, may I ask, is he?" Groucho gives him a whack over the shoulders with his staff and answers, "A golden-haired lion."

It had been, when I read it, only a vaguely pregnant piece of nonsense. Now it was all as clear as day, as evident as Euclid. Of course the Dharma-Body of the Buddha was the hedge at the bottom of the garden. At the same time, and no less obviously, it was these flowers, it was anything that I—or rather the blessed Not-I, released for a moment from my throttling embrace—cared to look at. The books, for example, with which my study walls were lined. Like the flowers, they glowed, when I looked at them, with brighter colors, a profounder significance. Red books, like rubies; emerald books; books bound in white jade; books of agate; of aquamarine, of yellow topaz; lapis lazuli books whose color was so intense, so intrinsically meaningful, that they seemed to be on the point of leaving the shelves to thrust themselves more insistently on my attention.

"What about spatial relationships?" the investigator inquired, as I was looking at the books.

It was difficult to answer. True, the perspective looked rather odd, and the walls of the room no longer seemed to meet in right angles. But these were not the really important facts. The really important facts were that spatial relationships had ceased to matter very much and that my mind was perceiving the world in terms of other than spatial categories. At ordinary times the eye concerns itself with such problems as *Where?—How far?—How situated in relation to what?* In the mescalin experience the implied questions to which

the eye responds are of another order. Place and distance cease to be of much interest. The mind does its perceiving in terms of intensity of existence, profundity of significance, relationships within a pattern. I saw the books, but was not at all concerned with their positions in space. What I noticed, what impressed itself upon my mind was the fact that all of them glowed with living light and that in some the glory was more manifest than in others. In this context position and the three dimensions were beside the point. Not, of course, that the category of space had been abolished. When I got up and walked about, I could do so quite normally, without misjudging the whereabouts of objects. Space was still there; but it had lost its predominance. The mind was primarily concerned, not with measures and locations, but with being and meaning.

And along with indifference to space there went an even more complete indifference to time.

"There seems to be plenty of it," was all I would answer, when the investigator asked me to say what I felt about time.

Plenty of it, but exactly how much was entirely irrelevant. I could, of course, have looked at my watch; but my watch, I knew, was in another universe. My actual experience had been, was still, of an indefinite duration or alternatively of a perpetual present made up of one continually changing apocalypse.

From the books the investigator directed my attention to the furniture. A small typing table stood in the center of the room; beyond it, from my point of view, was a wicker chair and beyond that a desk. The three pieces formed an intricate pattern of horizontals, uprights and diagonals—a pattern all the more interesting for not being interpreted in terms of spatial relationships. Table, chair and desk came together in a composition that was like something by Braque or Juan Gris, a still life recognizably related to the objective world, but rendered without depth, without any attempt at photographic realism. I was looking at my furniture, not as the utilitarian who has to sit on chairs, to write at desks and tables, and not as the cameraman or scientific recorder, but as the pure aesthete whose concern is only with forms and their relationships within the field of vision or the picture space. But as I looked, this purely aesthetic, Cubist's-eye view gave place to what I can only describe as the sacramental vision of reality. I was back where I had been when I was looking at the flowers — back in a world where everything shone with the Inner Light, and was infinite in its significance. The legs, for example, of that chair — how miraculous their tubularity, how supernatural their polished smoothness! I spent several minutes — or was it several centuries? — not merely gazing at those bamboo legs, but actually *being* them — or rather being myself in them; or, to be still more accurate (for "I" was not involved in the case, nor in a certain sense were "they") being my Not-self in the Not-self which was the chair.

Reflecting on my experience, I find myself agreeing with the eminent Cambridge philosopher, Dr. C. D. Broad, "that we should do well to consider much more seriously than we have hitherto been inclined to do the type of theory which Bergson put forward in connection with memory and sense perception. The suggestion is that the function of the brain and nervous system and sense organs is in the main *eliminative* and not productive. Each person is at each moment capable of remembering all that has ever happened to him and of perceiving everything that is happening everywhere in the universe. The function of the brain and nervous system is to protect us from being overwhelmed and confused by this mass of largely useless and irrelevant knowledge, by shutting out most of what we should otherwise perceive or remember at any moment, and leaving only that very small and special selection which is likely to be practically useful." According to such a theory, each one of us is potentially Mind at Large. But in so far as we are animals, our business is at all costs to survive. To make biological survival possible, Mind at Large has to be funneled through the reducing valve of the brain and nervous system. What comes out at the other end is a measly trickle of the kind of consciousness which will help us to stay alive on the surface of this particular planet. To formulate and express the contents of this reduced awareness, man has invented and endlessly elaborated those symbol-systems and implicit philosophies which we call languages. Every individual is at once the beneficiary and the victim of the linguistic tradition into which he has been born — the beneficiary inasmuch as language gives access to the accumulated records of other people's experience, the victim in so far as it confirms him in the belief that reduced awareness is the only awareness and as it bedevils his sense of reality, so that he is all too apt to take his concepts for data, his words for actual things. That which, in the language of religion, is called "this world" is the universe of reduced awareness, expressed, and, as it were, petrified by language. The various "other worlds," with which human beings erratically make contact are so many elements in the totality of the awareness belonging to Mind at Large. Most people, most of the time, know only what comes through the reducing valve and is consecrated as genuinely real by the local language. Certain persons, however, seem to be born with a kind of by-pass that circumvents the reducing valve. In others temporary by-passes may be acquired either spontaneously, or as the result of deliberate "spiritual exercises," or through hypnosis, or by means of drugs. Through these permanent or temporary by-passes there flows, not indeed the perception "of everything that is happening everywhere in the universe" (for the by-pass does not abolish the reducing valve, which still excludes the total content of Mind at Large), but something more than, and above all something different from, the carefully selected utilitarian material which our narrowed, individual minds regard as a complete, or at least sufficient, picture of reality.

The brain is provided with a number of enzyme systems which serve to co-ordinate its workings. Some of these enzymes regulate the supply of glucose to the brain cells. Mescalin inhibits the production of these enzymes and thus lowers the amount of glucose available to an organ that is in constant need of sugar. When mescalin reduces the brain's normal ration of sugar what happens? Too few cases have been observed, and therefore a comprehensive answer cannot yet be given. But what happens to the majority of the few who have taken mescalin under supervision can be summarized as follows.

(1) The ability to remember and to "think straight" is little if at all reduced. (Listening to the recordings of my conversation under the influence of the drug, I cannot discover that I was then any stupider than I am at ordinary times.)

(2) Visual impressions are greatly intensified and the eye recovers some of the perceptual innocence of childhood, when the sensum was not immediately and automatically subordinated to the concept. Interest in space is diminished and interest in time falls almost to zero.

(3) Though the intellect remains unimpaired and though perception is enormously improved, the will suffers a profound change for the worse. The mescalin taker sees no reason for doing anything in particular and finds most of the causes for which, at ordinary times, he was prepared to act and suffer, profoundly uninteresting. He can't be bothered with them, for the good reason that he has better things to think about.

(4) These better things may be experienced (as I experienced them) "out there," or "in here," or in both worlds, the inner and the outer, simultaneously or successively. That they *are* better seems to be self-evident to all mescalin takers who come to the drug with a sound liver and an untroubled mind.

These effects of mescalin are the sort of effects you could expect to follow the administration of a drug having the power to impair the efficiency of the cerebral reducing valve. When the brain runs out of sugar, the undernourished ego grows weak, can't be bothered to undertake the necessary chores, and loses all interest in those spatial and temporal relationships which mean so much to an organism bent on getting on in the world. As Mind at Large seeps past the no longer watertight valve, all kinds of biologically useless things start to happen. In some cases there may be extra-sensory perceptions. Other persons discover a world of visionary beauty. To others again is revealed the glory, the infinite value and meaningfulness of naked existence, of the given, unconceptualized event. In the final stage of egolessness there is an "obscure knowledge" that All is in all—that All is actually each. This is as near, I take it, as a finite mind can ever come to "perceiving everything that is happening everywhere in the universe."

A Day In The Life
JOHN LENNON AND PAUL McCARTNEY

I read the news today oh boy
About a lucky man who made the grade
And though the news was rather sad
Well I just had to laugh
I saw the photograph.
He blew his mind out in a car
He didn't notice that the lights had changed
A crowd of people stood and stared
They'd seen his face before
Nobody was really sure
If he was from the House of Lords.
I saw a film today oh boy

The English Army had just won the war
A crowd of people turned away
But I just had to look
Having read the book.
I'd love to turn you on
Woke up, fell out of bed,
Dragged a comb across my head
Found my way downstairs and drank a cup,
And looking up I noticed I was late.
Found my coat and grabbed my hat
Made the bus in seconds flat
Found my way upstairs and had a smoke,
Somebody spoke and I went into a dream
I read the news today oh boy
Four thousand holes in Blackburn, Lancashire
And though the holes were rather small
They had to count them all
Now they know how many holes it takes to fill the Albert Hall
I'd love to turn you on

FROM
Naked Lunch
WILLIAM BURROUGHS

I can feel the heat closing in, feel them out there making their moves, setting up their devil doll stool pigeons, crooning over my spoon and dropper I throw away at Washington Square Station, vault a turnstile and two flights down the iron stairs, catch an uptown A train . . . Young, good looking, crew cut, Ivy League, advertising exec type fruit holds the door back for me. I am evidently his idea of a character. You know the type comes on with bartenders and cab drivers, talking about right hooks and the Dodgers, call the counterman in Nedick's by his first name. A real asshole. And right on time this narcotics dick in a white trench coat (imagine tailing somebody in a white trench coat—trying to pass as a fag I guess) hit the platform. I can hear the way he would say it holding my outfit in his left hand, right hand on his piece: "I think you dropped something, fella."

But the subway is moving.

"So long flatfoot!" I yell, giving the fruit his B production. I look into the fruit's eyes, take in the white teeth, the Florida tan, the two hundred dollar sharkskin suit, the button-down Brooks Brothers shirt and carrying *The News* as a prop. "Only thing I read is Little Abner."

A square wants to come on hip . . . Talks about "pod," and smoke it now and then, and keeps some around to offer the fast Hollywood types.

"Thanks, kid," I say, "I can see you're one of our own." His face lights up like a pinball machine, with stupid, pink effect.

"Grassed on me he did," I said morosely. (Note Grass is English thief slang for inform.) I drew closer and laid my dirty junky fingers on his sharkskin sleeve. "And us blood brothers in the same dirty needle. I can tell you in confidence he is due for a hot shot." (Note: This is a cap of poison junk sold to addict for liquidation purposes. Often given to informers. Usually the hot shot is strychnine since it tastes and looks like junk.)

"Ever see a hot shot hit, kid? I saw the Gimp catch one in Philly. We rigged his room with a one-way whorehouse mirror and charged a sawski to watch it. He never got the needle out of his arm. They don't if the shot is right. That's the way they find them, dropper full of clotted blood hanging out of a blue arm. The look in his eyes when it hit—Kid, it was tasty. . . .

"Recollect when I am traveling with the Vigilante, best Shake Man in the industry.

Out in Chi . . . We is working the fags in Lincoln Park. So one night the Vigilante turns up for work in cowboy boots and a black vest with a hunka tin on it and a lariat slung over his shoulder.

"So I says: 'What's with you? You wig already?'

"He just looks at me and says: 'Fill your hand stranger' and hauls out an old rusty six shooter and I take off across Lincoln Park, bullets cutting all around me. And he hangs three fags before the fuzz nail him. I mean the Vigilante earned his moniker. . . .

"Ever notice how many expressions carry over from queers to con men? Like 'raise,' letting someone know you are in the same line?

"'Get her!'

"Get the Paregoric Kid giving that mark the build up!'

"'Eager Beaver wooing him much too fast.'

"The Shoe Store Kid (he got that moniker shaking down fetishists in shoe stores) say: 'Give it to a mark with K.Y. and he will come back moaning for more.' And when the Kid spots a mark he begin to breathe heavy. His face swells and his lips turn purple like an Eskimo in heat. Then slow, slow he comes on the mark, feeling for him, palpating him with fingers of rotten ectoplasm.

"The Rube has a sincere little boy look, burns through him like blue neon. That one stepped right off a *Saturday Evening Post* cover with a string of bullheads, and preserved himself in junk. His marks never beef and the Bunko people are really carrying a needle for the Rube. One day Little Boy Blue starts to slip, and what crawls out would make an ambulance attendant puke. The Rube flips in the end, running through empty automats and subway stations, screaming: 'Come back, kid!! Come back!!' and follows his boy right into the East River, down through condoms and orange peels, mosaic of floating newspapers, down into the silent black ooze with gangsters in concrete, and pistols pounded flat to avoid the probing finger of prurient ballistic experts."

And the fruit is thinking: "What a character!! Wait till I tell the boys in Clark's

about this one." He's a character collector, would stand still for Joe Gould's seagull act.* So I put it on him for a sawski and make a meet to sell him some "pod" as he calls it, thinking, "I'll catnip the jerk." (Note: Catnip smells like marijuana when it burns. Frequently passed on the incautious or uninstructed.)

"Well," I said, tapping my arm, "duty calls. As one judge said to another: 'Be just and if you can't be just, be arbitrary.'"

I cut into the automat and there is Bill Gains huddled in someone else's overcoat looking like a 1910 banker with paresis, and Old Bart, shabby and inconspicuous, dunking pound cake with his dirty fingers, shiny over the dirt.

I had some uptown customers Bill took care of, and Bart knew a few old relics from hop smoking times, spectral janitors, grey as ashes, phantom porters sweeping out dusty halls with a slow old man's hand, coughing and spitting in the junk-sick dawn, retired asthmatic fences in theatrical hotels, Pantopon Rose the old madam from Peoria, stoical Chinese waiters never show sickness. Bart sought them out with his old junky walk, patient and cautious and slow, dropped into their bloodless hands a few hours of warmth.

I made the round with him once for kicks. You know how old people lose all shame about eating, and it makes you puke to watch them? Old junkies are the same about junk. They gibber and squeal at sight of it. The spit hangs off their chin, and their stomach rumbles and all their guts grind in peristalsis while they cook up, dissolving the body's decent skin, you expect any moment a great blob of protoplasm will flop right out and surround the junk. Really disgust you to see it.

"Well, my boys will be like that one day," I thought philosophically. "Isn't life peculiar?"

So back downtown by the Sheridan Square Station in case the dick is lurking in a broom closet.

Like I say it couldn't last. I knew they were out there powowing and making their evil fuzz magic, putting dolls of me in Leavenworth. "No use sticking needles in that one, Mike."

I hear they got Chapin with a doll. This

* See page 36.

old eunuch dick just sat in the precinct basement hanging a doll of him day and night, year in year out. And when Chapin hanged in Connecticut, they find this old creep with his neck broken.

"He fell downstairs," they say. You know the old cop bullshit.

Junk is surrounded by magic and taboos, curses and amulets. I could find my Mexico City connection by radar. "Not this street, the next, right . . . now left. Now right again," and there he is, toothless old woman face and cancelled eyes.

I know this one pusher walks around humming a tune and everybody he passes takes it up. He is so grey and spectral and anonymous they don't see him and think it is their own mind humming the tune. So the customers come in on *Smiles,* or *I'm in the Mood for Love,* or *They Say We're Too Young to Go Steady,* or whatever the song is for that day. Sometime you can see maybe fifty ratty-looking junkies squealing sick, running along behind a boy with a harmonica, and there is The Man on a cane seat throwing bread to the swans, a fat queen drag walking his Afghan hound through the East Fifties, an old wino pissing against an El post, a radical Jewish student giving out leaflets in Washington Square, a tree surgeon, an exterminator, an advertising fruit in Nedick's where he calls the counterman by his first name. The world network of junkies, tuned on a cord of rancid jissom, tying up in furnished rooms, shivering in the junk-sick morning. (Old Pete men suck the black smoke in the Chink laundry back room and Melancholy Baby dies from an overdose of time or cold turkey withdrawal of breath.) In Yemen, Paris, New Orleans, Mexico City and Istanbul — shivering under the air hammers and the steam shovels, shrieked junky curses at one another neither of us heard, and The Man leaned out of a passing steam roller and I coped in a bucket of tar. (Note: Istanbul is being torn down and rebuilt, especially shabby junk quarters. Istanbul has more heroin junkies than NYC.) The living and the dead, in sickness or on the nod, hooked or kicked or hooked again, come in on the junk beam and the Connection is eating Chop Suey on Dolores Street, Mexico D.F., dunking pound cake in the automat, chased up Exchange Place by a baying pack of People. (Note: People is New Orleans slang for narcotic fuzz.)

The old Chinaman dips river water into a rusty tin can, washes down a yen pox hard and black as a cinder. (Note: Yen pox is the ash of smoked opium.)

Well, the fuzz has my spoon and dropper, and I know they are coming in on my frequency led by this blind pigeon known as Willy the Disk. Willy has a round, disk mouth lined with sensitive, erectile black hairs. He is blind from shooting in the eyeball, his nose and palate eaten away sniffing H, his body a mass of scar tissue hard and dry as wood. He can only eat the shit now with that mouth, sometimes sways out on a long tube of ectoplasm, feeling for the silent frequency of junk. He follows my trail all over the city into rooms I move out already, and the fuzz walks in some newlyweds from Sioux Falls.

"All right, Lee!! Come out from behind that strap-on! We know you" and pull the man's prick off straightaway.

Now Willy is getting hot and you can hear him always out there in darkness (he only functions at night) whimpering, and feel the terrible urgency of that blind, seeking mouth. When they move in for the bust, Willy goes all out of control, and his mouth eats a hole right through the door. If the cops weren't there to restrain him with a stock probe, he would suck the juice right out of every junky he ran down.

I knew, and everybody else knew they had the Disk on me. And if my kid customers ever hit the stand: "He force me to commit all kinda awful sex acts in return for junk" I could kiss the street good-bye.

So we stock up on H, buy a second-hand Studebaker, and start West.

The Vigilante copped out as a schizo possession case:

"I was standing outside myself trying to stop those hangings with ghost fingers . . . . I am a ghost wanting what every ghost wants — a body — after the Long Time moving through odorless alleys of space where no life is only the colorless no smell of death. . . . Nobody can breathe and smell it through pink convolutions of gristle laced with crystal snot, time shit and black blood filters of flesh."

He stood there in elongated court room shadow, his face torn like a broken film by lusts and hungers of larval organs stirring in the tentative ectoplasmic flesh of junk kick (ten days on ice at time of the First Hearing) flesh that fades at the first silent touch of junk.

I saw it happen. Ten pounds lost in ten minutes standing with the syringe in one hand holding his pants up with the other, his abdicated flesh burning in a cold yellow halo, there in the New York hotel room . . . night table litter of candy boxes, cigarette butts cascading out of three ashtrays, mosaic of sleepless nights and sudden food needs of the kicking addict nursing his baby flesh. . . .

The Vigilante is prosecuted in Federal Court under a lynch bill and winds up in a Federal Nut House specially designed for the containment of ghosts: precise, prosaic impact of objects . . . washstand . . . door . . . toilet . . . bars . . . there they are . . . this is it . . . all lines cut . . . nothing beyond . . . Dead End . . . And the Dead End in every face. . . .

The physical changes were slow at first, then jumped forward in black klunks, falling through his slack tissue, washing away the human lines . . . In his place of total darkness mouth and eyes are one organ that leaps forward to snap with transparent teeth . . . but no organ is constant as regards either function or position . . . sex organs sprout anywhere . . . rectums open, defecate and close . . . the entire organism changes color and consistency in split-second adjustments. . . .

The Rube is a social liability with his attacks as he calls them. The Mark Inside was coming up on him and that's a rumble nobody can cool; outside Philly he jumps out to con a prowl car and the fuzz takes one look at his face and bust all of us.

Seventy-two hours and five sick junkies in the cell with us. Now not wishing to break out my stash in front of these hungry coolies, it takes maneuvering and laying of gold on the turnkey before we are in a separate cell.

Provident junkies, known as squirrels, keep stashes against a bust. Every time I take a shot I let a few drops fall into my vest pocket, the lining is stiff with stuff. I had a plastic dropper in my shoe and a safety-pin stuck in my belt. You know how this pin and dropper routine is put down: "She seized a safety pin caked with blood and rust, gouged a great hole in her leg which seemed to hang open like an obscene, festering mouth waiting for unspeakable congress with the dropper which she now plunged out of sight into the gaping wound. But her hideous galvanized need (hunger of insects in dry places) has broken the dropper off deep in the flesh of her ravaged thigh (looking rather like a poster on soil erosion). But what does she care? She does not even bother to remove the splintered glass, looking down at her bloody haunch with the cold blank eyes of a meat trader. What does she care for the atom bomb, the bed bugs, the cancer rent, Friendly Finance waiting to repossess her delinquent flesh . . . Sweet dreams, Pantopon Rose."

The real scene you pinch up some leg flesh and make a quick stab hole with a pin. Then fit the dropper *over, not in* the hole and feed the solution slow and careful so it doesn't squirt out the sides. . . . When I grabbed the Rube's thigh the flesh came up like wax and stayed there, and a slow drop of pus oozed out the hole. And I never touched a living body cold as the Rube there in Philly. . . .

I decided to lop him off if it meant a smother party. (This is a rural English custom designed to eliminate aged and bedfast dependents. A family so afflicted throws a "smother party" where the guests pile mattresses on the old liability, climb up on top of the mattresses and lush themselves out.) The Rube is a drag on the industry and should be led out into the skid rows of the world. (This is an African practice. Official known as the "Leader Out" has the function of taking old characters out into the jungle and leaving them there.)

The Rube's attacks become an habitual condition. Cops, doormen, dogs, secretaries snarl at his approach. The blond God has fallen to untouchable vileness. Con men don't change, they break, shatter—explosions of matter in cold interstellar space, drift away in cosmic dust, leave the empty body behind.

Hustlers of the world, there is one Mark you cannot beat: The Mark Inside. . . .

I left the Rube standing on a corner, red brick slums to the sky, under a steady rain of soot. "Going to hit this croaker I know. Right back with that good pure drugstore M. . . . No, you wait here—don't want him to rumble you." No matter how long, Rube, wait for me right on that corner. Goodbye, Rube, goodbye kid. . . . Where do they go when they walk out and leave the body behind?

Chicago: invisible hierarchy of decorticated wops, small of atrophied gangsters, earthbound ghost hits you at North and Halstead, Cicero, Lincoln Park, panhandler of dreams, past invading the present, rancid magic of slot machines and roadhouses.

Into the Interior: a vast subdivision, antennae of television to the meaningless sky. In lifeproof houses they hover over the young, sop up a little of what they shut out. Only the young bring anything in, and they are not young very long. (Through the bars of East St. Louis lies the dead frontier, riverboat days.) Illinois and Missouri, miasma of mound-building peoples, groveling worship of the Food Source, cruel and ugly festivals, dead-end horror of the Centipede God reaches from Moundville to the lunar deserts of coastal Peru.

America is not a young land: it is old and dirty and evil before the settlers, before the Indians. The evil is there waiting.

And always cops: smooth college-trained state cops, practiced, apologetic patter, electronic eyes weigh your car and luggage, clothes and face; snarling big city dicks, soft-spoken country sheriffs with something black and menacing in old eyes color of a faded grey flannel shirt. . . .

And always car trouble: in St. Louis traded the 1942 Studebaker in (it has a built-in engineering flaw like the Rube) on an old Packard limousine heated up and barely made Kansas City, and bought a Ford turned out to be an oil burner, packed it in on a jeep we push too hard (they are no good for highway driving)—and burn something out inside, rattling around, went back to the old Ford V-8. Can't beat that engine for getting there, oil burner or no.

And the U.S. drag closes around us like no other drag in the world, worse than the Andes, high mountain towns, cold wind down from postcard mountains, thin air like death in the throat, river towns of Ecuador, malaria grey as junk under black Stetson, muzzle loading shotguns, vultures pecking through the mud streets—and what hits you when you get off the Malmo Ferry in (no juice tax on the ferry) Sweden knocks all that cheap, tax free juice right out of you and brings you all the way down: averted eyes and the cemetery in the middle of town (every town in Sweden seems to be built around a cemetery), and nothing to do in the afternoon, not a bar not a movie and I blasted my last stick of Tangier tea and I said, "K.E. let's get right back on that ferry."

But there is no drag like U.S. drag. You can't see it, you don't know where it comes from. Take one of those cocktail lounges at the end of a subdivision street—every block of houses has its own bar and drugstore and market and liquorstore. You walk in and it hits you. But where does it come from?

Not the bartender, not the customers, nor the cream-colored plastic rounding the bar stools, nor the dim neon. Not even the TV.

And our habits build up with the drag, like cocaine will build you up staying ahead of the C bring-down. And the junk was running low. So there we are in this no-horse town strictly from cough syrup. And vomited up the syrup and drove on and on, cold spring wind whistling through that old heap around our shivering sick sweating bodies and the cold you always come down with when the junk runs out of you. . . . On through the peeled landscape, dead armadillos in the road and vultures over the swamp and cypress stumps. Motels with beaverboard walls, gas heater, thin pink blankets.

Itinerant short con and carny hyp men have burned down the croakers of Texas. . . .

And no one in his right mind would hit a Louisiana croaker. State Junk Law.

Came at last to Houston where I know a druggist. I haven't been there in five years but he looks up and makes me with

one quick look and just nods and says:
"Wait over at the counter. . . ."

So I sit down and drink a cup of coffee
and after a while he comes and sits beside
me and says, "What do you want?"

"A quart of PG and a hundred nembies."

He nods, "Come back in half an hour."

So when I come back he hands me a
package and says, "That's fifteen dollars. . . .
Be careful."

Shooting PG is a terrible hassle, you have
to burn out the alcohol first, then freeze out
the camphor and draw this brown liquid
off with a dropper — have to shoot it in the
vein or you get an abscess, and usually
end up with an abscess no matter where
you shoot it. Best deal is to drink it with
goof balls. . . . So we pour it in a Pernod
bottle and start for New Orleans past
iridescent lakes and orange gas flares,
and swamps and garbage heaps, alligators
crawling around in broken bottles and
tin cans, neon arabesques of motels,
marooned pimps scream obscenities at
passing cars from islands of rubbish. . . .

New Orleans is a dead museum. We
walk around Exchange Place breathing
PG and find The Man right away. It's a
small place and the fuzz always knows
who is pushing so he figures what the hell
does it matter and sells to anybody. We
stock up on H and backtrack for Mexico.

Back through Lake Charles and the dead
slot-machine country, south end of Texas,
nigger-killing sheriffs look us over and
check the car papers. Something falls off
you when you cross the border into Mexico
and suddenly the landscape hits you
straight with nothing between you and
it, desert and mountains and vultures;
little wheeling specks and others so close
you can hear wings cut the air (a dry
husking sound), and when they spot
something they pour out of the blue sky,
that shattering bloody blue sky of Mexico,
down in a black funnel. . . . Drove all night,
came at dawn to a warm misty place,
barking dogs and the sound of running
water.

"Thomas and Charlie," I said.

"What?"

"That's the name of this town. Sea
level. We climb straight up from here ten
thousand feet." I took a fix and went to

sleep in the back seat. She was a good
driver. You can tell as soon as someone
touches the wheel.

Mexico City where Lupita sits like an
Aztec Earth Goddess doling out her little
papers of lousy shit.

"Selling is more of a habit than using,"
Lupita says. Nonusing pushers have a
contact habit, and that's one you can't
kick. Agents get it too. Take Bradley the
Buyer. Best narcotics agent in the industry.
Anyone would make him for junk. (Note:
Make in the sense of dig or size up.) I
mean he can walk up to a pusher and
score direct. He is so anonymous, grey
and spectral the pusher don't remember
him afterwards. So he twists one after the
other. . . .

Well the Buyer comes to look more and
more like a junky. He can't drink. He can't
get it up. His teeth fall out. (Like pregnant
women lose their teeth feeding the stranger,
junkies lose their yellow fangs feeding the
monkey.) He is all the time sucking on a
candy bar. Baby Ruths he digs special.
"It really disgust you to see the Buyer
sucking on them candy bars so nasty,"
a cop says.

The Buyer takes on an ominous grey-
green color. Fact is his body is making
its own junk or equivalent. The Buyer has
a steady connection. A Man Within you
might say. Or so he thinks. "I'll just set in
my room," he says. "Fuck 'em all. Squares
on both sides. I am the only complete man
in the industry."

But a yen comes on him like a great black
wind through the bones. So the Buyer
hunts up a young junky and gives him a
paper to make it.

"Oh all right," the boy says. "So what
you want to make?"

"I just want to rub up against you and
get fixed."

"Ugh . . . Well all right. . . . But why cancha
just get physical like a human?"

Later the boy is sitting in a Waldorf with
two colleagues dunking pound cake. "Most
distasteful thing I ever stand still for," he
says. "Some way he make himself all soft
like a blob of jelly and surround me so
nasty. Then he gets wet all over like with
green slime. So I guess he come to some
kinda awful climax. . . . I come near wigging

with that green stuff all over me, and he stink like a old rotten canteloupe."

"Well it's still an easy score."

The boy sighed resignedly; "Yes, I guess you can get used to anything. I've got a meet with him again tomorrow."

The Buyer's habit keeps getting heavier. He needs a recharge every half hour. Sometimes he cruises the precincts and bribes the turnkey to let him in with a cell of junkies. It gets to where no amount of contact will fix him. At this point he receives a summons from the District Supervisor:

"Bradley, your conduct has given rise to rumors—and I hope for your sake they are no more than that—so unspeakably distasteful that . . . I mean Caesar's wife . . . hrump . . . that is, the Department must be above suspicion . . . certainly above such suspicions as you have seemingly aroused. You are lowering the entire tone of the industry. We are prepared to accept your immediate resignation."

The Buyer throws himself on the ground and crawls over to the D.S. "No, Boss Man, no . . . The Department is my very lifeline."

He kisses the D.S.'s hand thrusting his fingers into his mouth (the D.S. must feel his toothless gums) complaining he has lost his teeth "inna thervith." "Please Boss Man. I'll wipe your ass, I'll wash out your dirty condoms, I'll polish your shoes with the oil on my nose. . . ."

"Really, this is most distasteful! Have you no pride? I must tell you I feel a distinct revulsion. I mean there is something, well, rotten about you, and you smell like a compost heap." He put a scented handkerchief in front of his face. "I must ask you to leave this office at once."

I'll do anything, Boss, *anything*." His ravaged green face splits in a horrible smile. "I'm still young, Boss, and I'm pretty strong when I get my blood up."

The D.S. retches into his handkerchief and points to the door with a limp hand. The Buyer stands up looking at the D.S. dreamily. His body begins to dip like a dowser's wand. He flows forward. . . .

"No! No!" screams the D.S.

"Schlup . . . schlup schlup." An hour later they find the Buyer on the nod in the D.S.'s chair. The D.S. has disappeared without a trace.

The Judge: "Everything indicates that you have, in some unspeakable manner uh . . . assimilated the District Supervisor. Unfortunately there is no proof. I would recommend that you be confined or more accurately contained in some institution, but I know of no place suitable for a man of your caliber. I must reluctantly order your release."

"That one should stand in an aquarium," says the arresting officer.

The Buyer spreads terror throughout the industry. Junkies and agents disappear. Like a vampire bat he gives off a narcotic effluvium, a dank green mist that anesthetizes his victims and renders them helpless in his enveloping presence. And once he has scored he holes up for several days like a gorged boa constrictor. Finally he is caught in the act of digesting the Narcotics Commissioner and destroyed with a flame thrower—the court of inquiry ruling that such means were justified in that the Buyer had lost his human citizenship and was, in consequence, a creature without species and a menace to the narcotics industry on all levels.

Speed Is of the Essence
GAIL SHEEHY

They never go out. No need to. For this pair the whole magic theatre is inside these four walls on East Second Street. Mozart and Nina Simone on the stereo lapping up their ears. And the good books, the "I Ching," The Bible and "Steppenwolf," with pages curled over passages like "but I, the homeless Steppenwolf, the solitary, the hater of life's petty conventions"—these same books always dozing in the chairs like friends in old sweaters. And bathrobes and diaries . . . safe night smells . . . and no lights, no clock and no phone to disrupt. Sweet frozen time. Time at last for the tiny glass beads their friends next door bring, and teach them to string. Lovely hours of mindsoft work. And their dancing, all day some days, by which they learn to move

without exertion, and other important things. Like how to fall
>   up
>   up
>   up
the stairs. And to play jazz piano by g-o-i-n-g s-l-o-w.

The secrets of the universe, all waiting to be possessed right here within an old-law tenement.* How? With the help of the Magic Vitamin. (A temporary prop, he assures her.) Should it get dull inside, there is fine window theatre on East Second Street. Last month 19 people trussed up a boy in the apartment across the street and set him on fire. Thrill-killing is becoming fashionable here. Though more commonly the new neighborhood showmen—the motorcycle gangs—stick to raping girls and light stabbing of strangers. Bonfires are also popular. Christmas Eve the two watched out the window while a group of young boys set two armchairs and a standing lamp on the top of a derelict car. They found a Christmas tree and set that on top too. It was a replica of the linoleum living rooms in which these boys live. Then they threw on the kerosene and burned it all to the ground. It happened the week she moved in with him. They had jobs up till then, good ones with a hip agency. But they were coming home dead tired. Not enough juice to get into a good book, much less plumb the secrets of the universe. So on New Year's Day he gave her the surprise gift of her life. The Magic Vitamin. Ups, speed, amphetamine. It is all the same. What makes everyone fall in love with amphetamine is the magic of feeling like the beautiful, confident, convivial person we all want to be all the time. It was good when he slipped the needle in for her. RUSH—from vein to brain in less than one second. Her old self-hating self died. She was reborn. He renamed her Joy. Now they never have to go out for anything. Maybe a quick stroll up to Gems Spa because it's spring and everyone is coming out again and buying each other joint-rolling papers and strawberry cones, but . . . you never know

* An old apartment, built before hot water was legally required in New York.

when a bad vibration might hit you crossing the street and bring you down. So going out is expensive. For the Superior Man and his Joy, staying in is a groove. It is retirement at 23.

The parents' Buick hardtop with the Connecticut plates rolls onto East Second Street like an amphibious tank. Big and awkward. The East Village looks like a town that has already been taken. On these streets the old Buicks are flopped on their tire-less haunches because, down here, drugs are more important than wheels. The parents drive over Christmas trees in the gutter and park between garbage pails. Lots of garbage pails down here too, but no one bothers with covers, so the trash kites around the sidewalks into hallways and gets all wound up in people's legs and in the tire-less haunches of the old junk cars. It is three days after the New Year, 1969. The parents are here because, for the first time in her life, their young daughter did not come home for Christmas. She has no phone. Her letter said:

"I'm fine, Mom.
"Believe what you see, not what you hear."

What they heard was, their 23-year-old daughter has moved into a hippie asylum with an acquitted murderer by the name of Remy, who is a speed freak. The words they don't know. But the air of crisis pushed so hard up the Merritt Parkway, they couldn't breathe in their house. Like all those parents sitting on the other side of suburban exit ramps—parents who will be driving in thicker and faster now as warm weather comes and news from the East Village grows uglier than anyone can remember—they have three things stuck in their throats. Guilt, fury, fear. Biggest is the fear.

"Quick, going into the blue building. Is that Remy?" the stepfather says.
"I'd like to scratch his eyes out," the mother says.
"Fools rush in, remember?" The stepfather is repeating the lawyer's words.
"I don't think it's him, anyway."
Hard to see anything here. The street glimmers like an old gas lamp and every window on the blue building is frosted from

the inside. No heat. On this block of tenements and fishy-eyed storefronts, all jigsawed together by fire escapes, there is no traffic either. But other things move past the parents' car. Three young hairies with rich homes in their walks, pulling what they call "street furniture" (other peoples' throwaways) on wooden dollies. A bent woman with a *Beggar's Opera* face wheeling a baby carriage; it is filled with rags. Now they watch an old man climb up from the basement of the blue building one step at a time. His splintery dog forages in the trash while the old man pulls a gate across Dr. Gartenlaub's Corn Salve store. Then he shuffles up the street after the kids.

"Probably chasing them for rent," the stepfather says.

"Let's go up now."

The mother walks directly through the unhinged entrance and up past the lumping fish-roe paint to the top floor. No numbers on the doors. They all look the same: double metal doors with steel bars padlocked across. Like lockers in a slaughterhouse, the stepfather says. They knock on each one without success and go back into their Buick to wait.

Of course they have seen it all on TV. Parents today watch drug programs as regularly as the old *Hit Parade*. You can almost picture Snooky Lanson with a joint in his mouth, the Hit Parade Head. So of course the parents know what to expect — wiggy music, smoke and dozens of ragamuffin kids drifting between apartments in a blue funk while others perform unnatural sex acts on tumbling mats. Except when it happens to *your* daughter, what do you *do?* This is the course one family took.

You never really know when things start to go bad. Their early family life had been a picture of suburban togetherness. Everyone envied it and took photos of it for the local *Tattler:* Father and son, a candidate for medical school, dropping a putt at golf club. Mother and small daughter frolicking in the municipal pool next to the one perfect colored family in town. These were mini-Nixons. Father was an advertising executive, albeit a commuter, but a Nixon Republican back

when it counted. The town elected him for high office. Son Alan went to med school. But for daughter Pammie, 10 years younger, growing up was different.

Suburbia was middle-aged, affluence was old. Birth of the fantasy/drug/love culture was near. The parents were older. Having fairly well shot their bolt on the first model child, they were busy picking up their own lives. Mother had a bout with alcoholism. Father invited girls home from the golf club. They tried with Pammie. But in the rhythm of their family life, there was a sense of . . . effort.

Age 16. One of the daughter's most vivid memories lying in her room alone, in the prom dress she'd selected alone, savoring those last moments of delight in the boy who had selected her, before the quivers set in and reduced her to Silly Putty . . . she looked up to find her mother. In her room! Staring at her hands. Your nails are terrible, the mother said. Suddenly concerned. We must cut those nails. She hurried to find scissors. The father came with a nail clipper. The daughter held out her hands. That memory is still in her fingers. She had never felt so cared for.

The parents divorced that year. Both remarried. They kept in touch through child support checks and phone fights over who should come up with the next semester's tuition — until the daughter turned 21. Tired of the money hassle. The Peace Corps refused her. As of last summer she was a practicing college dropout in the West Village.

Shy, slightly plump. Still with a cheerleader smile and that nice emollient way about her that New York eats away like acid. She waitressed in a benign coffee shop, took courses and kept a token bohemian pre-marital apartment. Plaid Stamp stainless and old oaken donated from each parent's attic. She called and visited her mother and stepfather regularly, until . . . when exactly?

A letter came saying she had sublet her apartment for the summer. To save money. To shake herself out of the plant-watering rut. She could stay with friends and her brother in Long Island. And then the reports spaced out. The parents sat up in Connecticut living on wishbones, tossed them from the classic progression story:

—"Bought the most adorable dog in the world today, Mom."
"But $250, Pammie, isn't that what you meant to save by giving up your apartment?"
"Mom, I need *something* to love."

—Pammie is seeing a onetime medical student. Remy is recently back from a year in prison in France, where they accused him of killing a young girl under the influence of amphetamine. "He was *acquitted,* Mother. He's trying very hard now. Absolutely off drugs. I'm getting him a job in the company."

—Promotion. Her company loves her and is sending her to conventions now.

What's happening? I'm on my back in this Chicago hotel, can't move, sleep, can't get my head off the ceiling and when I try to dial, my fingers—look at them!—my fingers are square and the holes are round.

—Pammie is out sick with a carbuncle. Gingivitis. The brother reports she drinks a great deal for a girl her age. And never walks the dog.

—She brings Remy up for Labor Day. Surprise; he is charming, agreeable and plays Mozart sonatas on their piano. Pammie says it is torture to be away from him more than a few hours.

It was in medical school Remy got the idea of becoming the junkie's doctor. Meaning he would have to experience every kind of drug, while studying its pharmacology, physiological effects, etc., and then, of course, beat it. He could do everything else. Up from the Bronx with a face and guitar that made mothers faint for their girls, a poet's way with words and cum laude grades. Remy always was a little bigger than life. The Grand Concourse Christ. All his friends came for guidance. "Follow me into the water, don't hesitate,

don't ask me where, but I know I can take you there," he would tell them. Truly believing—
I exist
Therefore, I am
The center of the universe.
The last girl followed him through medical school and expulsion to France. People loved the story; especially those most scandalized, who regularly told it for their friends:
One day during psychiatric rotation Remy took his prettiest schizophrenic patient back to his apartment. For private sexual therapy. When the dean called him in, Remy looked shocked at the accusation. "Do you mean to tell me, Dean, you would take the word of a madwoman with gross sexual fantasies against the word of your best extern?" Would this extern's apartment have blue lights and a harpsichord? the dean asked. Yes, but how would the dean know? The extern's patient must have had a moment of clarity; she had described his apartment to the last detail. "Remsberg," the dean said, "you are not only perverted, you are a liar." Remy told his friends: "I had to admit, he had me on both counts."
So they went to Paris, Remy and his childhood sweetheart, where medical school is six years and he would try it in French. His parents sent $10,000 a year. He married the girl and she worked every night in the American jazz club, but always they lived in a one-room flat. Most of the money went for Remy's research materials. He made it through hashish, barbiturates, cocaine, mescaline and LSD, relying on his old friend marijuana to give focus to those all-night bouts with the texts. Often Remy and his wife took a few weeks off to drop a little acid on a Greek island or ski in the Austrian Alps, "to get our bodies back in shape." Preparatory, always, to getting their heads into shape. Remy even got through heroin. But that last winter back in the windowless Paris flat, Remy met up with Uncle Max.
Maxitone is the most popular brand of speed in Paris. Well, Remy took Uncle Max into his veins. And Uncle Max got to Remsberg the way it is to feel 18 again. Jolt, whooosh, flyyyiiiing—he was back at his piano and they didn't see him in medical

school anymore. His wife had to step over the bodies on the floor to go to work. First it was friends, then girls, sometimes two in his bed at once, but Remy would be asleep. Amphetamine plays mean tricks with sex. It prolongs orgasm to the point of ecstatic frenzy, sometimes driving people for hours, but in the end there is usually no orgasm. Remy became concerned about his manhood. His wife found the refrigerator filled with hot dogs. She made up a little song to sing herself to sleep.

Just Remy and me
And Uncle Max makes three
We're happy in my Blue Heaven.

—Pammie is asking for too many diet pills, reports her brother, the Long Island doctor.

—Madelaine, who is the second wife of Pammie's real father, calls from Boston. "Pamela, we haven't heard a word in eight months. Your father is ready to give up."

"Oh," Pammie says. "Is he still around?"

—Pammie won't be coming home for Thanksgiving. Flu.

"Honey, you're associating with a boy who's been connected with dope, murder, rape and ruined a marriage. It's *him* making you sick." Pammie says her mother is being negative.

"Are you on dope?"

"No. But everybody in New York carries some kind of pills in their pocketbook."

—Their daughter comes home unexpectedly. Finished with Remy. He went back on the one promise she couldn't forgive. He was back on amphetamine. It's all right. She feels, somehow, superstrong. Then in the kitchen sobs jump out and she buries them in her mother's neck.

He didn't come to work—three days—a hell—it's a girl, I thought—I went over—he wouldn't open the door—I sat on the stairs—oh God, I sat on those stairs 12 hours and in the morning he let me in; he said, "Can't you see I have nothing to give you now" and I said all I wanted was to crawl into the corner and go to sleep. He'd been shooting for three days straight —oh Mom, why couldn't it have been a girl?

Later Pammie played on the lawn with her dog and left with the flush of resolution high in her cheeks.

—Pammie has no phone; write to her office.

—She is back with Remy but he's hung up his gun.

It means he's promised not to shoot speed again. She is the keeper of the works, the equipment, for him and his friends. Keep writing.

—"Don't *worry,* Mom. Sure, they tease me about trying it all the time. But *you* know what my poison would be, if it ever got to that. Liquor." The mother knows because she spent several years as an alcoholic.

—Now the only reports come from her brother and old friends. Pammie can't shake the flu. Conjunctivitis. Probably anemic, possible liver damage. She and Remy appear to live on frankfurters and Wing Dings. And pills. Don't push her. Pammie is withdrawing from everyone. Write. Come. Best we can do is keep all the lines open for when she calls for help.

—Christmas. The letter to the parents says: "My love for you both is so strong, I want to use all I have to make you understand and believe in me. I say believe in me, rather than trust me (as you always have), because the latter is what an unformed child asks from a parent. I'm asking for a lot more. This is an emotional time, intense with both joy and pain, but one I must do alone. A day doesn't go by without my being excited about being alive. All I ask is that you be you, and I will be me. *Believe what you see, not what you hear.*"

—"Pamela Burr? She's not in the office. We haven't heard from her or Mr. Remsberg in six days."

"Noooooo! No, no, no—"

The stepfather takes the phone out of the mother's hands. That's it, he says. They are going down with the police and a doctor and put the girl in a state hospital. Let them pull her off dope while a psychiatrist straightens out her thinking. Or they'll all go crazy.

It's not that easy. They find by making a few calls:

New York City hospitals won't admit amphetamine abusers to their drug withdrawal programs; neither will state hospitals (unless it is amphetamine habituation mixed with heroin addiction).

"Physical withdrawal isn't the problem," the brother explains. "Amphetamine is not heroin, it's a psychiatric problem."

"It's common for a girl to be hooked by her boyfriend," says Dr. Harold Trigg at Beth Israel Medical Center's Drug Addiction Service. "It's a tough one for parents."

Can a user control amphetamine and get off when he wants to?

"I don't think anyone can handle it," says Dr. Trigg. "It makes you feel too good. The original goal for taking it is lost. The root of your depression is masked. Maybe you really hate yourself, or your boyfriend. But on amphetamine, all that matters is how good you feel. You don't *want* to give it up."

Their lawyer was next.

"Law is on Remy's side. He can throw you out of his home, and he might have weapons." The mother says she plans to tell the daughter all doors will be closed to her unless she changes immediately. "Absolutely not!" the lawyer says, having made trips with parents to the East Village before. "Open all doors and keep them open. If you must go down, go for your *own* sake."

It is now 7 P.M. and the parents go back into the blue building and knock on the first door on the top floor. Remy answers in jockey shorts.

"May we come in?"

"Depends who you are."

"Pammie's parents."

"Oh. Excuse me while I get some pants on."

Through the door can be glimpsed a thin, eye-rubbing version of their daughter Pammie, stumbling off a floor mattress in black baby-dolls.

"We, uh, were just sleeping for 10 hours."

"That's a funny time to sleep, through the day," says the mother.

"I'll wash my face." The daughter reaches for the Noxzema over the tub-in-kitchen, and buckles in the knees.

Now there is a lot of dialogue like one-way tennis balls. What time is it? What day is it? Should Remy go next door? Do you want coffee? Where's the cup? Remy goes next door for the cup. The stepfather examines Pammie's eyes. Transparent, he is thinking, like an alcoholic waking up. Remy comes back with a friend and no cup. We just love Pammie, the friend says. You should, the mother says, she's a very nice girl. Remy starts the coffee. Why is Pammie shaking? Remy says this is morning, for Pammie. How can anyone tell the difference in *here!*

The mother is staring at Pammie's legs. There's nothing *to* you, honey. Oh, but people tell me I look great, it's nice to be on the thin side for once. But your legs, almost deformed, they look like the legs of an alcoholic—

"Pammie hasn't had a drink since Thanksgiving," Remy dramatically announces. Pammie nods. She nods at everything Remy says.

"Know what we had New Year's Eve? Chocolate mallows and milk." This is their ace in the hole, and they know it.

"Well, we're here in answer to your letter," the stepfather says. He takes the only chair. Pammie sits on the mattress, forgetting the coffee. A 10-watt hangs over the mattress.

"Well, you can see we're not angry and we're not here to hurt you. We're here to offer our love. Now, what can we do to help you?"

The lights go out.

So the parents sit in the flashlight mark drinking something out of paper cups and put the what-can-we-do-to-help question again.

Pammie: I need no help. I'm happy and I'm doing what I want to do.

Parents: What do you want from life?

Pammie: Actually, nothing. These things are going on in my mind, so many things I haven't had time to think about.

Parents: What things?

Pammie: Well, I just sit here and keep getting these things.

Parents: How can anything come through these filthy windows? You must get out in the world to see things as they are. Why do you have to take pills?"

Pammie: I like the way they make me feel. I can think better.

Parents: Why did you quit your job?

Remy: We were working in an office, and not only that but inside a cubicle inside an office. We came home uptight.

Mother: What are you going to live on?

Pammie leans, yawns, a grin flops down (it is the way she begins all her answers) and asks, What was the question again?

Six days straight, no sleep, the dayless night. A war waged between three different Pammies, directed by Remy, the rebirth! How to tell it? About the old Pammie, inhibited, unable to please a man, promiscuous but nearly frigid, she made f---, not love. Then "Julia" came out one day, confident, mysterious, a sexual aggressor, ah, a woman, but, Julia quickly disappeared. Then trouble. One night during lovemaking Pammie's gears went flooey, the arms and legs were clutching, in-grabbing, and when it was over she remembered nothing. Remy could not engage her. The quivers, he called them, went on for weeks. New Year's Day he shot her with the Magic Vitamin. He looked down and—Pammie was not in her own face. It was a child of 7, a moaning, quivering mass of uncontrolled in-clutching auto-eroticism. He quickly cast the "I Ching" for Pammie. Darkening of the light, omens of death, the book said. His own hexagram told Superior Man the time had come to direct another's destiny. He went back to the bed and struck the quivering spook. Did he kill her? No, "Pammie" came back. Or was it "Julia?" "So here we are, folks, at the movies," he said. "Three Faces of Eve." For six days, then, he has been directing the war between them. Pammie and the spook will kill each other. Julia will prevail. Remy says so, and Remy is the Superior Man.

Mother: There *are* kicks in life without stimulants or alcohol.

Suddenly it hits the parents. They cannot use their own lives for arguments. Coming into the ring exposed, having played over half the rounds, they can't hide the trick knees and broken ribs of their own false dreams. Remember? Bottles under the motel bed, clock and phone ripped out. Live a Day at a Time. Can they now fight her pills with their gin?

The parents switch tack.

Do you need money?

Remy: I pay the rent and we live on her savings. We need time to look around for what we want to do.

Pammie: Lots of ways to make money in New York without working. From Unemployment. Welfare.

Mother: Prostitution?

Pammie: Oh no.

Mother: You're both perfectly able to work. Is it right to take welfare?

Stepfather: I pay war-size taxes for people like you. You know, you're not unique. I broke up my home, took a housekeeper for my child and kept going into the hole until I quit my job. Then I started a business I could run from home. Florida land development. The difference is, I had a sense of direction and responsibility.

Pammie: Material things don't interest us. Remy is frantic when he can't get four hours in on the piano.

Mother: Are you going to continue the drugs?

Remy: I'm glad you asked that. No, not when she can do what she wants without them.

Stepfather: *You people want to retire at 23!*

Laughter engulfs generation gap. The scene becomes a mock sales meeting.

Stepfather: You know, for $19 down you can buy a dream. I expect to retire too, in Florida, with a brand new home, central air-conditioning and an automatic-pilot airplane. But to retire before you've lived . . . why?

Mother: Why can't you answer these questions?

Remy: They asked Einstein the same thing.

Stepfather: Einstein had direction.

Mother: We found beauty in Florida.

Remy: The day we found beauty, we made a sign. *It's illegal not to be free.*

Stepfather: That and 15 cents will get you a glass of beer.

Remy: We don't drink.

Stepfather: Do you know what empathy is?

Pammie: The ability to put yourself in another's shoes.

Stepfather: I'm a salesman. My life is spent selling a way of life. Now, I've put myself in your shoes for two hours. I've found no possible way to motivate you. Inability to motivate means I do not have empathy. I can't make the sale.

Remy: Oh no, I'll admit, speed is the worst drug in the world.

Stepfather: You know, when you make an easy sale, you forget the person. When someone turns you down flat, you're at the corner every time they turn around.

Remy: I can see what makes you a great salesman.

At the door, the stepfather notes Remy's grip has improved. Halfway up the Merritt Parkway he turns to the mother.

"I like him."

It's par. Sociopaths like Remy are some of the world's favorite people. Books are woven of them. Raskolnikov, Siddartha, the Steppenwolfs, the wanderers, "unbound by life's petty conventions" — the mother is reading the books now. She turns to the stepfather. "You know, they are what we all might be, if we dared."

MARCH   You may never know when things start to go bad, but when things are worse you know it. By March, when the parents drive down to surprise the daughter, there are only two things to see.

Gray circles. Little clumps of them, like old cigarette burns, in the crooks of her arms. And the prescription pad on top of the typewriter.

Dr. Alan Burr, M.D.
Obetrols — 20 mg.
100 tabs

There is one last prescription on the stolen pad. A typewritten copy has been mimeographed on dozens of large white sheets, which Pammie is now cutting out like large paper dolls. The doctor is her brother.

She can't speak. When she tries to put together more than 10 words running, a yawn peels at her lips and her head slumps. She asks nothing about anybody. Says she is fine. Except that Remy has gone on a three-day trip to Chicago to appear in a

happening. She feels bad just now because in all these months, he hasn't been out of her sight more than two hours. The bookcase is draped in paisley prayer cloth. Syringes and rubber hosing spill out the sides. The two capsule jars on the table are empty.

Pammie is home alone with an empty doughnut box and a jar of Bosco. *Old lady* is what men call their girls down here. It fits. The daughter looks the way old ladies in rest homes do when their husbands pass on. Suddenly they don't asked to be wheeled to the solarium anymore and start soiling their beds.

SATURDAY   "I'm going to stop the drugs."

It is the next afternoon and Pammie is at her brother's door. He hugs her long. (No one mentions the stolen prescription pad.) Later, carefully . . .

"What brought you to this momentous decision?"

"Actually, I had no choice. Remy didn't leave me anything." Pammie smiles. Her words are still a whisper but about her is a general lightening. "I don't know how to shoot myself anyway. He always does it for me."

The brother makes tea and they talk about Obies.

"Obetrol, for obesity control I guess. It's four amphetamines in one. We dilute five tablets, strain it and shoot. Oh, maybe twice a day. Sometimes every hour for five or six hours, and then we coast for two days."

Her brother gives a very rough translation of what she is doing. One asprin-sized amphetamine tablet gives roughly the lift of five cups of black coffee, drunk rapidly. Pammie is shooting into her veins 20 times that jolt, three times a day. Or 300 cups of black coffee straight to the brain.

"No kidding."

Has she noticed the contradiction of amphetamine? How on one day a large dose can put a person into a frenzy? While on another day, when he's down—

"Yes!" This strokes home. Gene, their friend, who shoots 1,000 mg., or enough to put a horse over the moon, can think all day how nice it's going to be to get high. "After supper he gets ready, shoots, *crash.* Dead sleep."

And for Pammie?

"After a while it's not a high anymore. You take it to feel better, but you can't remember what was bothering you. Some nameless anxiety. So you take more and suddenly say to yourself—am I high? I'm not sure anymore. It's just outer space."

Pammie leans on her own words, as though forming with them a little rope ladder up to the light.

"Listen to yourself, honey," the brother says. "Know what you're saying."

"Well, you can know it, but then the panic sets in. Like, what are you going to do about it?"

The brother tells her about Encounter. A new nonresidential drug therapy center at 150 Spring Street. They work with pre-addicts, age 13 to 27, from the outside in—by changing behavior first. Over half used speed. Two things you do before starting are : 1) give up getting high, 2) give up your drug-using friends.

"They're young, good people, you'd like them," the brother says. "It's a good way to find new friends and a roommate."

Yes, Pammie sounds very interested. She'll call Encounter tomorrow. "If I don't go to sleep again."

It seems the fever has broken.

NEXT MORNING, 6 A.M. Pammie calls her brother.

"I just got raped in my apartment. Could someone come down and bring a tranquilizer?"

She is next door under a blanket. The eyes and frail arms belong to those broken sparrows and half-drowned cats that children nurse and pray over, and which usually die. He was a Japanese man, but big, a karate type. It was exactly like the dream all alone women have had. She opened her eyes and he was there, standing over her with a handkerchief in his hand. Don't move or I'll kill you, he said, and she believed it and he came down on her with his 200 pounds.

He couldn't enter and told her to raise her knees. She said she had just had an operation and was in pain. Could she give him money instead? He hopped off. A pillow came down on her face. Don't move or I'll

kill you, he said. She heard footsteps running down the stairs.

When the mother arrives and goes to Pammie's apartment, the first thing that strikes her is how . . . cheerful . . . it looks. It's the first time she has seen light in it. Morning sun creams the rough walls and greens the plants. Grain pushes up in the oak table. The typewriter and prescriptions are gone. Bright paper flowers are on the table instead. Pammie had happied the apartment for Remy's return. Only one thing is wrong:

Remy went away for three days and left his old lady with no drugs. Supposed to call last night. He didn't. So the girl, whose mind it is destined for this Superior Man to control, fell apart in amphetamine withdrawal and was raped by a Japanese karate expert. Neat. Predictable.

The mother sits on the hall steps turning the crisis over in her hands. It comes, first, in shapes and colors. All the things in this building—the food in the apartments, chocolate-coated marshmallow mallows, Bosco, orange soda, sugar doughnuts; and the furniture, all in miniature, boxes with tiny pillows for seats and doll-size trunks from the street—all of it is for children. How did we make them hate to grow up? It must be very bad in this country, she is thinking. So bad that it is driving our kids crazy. They turn on in high school at the age of 12 now. At PTA meetings in substantial communities the parents get it straight: "Your child will be involved with drugs one way or another before he graduates. Be prepared to deal with it." Now, if she, the mother, sits here all day, like they do, and really thinks about Vietnam, for instance, or the Chicago convention or Kennedy and King, or about why our best young men are deserting their army and another 3,000 choose to live in Canada without a country . . . and if she then flipped on the radio to hear a glowing Dow Jones and thought about America's fat turning to gristle in the last five years, until radical attacks radical and black and white desiring the same revolution turn on one another in civil war— and if she had a couple of parents in the next room flipping out on a dinner of martinis and Miltowns — well. This must be what drugs are all about. The young people of this nation would rather go crazy their way than ours.

MONDAY   Remy returns. Pammie can't be reached.

TUESDAY   Pammie just went to sleep behind a Nembutal, the people next door say. Can she call back later?

WEDNESDAY   "I never knew anyone who stopped shooting by himself," says Margie Nichols at Encounter. She is a beautiful, smart, 24-year-old veteran of speed. The parents ask how, then, do people stop?

"Death. That's number one. Two: move on to heroin. Three: unable to get it, but that's temporary. If you stay in the same setting with the same friends, there's no hope of stopping. The friends get uptight and pressure you in subtle ways."

Remy, she says, sounds like the boyfriend who started her on drugs. "It was a relief to give up everything of my own and make my whole purpose in life whatever he wanted. It's terribly common here." To help Pammie, she says, you start by getting her away from the boyfriend.

"I hope you're aware," says Margie at the door, "that your daughter could kill herself any day."

THURSDAY   You can talk and write letters, but the bottom line is you go to 52 Chambers Street and into the gangrenous Criminal Court building, and here — you ask to swear out a warrant for your daughter's arrest. Because today you are a good parent if you can do one thing. Get your child past 25 and still alive.

An off-duty cop takes the parents aside. He knows they are nice people but wet behind the ears. He gives it to them straight.

"Are you ready to lie? Okay, she stole some prescriptions; what's she done to you? We're not talking about a minor. Nothing's gonna happen without a warrant. Trying to get a warrant in this town for a 23-year-old girl is like trying to get a check cashed on Sunday. So they've got pills and needles in the apartment. Possession of

one pill or 800 pounds of amphetamine is all the same. A misdemeanor. Unless you can prove intent to sell, which you never can in court. First offenders on any drug besides heroin get probation or an s.s. [suspended sentence] 100 percent of the time.

"You really want to get your daughter away from this creep and his drugs? Tell them she stole your wedding ring and you saw her do it. Throw in the hundred bucks she pinched from your cash box at Thanksgiving. Why the face? You said you didn't mind a white lie. Whad'll they do to her? Lock her up until trial, couple weeks. Sure it means the Women's Detention Home, you think she'll get the Sheraton? Maybe it'll be the Bellevue psycho ward. Depends on the judge. But you'll get his ear before the trial. They know the difference between junkies [heroin] and the kids playing with speed. They see concerned relatives in court, they're not gonna send the girl out to Pilgrim State [mental hospital] for three years. You tell the judge what you want. Meantime your daughter's better off in ladies' jail than letting some bastard put holes in her arm. Shake her up a little. Where else you going to keep her till the trial? What, with handcuffs? Sure, then the two of them take off for Mexico. You going squeamish on me now?

"Okay. Remember, you counted the cash box just before she walked in and you saw her in the drawer. It was $100 lighter when she left. You ready to tell it like that to the judge's face? It's too bad, but the law isn't set up for decent people."

A little paler for the psychodrama, the parents approach the court clerk.

"Nobody but a peace officer gets a warrant here. Go to the Ninth Precinct. Whad'ya mean, they sent you here? This is the court's department!"

At the Ninth things are loud and full. The upstairs swarms with detectives, narcos, suspects being fingerprinted and four prisoners sitting on the floor of a small cage in the corner. Everyone else is phoning, running or shouting. Complainants are being waved away midway through their second sentence.

"Yes dear," to the mother. "Whada you want?"

"I'd like to swear out a warrant for my daughter's arrest."

"For what?" Mild suprise on the detective.

"Stealing $100 from my cash box and—"

"Where?"

"Connecticut, and also—"

"No no no!" the detective is waving them out the gate when the stepfather shouts back:

"She stole prescription blanks in New York and forged them. To get drugs."

Reluctantly, the detective picks up his clipboard. He lets them inside the gate.

"Okay, what I want to know is nothing about Connecticut. What happened here, when, and who's the complainant?"

The brother from Long Island steps up and adlibs the story. The detective says okay, the only way they're going to get the girl out of there is to get a warrant on her for forging prescriptions.

"Which the D.A. probably won't give you anyway." He excuses himself and returns with a young man in hippie costume jeans, kerchief and long curly red hair.

"This is Ritchie Toes, narcotics squad."

Ritchie Toes has a face like a person who is still listening. He smiles. The brother almost dives at him.

"Who's the guy?" They give Remy's history. "Sounds like a beaut."

The detective is still shaking his head.

"Can *he* be arrested then?" the stepfather interrupts. "He stole my wife's wedding ring."

"Nah, a ring theft is hard to prove."

The mother's voice splits. "What do I have to do to get him arrested, kill the man? Because I will if I have to."

Ritchie Toes catches her arm; his voice is very quiet. "We'll get the warrant. You tell the D.A. all you've told me. Maybe they'll set a big bail for the guy and give your daughter $500."

"How long will it take?" the brother asks.

Smack. The detective's clipboard sails across his desk and hits a two-foot pile of complaints.

"When we get time," he announces with official finality. "We take 1,700 cases a year. Right now we got two homicides back to back. The motorcycle kids. You know what I'm gonna do with this?"

"Throw it away?"

The detective smiles. These people are learning. "If it's something's gonna take time, like your warrant, we get to it when we can."

The mother suddenly remembers . . .

"You had two detectives in her apartment on Sunday. My daughter was almost raped. They have pills, syringes and illegal prescriptions all over the place. Your men probably reported it already."

"If they would have seen it, they would have locked up somebody. Sunday?" Shouting to the back, "Charlie, you got a rape on Sunday for, what's her name?"

"No rapes on Sunday. Saturday neither," Charlie says.

"But two detectives fingerprinted her."

"Sorry, no rapes on the arrest record."

Out of the Ninth Precinct the parents walk like cardboard dolls. From Ratner's, with automatic futility, they call Pammie. She comes over in a wig and a smart pantsuit, looking, as she herself comments with a proud twirl:

"Like a model. Isn't it wonderful—I'm thin!"

The mother cries and begs without shame. Please come home. Pammie says she knows now she has a decision to make. Remy's way of life or—she must leave. The parents go home to Connecticut knowing all their daughter's apparent decisiveness came out of a syringe.

"Don't call us," the stepfather tells the brother, "unless the news is good."

APRIL   Out of East Second Street, life force has begun vibrating. Twelve people now rotate through the apartment to participate in the Grand Magic Vitamin Experiment. Remy cures ulcers and revives souls. Pammie cooks. The psychic sensitivity between them all becomes so acute, doors might be made of smoke. Which is fine when anyone needs help; not so fine when one feels a bone crusher coming on.

Bone Crusher: Like being caught forward and reverse. . . . grinding muscle contractions. It happens without warning. The afflicted one goes outside to hide it. But soon, Pammie-Gene-Sunny Smiles-everyone feels a bone crusher coming on too. One by one they crawl into a hot tub.

Paranoia is the big one. "It begins inside, imagining peep-holers, and moves out to make you the controller of cosmic forces: you are making the storm, wind, bad-tripping the world, and there's no way to stop yourself," Pammie explains.

In those speed freaks who "hit and skip" through institutions, the paranoia is so bad they cannot speak. It is raw fear. For a user like Pammie, doctors warn, the longest part of withdrawal is getting over the paranoia. *It can take two years.*

Otherwise, Pammie says, the vibrations are beautiful. Closeness and love. She has begun to draw.

But the shleppers are the truly unattractive segment of any unconventional group: the parasites. So long as there is food on the stove, the shleppers bring Pammie Italian shoes from the trashcans and wig out over Remy's piano. On Remy's pills. All sharesies. Until there is no bread at all.

So now it is farina and water. For three days. The shleppers have disappeared through the cracks. One straggler still sleeps under Remy's piano bench.

"Get out! Shoo! Split!" Pammie is finally asserting herself. She shakes out the shlepper like a carpet beetle. She and Remy set to fighting. At the peak, the new man from next door walks in unannounced.

"You're wrong about that, Pammie."

"Another peepholer! They're everywhere!"

Pammie packs a shopping bag and runs out, pushing, running, down steps, bursting onto a subway platform. On the sign it all comes in letters and numbers.

E Train, Local on Track —, Between 5:31 and 6:02

F Train between hours of ——

Where to go? Who would be there? Parents. Nice parents. Different language. Grief, the last thing they will give up is their grief. This thing, it's a way of life . . . my friends, my work, my home, my love, where I feel cared for. Hello out there . . . can you hear the voice of a stranger? Tell me. Call to me. What language do you speak?

"Remy, where are the Al Jolson records?"

Pammie is back, making a pile of valuables by the door.

"It's all going to the pawnshop. I'm not beaten yet."

Remy can rouse himself only up on one elbow.

"Pammie? I'm glad you're back." He motions her to come and rest.

"But I'm hungry! I am hungry, Remy, *hungry!*"

His eyebrows lift.

"I guess I never took you seriously before."

Three days after their visit to the Welfare Department, the welfare investigator is coming to visit the couple.

"Look at this ritzy place!" Sunny Smiles from downstairs bursts into their apartment and begins scooping chairs and lamps under his arms. "You gotta ditch this furniture, man, this place'll go down for a palace." Plants go out on the fire escape, everything else downstairs to Sunny Smiles' apartment, leaving only the rag rug, piano and one chair.

He is a regular class picture, the welfare investigator. Crew-cut, flushed of cheek, Yale in speech, earnest. Standing in the doorway with a briefcase clasped to his chest, so very earnest . . .

"I'm a professional and we can all just be very professional about this thing because, really, it's nothing to be ashamed of." He takes a quick, embarrassed look around the room. "Uh, do you have a chair?"

"Why yes, we *do* have a chair." Remy sounds delighted with himself. He pulls the one chair to the center of the room. Yalie sits. The couple curl round his feet as for story hour at the public library.

"And, uh, where's the bed?" Yalie asks.

"There."

"That single mattress on the floor? I see. Well, let's get the sleeping arrangements straight before we go any farther. Um, where do you sleep, Pamela?"

Pammie tries very hard not to sound flip. "There, with Remy."

"You both sleep on that tiny mattress on the floor!"

Now Remy will give his whole story. Beginning with the Army declaring him a lunatic — he speaks dispassionately, plying his audience with endearing eccentricities. Yalie sits by the hour, enraptured.

"You'll notice I'm taking more time than is normal on this interview."

Remy leaps up in mid-sentence —

"I declare a musical break!"

Remy comes down on the piano with a Chopin polonaise—bronk, bronk, BAAARONK—like a Strindberg character in the advanced stage of syphilitic brain disease. He follows it up with a soothing *Clair de Lune.* Yalie is out of his horn-rimmed mind with digging this beautiful lunatic, and the girl who would rather turn the pages of his Schirmer Classics and sleep at his feet than on foam-rubber Connecticut.

"I'll dictate this right away, right off today. Don't you worry about a thing."

"It's been our pleasure . . ."

Remy was declared Non-Functional. Pammie was declared his common-law wife. Several days later they walked over to the Service Center at 9 West 13th Street to pick up a $50 (monthly) welfare check. That simple. Don't worry about the eviction notice, they were told. A check for your back rent is on its way.

For supplemental income the couple consulted a booklet popular in East Village homes. A sort of variation on *Reader's Digest,* called "F--- the System."* It tells how to get everything free in New York. Under Free Meat and Poultry, for instance, it suggests: "Get a letter from Rev. Michael Allen of St. Mark's Church, saying you need some meat for a church sponsored meal. If you want to be really professional, dress as a priest when you ask. Bring a car or truck. The closest slaughterhouse area is in the far West Village, west of Hudson Street and south of 14th Street. Turning a guy onto the free idea will net you a week's supply of top quality meat."

What Pammie is learning on the Lower East Side is what all white middle-class kids learn from living side by side with genuinely poor blacks and Puerto Ricans. She is absorbing their frustrations, duplicating their street hip, their language, the canned heat of their tenement lives. And their criminal savvy. Total identification with the anger of the real poor gives the kids, to their way of thinking, the right of equal violence. Angry, angrier, angriest . . . con society . . . screw the system . . .

"We're *entitled* to welfare," Pammie tells

her brother. He clears his throat but never gets his lecture past the dial tone.

"You and your nobility!" Pammie hisses. "I've always despised your nobility." End call.

If it wasn't for . . . one tiny niggling haze-glo memory of self-respect . . . Pammie would feel fine.

"Hey, it's Bonnie and Clyde!"

Back to back, slim and devilish-eyed, in beads, head ribbons and silk jersey pantsuits, Pammie and Remy take a bow before the members of the Grand Magic Vitamin Experiment.

"*Wooowow,* beautiful."

Remy has made contact with two spade cats from Jersey, Angel and Boy. They have a partnership selling Seconal and Tuinal (barbiturates with a big market). Angel forges the scrips. Boy, age 15 with a Sweet Pea face, can sell the stuff on the street for $1 a pill. They need nice white trusty-looking middlemen to "score" the drugs (cash the phony prescriptions at the drug store).

"That's us," Remy says. "This is probation. From here, the deals these guys have are dynamite."

"One question," says Sunny Smiles. "How come one spade cat calls the other one 'Boy'?"

"I don't know. He's a bigot."

Timing is critical. Druggists are wising up on the forged prescriptions. The heat is on from "takeoff artists." These are older and wiser drug dealers who wait for amateurs like Remy to leave their apartments unguarded. The takeoff artist appears at a neighbor's door and with quiet persuasion—a knife or several large friends—asks to use the fire escape. Once inside, he either cleans out the apartment, lives in it until the tenant returns (unbeknown to the landlord, who gets no rent) or he calls the tenant and demands a ransom. A hundred or so to get his apartment back.

Pammie is frightened. She throws a fit whenever Remy tries to leave the apartment. To which Remy, with mounting frustration, posed at the door in traditional male outrage, hollers back:

"Dammit, you've got to let a man get his work done!"

SUNDAY IN APRIL   When the brother stops unexpectedly by his office, Remy is sitting at his desk. Under the cornflower blue eyes he works his long, scared mouth into a smile.

"We, uh, as you know we speed freaks are a little paranoid. I thought you might have been making some notes, or maybe some calls about us."

"Not yet. But I'm glad you asked. You have a deadline, Remsberg. Two weeks. If Pammie isn't out of your life in two weeks, if I have to plant a kilo of heroin in your apartment, I'll put you behind bars." The brother slides his desk chair and spills Remy out. Bravado is all that counts. He has been many times to the Ninth Precinct. The police are sympathetic. They keep saying, "This is a case for the books." Except they never book anyone.

"That's heavy, heavy talk." Remy drops his head. "Hey, do you like me?"

"Remy, I give you credit for what you say you are. Just one thing. Get Pammie out. You are the only one who can do it."

The handshake is firm. Remy throws an arm around the brother's shoulder.

"By the way, from one former doctor to another," Remy drawls, "would you have an extra prescription or two lying around?"

Pammie was angry when she saw the new Alan Burr, M.D. pad. Stolen, of course. Pammie is either angry—or high—all the time now. "Why the second eviction notice, Remy? Welfare sent us two months' rent." He couldn't remember what he did with the check. "Why has Welfare cut us off, Remy?" "Beats me." Welfare apologizes; Mr. Remsburg has kept none of his employment appointments.

He was busy, he says, doing second-step work with Angel and Boy. Credit cards.

"Dress up, baby. We'll take a little happy needle and then we'll take a leisurely walk over to Hertz and rent the car of your choice. Like a nice young couple off to the Hilton for the evening. Yes?"

He holds out the Hertz credit card.

"Who's Ephraim Frisch?"

"Who's Ephraim *Frisch?* First of all, he's a cat who doesn't take good care of his credit cards. Second of all, his name has a

ring to it, wouldn't you say? I think I'll take it for my *nom de plume.*"

Driving home, they stop at the record store. "Keep the purchase small, this is only a digit check," Remy whispers. "What's a digit check?" Remy explains that one of the numbers on the credit card is used by the store in checking with the central credit bureau. "The idea is to find out which digit the store uses."

Next day they call the credit bureau, pretending to be the store. On the third call they choose the right digit and get their answer. The card is clean.

"Okay, baby, back for more. Ephraim has become a businessman."

"We can't eat records, Remy. I mean Ephraim."

"This is the beginning, *dig it.*"

Pammie has little choice: The shleppers are back. Everyone is shooting heavily. When 16 people are in the room, high, laughing, dealing, Pammie loses hold of everything. She is on everyone else's trip, 16 trips at once. Praying for a blank wall to stare at.

Remy, she begs, *make them go away. I forget who we are.*

But Remy and his friends are working night and day. That is, under amphetamine, when one sets out to accomplish a particular task (go to the drugstore, for instance), one is compelled first to talk about it, make a plan, make a list, put on shoes, take off shoes and polish them, etc. This takes time. All day, perhaps. And all night Remy practices his aliases on yellow legal pads.

He is about to close a $1,300 marijuana deal, having come into 100 pounds of Tijuana Gold from Mexico. Orders from uptown artists are coming in for Obetrols, 1,000 pills per order. The plan is to turn the grass over to certain minor Mafiosi in Lefrak City and split. The whole Magic Vitamin Experiment group will split to Greece and write a book.

Sunny Smiles shakes his head. Remy is a strung-out man, he says. And this is a business that takes cool. The atmosphere on East Second Street is taking on the tension of Wall Street during a money crunch.

Spring urges Pammie outdoors to walk.

She has "hung up the gun" for two days. Simple, just as she thought. Sun along Third Avenue eddies up her legs and arms like drops of oil in her joinings. She walks for blocks, grooving on Reality! Maybe, if she doesn't go back inside . . .

"I want to be healthy." She confronts Remy at his door. "I can't live your drug life. The shleppers and the wheeling and dealing—it's driving me crazy."

"That's a fact. You'd better leave."

"No! Please, let's give it all up and go away. In the sun—"

"I'm not changing my life. I don't believe in the outside. You go."

"No."

"Then I'll go," Remy scoops his customers list.

"If you do, I'll turn on the gas."

"No you won't."

"Yes I will."

"Sobeit."

Gas rose behind the top-floor windows on East Second Street three times in the next weeks. Neighbors came to the rescue. No one could sleep. If Pammie wasn't making a suicide gesture, she and Remy were shouting and nailing up the door to keep one or the other out. One night Remy calls the brother in Long Island.

"Your sister took a knife to her wrists today. I need your help to get her out of here. I lost $1,000 today because of her."

The brother arrives with the Rev. Michael Allen from St. Mark's Church. Pammie shows a flicker of recognition. She was once a parishioner.

They are all in Sunny Smiles' apartment. Remy's parents included this time. Mrs. Remsberg talks non-stop. She is *very* concerned. It cost her $50,000 to get Remy out of that old murder charge in Paris. She would not like her son to have a suicide in his apartment. Mr. Remsberg sits throughout the proceedings in a captain's chair, reading the newspaper.

"How badly do you feel, Pam?" Michael Allen asks.

"Pretty bad."

"Bad enough to walk out of here?" Rev. Allen talks directly to Pamela. She looks pleadingly at Remy. He gives back the look that says: What can I do? *They* are intruding again.

"No," says Pammie.

"It's taken me five minutes to figure out this man of yours is a bastard," Father Allen says to Pammie. "How long is it going to take you?"

"Could I just . . . talk to him a minute?"

"Will you come with us to the hospital after the talk?"

"Yes, if I can just talk to Remy alone one minute—"

"Talk talk all you want," Mrs. Remsberg says. "I'm not leaving this apartment."

There is only one way to admit a suicidal person, involuntarily, to psychiatric service in Manhattan. Police must make an arrest. The patient is taken to Bellevue. It is the clearing house for all involuntary psychiatric admissions. The catch is this: Police will not make an arrest unless the person is *in the act* of suicide. If the gas is thin or the blood dry, no arrest.

The lovers go upstairs, the brother standing guard. *Clair de Lune* strains through the door. Father Allen calls Bellevue.

"Is she rational?"

"By now, yes," says Michael Allen.

"Sorry. We can't take her in."

Mr. Remsberg looks up from his paper for the first time. He must have turned off 20 years ago. What he does is keep quiet and pay the bills.

"I don't get these kids," he says. "You take a balloon. It's empty. You blow it up with air." He gestures a big circle. "So you got a great big balloon filled with air. It's still empty."

Everyone goes upstairs. Pammie is asleep at the feet of Remy, who is playing his heart out on the piano.

Michael Allen looks at the brother. "You have to know when you're beat."

Deputy Inspector Joseph Fink receives the brother warmly. His brassy hair and snapping eyes live up to the TV image of that sharp young inspector at the Ninth Precinct, the "good cop." He is powerfully built but theatrical in manner, evoking images of John Cassese playing stunt man for Johnny Cash. The brother empties on Fink's desk a paper bag of evidence, collected from Remy's wastebasket. Three forged prescriptions, a pad of aliases, two orders for 1,000 Obetrols each.

"Nothing here we can get our teeth into. Have you talked to our detectives?"

"My sister is on her fourth suicide attempt. I have talked to the detectives more than four times."

"Why don't you get some big friends, put her in the car and take her to Bellevue yourself?"

"Because I need two psychiatrists to certify her before Bellevue will admit."

Inspector Fink looks down at the contents and shakes his head.

"I'd like to help, I really would. Not enough here to put our teeth into . . ."

"Inspector, three men are about to leave the building on East Second Street for a payoff in Lefrak City on 100 pounds of marijuana. I will be glad to identify them and accompany your men."

"You know, this sounds a little big for us. We might mess it up. Why don't you go down to the Federal Narcotics Bureau. I'll give them a call—"

The brother goes home to bed.

NEXT DAY   Remy has a Master Plan!

"I have gathered you here together to say: The whole Grand Magic Vitamin Experiment will be in Greece by next week."

Skeptical oohs and ahs.

"I have here 12, count them, 12 credit cards. American Express, Carte Blanche, Uni-Card, Master Charge, Abercrombie's —you name it. Angel and Boy came through. Now, in the other hand, I have eight blank checks. From my phony Ephraim Frisch account."

"Watch that Uni-Card, man," Sunny Smiles warns. "Never charge over $50. They call up central credit over $50."

"Paltry concern," Remy says. "Now. You can cash up to $300 in any bank on American Express, right? So eight blank checks cashed in eight banks equals $2,400 in cash. Next step. Tickets for everyone on this Air Travel Card."

"Mr. Frisch, you're a genius."

"Howsomeever, speed is of the essence." Everyone laughs.

"Credit cards are hot after three days. This is Friday. The cat doesn't get a letter off to his credit people until Monday. Can we work that fast?"

"Speaking of speed . . ." says Sunny Smiles . . . and they get off in a celebration

shoot. The next morning Remy is in a cold sweat. It's too much, too much in three days. Got to make a list.

Pammie can no longer go outside. She is afraid to talk to people. They make lists. Later Remy goes out. After 12 hours alone Pammie wrecks the apartment. Pulling out drawers, tearing up his pictures, scrambling beads and sheet music, tearing at the paper flowers.

Sunny Smiles brings her a Wing Ding for lunch.

"By the way. Did you hear Remy got busted?"

"How!"

"He bought a tape recorder on Uni-Card. Fifty-five dollars."

They bailed him out with $500 from the marijuana deal. Pammie, Remy and Sunny Smiles came out of the Criminal Courts Building into the warm evening, trembling in unison. Remy had told the judge his whole Master Plan.

The lovers are sitting now, face to face, in the downstairs apartment. Shot, down. Shot, downer. Shot—

"Remy," she whispers. "Tell me again how it is to get high."

His head rolls to the ceiling, the face pressurized as in a space cabin. "Oh God, I can't stand how everything is my fault. Doesn't anyone care about me?"

Through this last night, on the neighbor's floor, the young man is sleepless. "Please talk to me," he pries at Pammie, "Please —let's go upstairs and fix up the apartment again. The way it used to be when everything was beautiful. Paper flowers and all. I loved that apartment . . ."

"I can't, Remy. I am so tired." The weight of all the times they had let one another down presses Pammie into sleep.

He was packing the next morning.

"But you wouldn't do that to me, Remy? Leave me with a grand larceny rap? I can't even talk to people."

They are both on the fire escape.

"Get out of my way, Pammie."

"You wouldn't leave me like this. I don't know how to go out anymore. Without you, I can't remember who I am. Talk me back up, Remy. You're the only one left who can."

"I don't want to hit you, Pammie."

There is still time to talk him out of it,

Pammie is thinking. She climbs in the window. He couldn't do this to her. The Superior Man doesn't do this.

Remy runs, suitcase banging on metal like a bell's clapper, down the tin-chiming fire escape. He jumps the last two floors.

Remy Remy Remy Help me Remy Remy Remy . . .

When the door opens, Pammie wheels and falls into a pair of broad arms. The other two policemen put away their guns.

Pamela Burr has been sitting by the locked door in her striped Bellevue bathrobe for three days. Not eating, not speaking. A woman called Loudmouth tells her where to line up for food. She asks about a bed. Most of the beds are locked in the wall during the day. There are many old women with hair on their chins. Smells like a stable. When Pammie looks up, an old woman, standing, spreads her legs and defecates. Don't worry, says Loudmouth. They're closing this ward in a few weeks.

On the fourth day Pammie borrowed a quarter from Loudmouth. She bought a chocolate mallomar bar. With the dime she called Remy. A girl answered and said he was out.

Where It's At
FROM A BLACK STUDENT PAPER

When we begin to see how drugs are used against us we see that being strung out keeps us apart. And we begin to think, well how can we begin to break this problem down, you know. How do we begin to get to the sisters and brothers noddin' on the block or in the parks? How do we deal with the MAN who's hustlin dope: very often the pusher man is strung out on his own habit and only uses us to keep it going. All these things make it hard for us to make contact with the real enemy.

Smack, speed, and downs are just a few of the weapons used to keep us down; keeping us down means keepin' us apart. As long as we think it's just his problem or her problem there's no solution. Alone

we have no alternative. The Man picks us up one by one. But together we can begin to fight back.

There used to be a lot of gangs in New York. These gangs were bought off with dope and money. In Chicago they still have a lot of gangs: Black gangs like the Stone Rangers; Brown like the Young Lords or Young Commancheros; and White like the Patriots or Corps. These gangs ran on each other a lot at the same time the Pig was vampin on all of them. The Black Panthers led the way by showing us who the real enemy was; that fighting amongst ourselves was making the Man's work easier cause all of us Black Brown and Yellow and White have a common enemy who can be defeated if we struggle together. Getting together means defending our sisters and brothers from the Pig. It means running a rap on the pusher man that by pushing junk, that by cutting grass with other shit, he's siding with the man. If he doesn't understand what we're talking about we got to deal with that too. Those of us that are strong got to move to stop more of us from getting into the heavy drug scene. That's why being tight is important because it shows an example to others around us, like the Panthers in Chicago. Cause gangs in Chicago are getting political in the same way that the Panthers are. These gangs which were social clubs are now beginning to relate to the political needs of their communities.

In our communities, drugs are a political problem because they're used to keep us down; in rich upperclass set-ups drugs are a kick, a goof; these dudes got the time and the bread to trip out casually like they can afford rich habits.

Tricky Dick Nixon's "operation intercept" is the Man running his game on us again cause cuttin off the grass makes it easier for the Man to push smack, and goof balls. The man can burn grass fields in Mexico but you don't see him hittin on drug companies or burning poppy fields in Turkey to cut the flow of the hard stuff. So for some people drugs are entertainment but for us they are like handcuffs to keep us from moving.

When we begin to move on this drug thing we are also moving on the other crap which is dragging us. In New York City about 27 million dollars are spent in relation to 'drug-addiction'. This bread keeps a lot of people in well paid jobs; this bread also pays a lot of agents and informers. But this bread is not being used to deal with our problems. This bread allows the man to continue to run his jive-ass programs on us. The latest trick the Man is running on junkies is the Methadone program. Methadone is plastic heroin: it keeps you strung out longer and cheaper because the man provides the methadone. Instead your connection is some city hospital or 'drug center'. Methadone isn't kicking it's substitution; in this way the pig power structure is able to control us more directly.

This messed up society is the reason many brothers and sisters move into smack. The H-head is a good head compared to the ordinary reality of our daily lives. To kick any habit whether its smack or downs there must be real alternatives to the life which drove us toward drugs first of all. A lot of us are digging on the fact that revolution begins to open the door on a lot of shit and misery. That working in a revolutionary way with our brothers and sisters is a real alternative to the down-head of goofballs, that when we realize that each of us has a stake in the revolution our lives become more meaningful and our time is better spent making that revolution than laying-in strung-out.

IN THE GHETTO

Recently, after lecturing on Ralph Ellison's *Invisible Man,* a professor at an urban university confided: "Hell, what's so invisible about them? They're the most *visible* people in society." Besides revealing the racial attitudes of one man, the remark illustrates the dramatic change which has taken place in the public awareness of nonwhite minority groups and their problems. Ellison's point, made in 1952, is still well-taken; but in 1971 the power that Ellison's hero was conserving underground has generated a rapidly expanding public eloquence on the part of ghetto people. This section attempts to capture some of that verbal power.

PART SEVEN

FROM
The Invisible Man
RALPH ELLISON

PROLOGUE

I am an invisible man. No, I am not a spook like those who haunted Edgar Allan Poe; nor am I one of your Hollywood-movie ectoplasms. I am a man of substance, of flesh and bone, fiber and liquids—and I might even be said to possess a mind. I am invisible, understand, simply because people refuse to see me. Like the bodiless heads you see sometimes in circus sideshows, it is as though I have been surrounded by mirrors of hard, distorting glass. When they approach me they see only my surroundings, themselves, or figments of their imagination—indeed, everything and anything except me.

Nor is my invisibility exactly a matter of a bio-chemical accident to my epidermis. That invisibility to which I refer occurs because of a peculiar disposition of the eyes of those with whom I come in contact. A matter of the construction of their *inner* eyes, those eyes with which they look through their physical eyes upon reality. I am not complaining, nor am I protesting either. It is sometimes advantageous to be unseen, although it is most often rather wearing on the nerves. Then too, you're constantly being bumped against by those of poor vision. Or again, you often doubt if you really exist. You wonder whether you aren't simply a phantom in other people's minds. Say, a figure in a nightmare which the sleeper tries with all his strength to destroy. It's when you feel like this that, out of resentment, you begin to bump people back. And, let me confess, you feel that way most of the time. You ache with the need to convince yourself that you do exist in the real world, that you're a part of all the sound and anguish, and you strike out with your fists, you curse and you swear to make them recognize you. And, alas, it's seldom successful.

One night I accidentally bumped into a man, and perhaps because of the near darkness he saw me and called me an insulting name. I sprang at him, seized his coat lapels and demanded that he apologize. He was a tall blond man, and as my face came close to his he looked insolently out of his blue eyes and cursed me, his breath hot in my face as he struggled. I pulled his chin down sharp upon the crown of my head, butting him as I had seen the West Indians do, and I felt this flesh tear and the blood gush out, and I yelled, "Apologize! Apologize!" But he continued to curse and struggle, and I butted him again and again until he went down heavily, on his knees, profusely bleeding. I kicked him repeatedly, in a frenzy because he still uttered insults though his lips were frothy with blood. Oh yes, I kicked him! And in my outrage I got out my knife and prepared to slit his throat, right there beneath the lamplight in the deserted street, holding him by the collar with one hand, and opening the knife with my teeth—when it occurred to me that the man had not *seen* me, actually, that he, as far as he knew, was in the midst of a walking nightmare! And I stopped the blade, slicing the air as I pushed him away, letting him fall back to the street. I stared at him hard as the lights of a car stabbed through the darkness. He lay there, moaning on the asphalt; a man almost killed by a phantom. It unnerved me. I was both disgusted and ashamed. I was like a drunken man myself, wavering about on weakened legs. Then I was amused. Something in this man's thick head had sprung out and beaten him within an inch of his life. I began to laught at this crazy discovery. Would he have awakened at the point of death? Would Death himself have freed him for wakeful living? But I didn't linger. I ran away into the dark, laughing so hard I feared I might rupture myself. The next day I saw his picture in the *Daily News,* beneath a caption stating that he had been "mugged." Poor fool, poor blind fool, I thought with sincere compassion, mugged by an invisible man!

Most of the time (although I do not choose as I once did to deny the violence of my days by ignoring it) I am not so overtly violent. I remember that I am invisible and walk softly so as not to awaken the sleeping ones. Sometimes it is best not to awaken them; there are few things in the world as

Photograph by DeFrancis.

dangerous as sleepwalkers. I learned in time though that it is possible to carry on a fight against them without their realizing it. For instance, I have been carrying on a fight with Monopolated Light & Power for some time now. I use their service and pay them nothing at all, and they don't know it. Oh, they suspect that power is being drained off, but they don't know where. All they know is that according to the master meter back there in their power station a hell of a lot of free current is disappearing somewhere into the jungle of Harlem. The joke, of course, is that I don't live in Harlem but in a border area. Several years ago (before I discovered the advantage of being invisible) I went through the routine process of buying service and paying their outrageous rates. But no more. I gave up all that, along with my apartment, and my old way of life: That way based upon the fallacious assumption that I, like other men, was visible. Now, aware of my invisibility, I live rent-free in a building rented strictly to whites, in a section of the basement that was shut off and forgotten during the nineteenth century, which I discovered when I was trying to escape in the night from Ras the Destroyer. But that's getting too far ahead of the story, almost to the end, although the end is in the beginning and lies far ahead.

The point now is that I found a home—or a hole in the ground, as you will. Now don't jump to the conclusion that because I call my home a "hole" it is damp and cold like a grave; there are cold holes and warm holes. Mine is a warm hole. And remember, a bear retires to his hole for the winter and lives until spring; then he comes strolling out like the Easter chick breaking from its shell. I say all this to assure you that it is incorrect to assume that, because I'm invisible and live in a hole, I am dead. I am neither dead nor in a state of suspended animation. Call me Jack-the-Bear, for I am in a state of hibernation.

My hole is warm and full of light. Yes, full of light. I doubt if there is a brighter spot in all New York than this hole of mine, and I do not exclude Broadway. Or the Empire State Building on a photographer's dream night. But that is taking advantage of you. Those two spots are among the darkest

of our whole civilization—pardon me, our whole culture (an important distinction, I've heard)—which might sound like a hoax or a contradiction, but that (by contradiction, I mean) is how the world moves: Not like an arrow, but a boomerang. (Beware of those who speak of the spiral of history; they are preparing a boomerang. Keep a steel helmet handy.) I know; I have been boomeranged across my head so much that I now can see the darkness of lightness. And I live light. Perhaps you'll think it strange that an invisible man should need light, desire light, love light. But maybe it is exactly because I am invisible. Light confirms my reality, gives birth to my form. A beautiful girl once told me of a recurring nightmare in which she lay in the center of a large dark room and felt her face expand until it filled the whole room, becoming a formless mass while her eyes ran in bilious jelly up the chimney. And so it is with me. Without light I am not only invisible, but formless as well; and to be unaware of one's form is to live a death. I myself, after existing some twenty years, did not become alive until I discovered my invisibility.

That is why I fight my battle with Monopolated Light & Power. The deeper reason, I mean: It allows me to feel my vital aliveness. I also fight them for taking so much of my money before I learned to protect myself. In my hole in the basement there are exactly 1,369 lights. I've wired the entire ceiling, every inch of it. And not with fluorescent bulbs, but with the older, more-expensive-to-operate kind, the filament type. An act of sabotage, you know. I've already begun to wire the wall. A junk man I know, a man of vision, has supplied me with wire and sockets. Nothing, storm or flood, must get in the way of our need for light and ever more and brighter light. The truth is the light and light is the truth. When I finish all four walls, then I'll start on the floor. Just how that will go, I don't know. Yet when you have lived invisible as long as I have you develop a certain ingenuity. I'll solve the problem. And maybe I'll invent a gadget to place my coffeepot on the fire while I lie in bed, and even invent a gadget to warm my bed—like the fellow I saw in one of the picture magazines who made himself a gadget to warm his shoes! Though invisible, I am in the great American tradition of tinkers. That makes me kin to Ford, Edison and Franklin. Call me, since I have a theory and a concept, a "thinker-tinker." Yes, I'll warm my shoes; they need it, they're usually full of holes. I'll do that and more.

Now I have one radio-phonograph; I plan to have five. There is a certain acoustical deadness in my hole, and when I have music I want to *feel* its vibration, not only with my ear but with my whole body. I'd like to hear five recordings of Louis Armstrong playing and singing "What Did I Do to Be so Black and Blue"—all at the same time. Sometimes now I listen to Louis while I have my favorite dessert of vanilla ice cream and sloe gin. I pour the red liquid over the white mound, watching it glisten and the vapor rising as Louis bends that military instrument into a beam of lyrical sound. Perhaps I like Louis Armstrong because he's made poetry out of being invisible. I think it must be because he's unaware that he *is* invisible. And my own grasp of invisibility aids me to understand his music. Once when I asked for a cigarette, some jokers gave me a reefer, which I lighted when I got home and sat listening to my phonograph. It was a strange evening. Invisibility, let me explain, gives one a slightly different sense of time, you're never quite on the beat. Sometimes you're ahead and sometimes behind. Instead of the swift and imperceptible flowing of time, you are aware of its nodes, those points where time stands still or from which it leaps ahead. And you slip into the breaks and look around. That's what you hear vaguely in Louis' music.

Once I saw a prizefighter boxing a yokel. The fighter was swift and amazingly scientific. His body was one violent flow of rapid rhythmic action. He hit the yokel a hundred times while the yokel held up his arms in stunned surprise. But suddenly the yokel, rolling about in the gale of boxing gloves, struck one blow and knocked science, speed and footwork as cold as a well-digger's posterior. The smart money hit the canvas. The long shot got the nod. The yokel had simply stepped inside of his opponent's sense of time.

So under the spell of the reefer I discovered a new analytical way of listening to music. The unheard sounds came through, and each melodic line existed of itself, stood out clearly from all the rest, said its piece, and waited patiently for the other voices to speak. That night I found myself hearing not only in time, but in space as well. I not only entered the music but descended, like Dante, into its depths. And *beneath the swiftness of the hot tempo there was a slower tempo and a cave and I entered it and looked around and heard an old woman singing a spiritual as full of Weltschmerz as flamenco, and beneath that lay a still lower level on which I saw a beautiful girl the color of ivory pleading in a voice like my mother's as she stood before a group of slave owners who bid for her naked body, and below that I found a lower level and a more rapid tempo and I heard someone shout:*

"Brothers and sisters, my text this morning is the 'Blackness of Blackness.'"

And a congregation of voices answered: "That blackness is most black, brother, most black . . ."

"In the beginning . . ."

"At the very start," they cried.

". . . there was blackness . . ."

"Preach it . . ."

". . . and the sun . . ."

"The sun, Lawd . . ."

". . . was bloody red . . ."

"Red . . ."

"Now black is . . ." the preacher shouted.

"Bloody . . ."

"I said black is . . ."

"Preach it, brother . . ."

". . . an' black ain't . . ."

"Red, Lawd, red: He said it's red!"

"Amen, brother . . ."

"Black will git you . . ."

"Yes, it will . . ."

". . . an' black won't . . ."

"Naw, it won't!"

"It do . . ."

"It do, Lawd . . ."

". . . an' it don't."

"Halleluiah . . ."

". . . It'll put you, glory, glory, Oh my Lawd, in the WHALE'S BELLY."

"Preach it, dear brother . . ."

". . . an' make you tempt . . ."

"Good God a-mighty!"

"Old Aunt Nelly!"

"Black will make you . . ."

"Black . . ."

". . . or black will un-make you."

"Ain't it the truth, Lawd?"

And at that point a voice of trombone timbre screamed at me, "Git out of here, you fool! Is you ready to commit treason?"

And I tore myself away, hearing the old singer of spirituals moaning, "Go curse your God, boy, and die."

I stopped and questioned her, asked her what was wrong.

"I dearly loved my master, son," she said.

"You should have hated him," I said.

"He gave me several sons," she said, and because I loved my sons I learned to love their father though I hated him too."

"I too have become acquainted with ambivalence," I said. "That's why I'm here."

"What's that?"

"Nothing, a word that doesn't explain it. Why do you moan?"

"I moan this way 'cause he's dead," she said.

"Then tell me, who is that laughing upstairs?"

"Them's my sons. They glad."

"Yes, I can understand that too," I said.

"I laughs too, but I moans too. He promised to set us free but he never could bring hisself to do it. Still I loved him . . ."

"Loved him? You mean . . ."

"Oh yes, but I loved something else even more."

"What more?"

"Freedom."

"Freedom," I said. "Maybe freedom lies in hating."

"Naw, son, it's in loving. I loved him and give him the poison and he withered away like a frost-bit apple. Them boys woulda tore him to pieces with they homemake knives."

"A mistake was made somewhere," I said, "I'm confused." And I wished to say other things, but the laughter upstairs became too loud and moan-like for me and I tried to break out of it, but I couldn't. Just as I was leaving I felt an urgent desire to ask her what freedom was and went back. She sat with her head in her hands, moaning softly; her leather-brown face was filled with sadness.

"Old woman, what is this freedom you love so well?" I asked around a corner of my mind.

She looked surprised, then thoughtful, then baffled. "I done forgot, son. It's all mixed up. First I think it's one thing, then I think it's another. It gits my head to spinning. I guess now it ain't nothing but knowing how to say what I got up in my head. But it's a hard job, son. Too much is done happen to me in too short a time. Hit's like I have a fever. Ever' time I starts to walk my head gits to swirling and I falls down. Or if it ain't that, it's the boys; they gits to laughing and wants to kill up the white folks. They's bitter, that's what they is . . ."

"But what about freedom?"

"Leave me 'lone, boy; my head aches!"

I left her, feeling dizzy myself. I didn't get far.

Suddenly one of the sons, a big fellow six feet tall, appeared out of nowhere and struck me with his fist.

"What's the matter, man?" I cried.

"You made Ma cry!"

"But how?" I said, dodging a blow.

"Askin' her them questions, that's how. Git outa here and stay, and next time you got questions like that, ask yourself!"

He held me in a grip like cold stone, his fingers fastening upon my windpipe until I thought I would suffocate before he finally allowed me to go. I stumbled about dazed, the music beating hysterically in my ears. It was dark. My head cleared and I wandered down a dark narrow passage, thinking I heard his footsteps hurrying behind me. I was sore, and into my being had come a profound craving for tranquillity, for peace and quiet, a state I felt I could never achieve. For one thing, the trumpet was blaring and the rhythm was too hectic. A tom-tom beating like heart-thuds began drowning out the trumpet, filling my ears. I longed for water and I heard it rushing through the cold mains my fingers touched as I felt my way, but I couldn't stop to search because of the footsteps behind me.

"Hey, Ras," I called. "Is it you, Destroyer? Rinehart?"

No answer, only the rhythmic footsteps behind me. Once I tried crossing the road, but a speeding machine struck me, *scraping the skin from my leg as it roared past.*

Then somehow I came out of it, ascending hastily from this underworld of sound to hear Louis Armstrong innocently asking,

What did I do
To be so black
And blue?

At first I was afraid; this familiar music had demanded action, the kind of which I was incapable, and yet had I lingered there beneath the surface I might have attempted to act. Nevertheless, I know now that few really listen to this music. I sat on the chair's edge in a soaking sweat, as though each of my 1,369 bulbs had everyone become a klieg light in an individual setting for a third degree with Ras and Rinehart in charge. It was exhausting—as though I had held my breath continuously for an hour under the terrifying serenity that comes from days of intense hunger. And yet, it was a strangely satisfying experience for an invisible man to hear the silence of sound. I had discovered unrecognized compulsions of my being—even though I could not answer "yes" to their promptings. I haven't smoked a reefer since, however; not because they're illegal, but because to *see* around corners is enough (that is not unusual when you are invisible). But to hear around them is too much; it inhibits action. And despite Brother Jack and all that sad, lost period of the Brotherhood, I believe in nothing if not in action.

Please, a definition: A hibernation is a covert preparation for a more overt action.

Besides, the drug destroys one's sense of time completely. If that happened, I might forget to dodge some bright morning and some cluck would run me down with an orange and yellow street car, or a bilious bus! Or I might forget to leave my hole when the moment for action presents itself.

Meanwhile I enjoy my life with the compliments of Monopolated Light & Power. Since you never recognize me even when in closest contact with me, and since, no doubt, you'll hardly believe that I exist, it won't matter if you know that I tapped a power line leading into the building and ran it into my hole in the ground. Before that I lived in the darkness into which I was chased, but now I see. I've illuminated the blackness of my invisibility—and vice versa. And so I play the invisible music of my isolation. The last statement doesn't seem just right, does it? But it is; you hear this music simply because music is heard and seldom seen, except by musicians. Could this compulsion to put invisibility down in black and white be thus an urge to make music of invisibility? But I am an orator, a rabble rouser—Am? I *was,* and perhaps shall be again. Who knows? All sickness is not unto death, neither is invisibility.

I can hear you say, "What a horrible, irresponsible bastard!" And you're right. I leap to agree with you. I am one of the most irresponsible beings that ever lived. Irresponsibility is part of my invisibility; any way you face it, it is a denial. But to whom can I be responsible, and why should I be, when you refuse to see me? And wait until I reveal how truly irresponsible I am. Responsibility rests upon recognition, and recognition is a form of agreement. Take the man whom I almost killed: Who was responsible for that near murder—I? I don't think so, and I refuse it. I won't buy it. You can't give it to me. *He* bumped *me, he* insulted *me.* Shouldn't he, for his own personal safety, have recognized my hysteria, my "danger potential"? He, let us say, was lost in a dream world. But didn't *he* control that dream world—which, alas, is only too real!—and didn't *he* rule me out of it? And if he had yelled for a policeman, wouldn't *I* have been taken for the offending one? Yes, yes, yes! Let me agree with you, I was the irresponsible one; for I should have used my knife to protect the higher interests of society. Some day that kind of foolishness will cause us tragic trouble. All dreamers and sleepwalkers must pay the price, and even the invisible victim is responsible for the fate of all. But I shirked that responsibility; I became too snarled in the incompatible notions that buzzed within my brain. I was a coward . . .

But what did *I* do to be so blue? Bear with me.

Felipe Luciano is one of "The Last Poets," a group who read their poems to the accompaniment of conga drums, live, on record, and in the recent movie *Right On.*

Puerto Rican Rhythms
FELIPE LUCIANO

Do loo loo la la la la
Como esta Miguel?
Do loo loo la la la la
Como esta Miguel
Sweetness lies embedded in pores of our
Black brown beige bodies.
Don't need French perfume.
Sugarcane smells drive our women crazy.
Look at them coming out of garment center
subway holes untouched by the putrid odors of
subterranean monsters.
Look at those big, brown buttocks
Sway, play, invite, delight
Under dresses as tight as their rich, brown velvet skin.
Yi si me cortan mi palo de mango me voy a morir.
Look at the rippling muscles of the Puerto Rican
pack mules pulling racks of cheap dresses
down foggy 8th Ave.
Handkerchief 'round their heads catch the
Indian sweat.
Don't let it fall on unfertile soil.
Rhythms, rhythms, rhythms
We eat rhythms, we sleep rhythms, we make love to rhythms.
Ain't no rinky tink, ain't no dinky dink
Just booming timbales creating
Sandy Beaches for the homeless
and Machettes for the angry
The bodegas jump
Women hanging out windows jump
Naked babies on firescapes jump
Domino players on 104th St. jump
Strung out, tracked armed junkies jump
little number runners jump
Prostitutes jump, pimps jump
And the barber is cutting up a brother's face
'cause the lined streets, the street lines,
the lines in the middle of the street
ain't straight no more.
They're curving, bending, twisting
to the rhythms of the asphalt.
The rich, black asphalt makes the yellow line
droop its head as it grinds with the brown tenements.
And spirits nod their approval
'cause they know we a partying people
Piano, drums
Drums, piano
All we think is rhythm.

Goose pimples cha cha on my cheek muscles.
Boricua, Boricua, Boricua
You live in snapping fingers and
shingalinging sneakers bought on Park Ave.
You live as long as we're able to croak a tune.
And rhythms, rhythms, rhythms, rhythms, rhythms.
Rhythms, Rican rhythms are the masters of ceremony
Brothers and sister's
I have great pleasure in
introducing to you tonight,
Mr. Tito Rodriguez
Baaa Yaaaaaaaa

FROM

The Cool World
WARREN MILLER

AFTER THE BIG NIGHT

I locked the door and listened to they steps
goin down the stairs. Then I put out the
candles an walked in to the front room
where Lu Ann layin on the bed smokin an
lookin at a comic book. I blew out her
candle an went an watched the street from
the winda.

Lu Ann say. "Whut was goin on?"

I watchin the out side an I dont answer
her.

She say. "I thought I hear Bloods voice.
Whut was goin on all that noise an all that
quiet I knew somethin goin on."

I lean out the winda a little ways an see the
guys comin out one & two at a time an
disapeerin on the street. One right after an
other like they meltin right inta the side
walk. They know that street Man. They
know evry hole and corner. I see Blood
walkin off by him self. No one with him. He
stumble down the street. Headin for Ritzies
prolly.

Lu Ann say. "Man you blockin whut air
they is. Get away from that winda."

I wait till all my boys is out an away. Then
I go over an stretch out on the bed. Lu Ann
say. "Whut was goin on in there? Did I hear
right thinkin it Bloods voice I hear?"

"You hear right." I say. I tell her whut
happen. About Rod an Cowboy an Blood
an me.

She say. "Blood really thru now."

"He thru all right." I say.

"You the big man now Duke." She say.
She lean up on her elbow and look at me.
"I knew it first time I saw you Duke you was
gonna be the big man." She touch my
mouth with her fingers an lookin at me.
Then she put her hand under my shirt and
touch my chest. "You want to make it with
me now Duke?"

I dont answer. I dont feel like talkin. "Any
thing you want Duke Honey?" She ask me.

I tell her Im tired and want to go to
sleep.

"I will go to sleep too." She say.

But I cant sleep an jus lay there lookin at
the ceelin where a square of light from the
winda is. So tired I dont even take off my
clothes. No wind comin in that winda even
when no one in front of it. Lu Ann say.
"Youd think a skinny girl like me woulden
feel the heat so bad but I do."

I lay there an look at the light on the ceelin
an I can hear people movin aroun up stairs
on the floor above an I hear some cars pass
on the street. Some one cryin below. A baby
or a girl. An you can hear the cryin comin
up the air shaft an voices not sayin anythin
you can make out. I think about Little Man.
In the cooler now. In the cold box. Waiten
to be identifyd. Old Little Man. Thinkin about
how Rod wearen his shirt now. Thinkin
about how we gonna revenge them
motheren Wolves for what they done to
Little Man. Old Little Man no one ever goin
to come identify. Finely they bury him some
place.

"San Fran cis co." Lu Ann say. "I like that
name." She say it again. "San Fran cis co.
San Fran cis co." She raise up on her elbow
again holdin her little face in her hand.
"Duke you ever think about San Fran cis co?

About ever goin there? Some times I think about it all the time." She say.

"You been there?" I ask her.

"No I never been there. But I seen it in the movies. It look so cool and clean Man you know. Some time I jus gonna take off for that olace like a big bird."

"You gonna walk?"

"Buy a ticket on the Grey Hound for all the money I got. Go as far as I can go. Then work for a while an start out again. I know I could make it if I ever get started."

"Whut you gonna do when you get to San Francisco?"

"I will always find some thing." She say. Then she quiet for a while an the cryen in the air shaft stopped. "You know they got an ocean in San Fran cis co?" She say.

"I know it." I tell her.

She look at me. "Then whut ocean they got?"

"They got the Pacific ocean." I tell her.

"Now Duke how did you know that?"

"Jus know it."

She say. "You know whut Duke? I would go all that way jus to see the ocean? You know that?"

"You dont have to go all that way jus to see an ocean." I tell her but she aint listenin. She say. "I see pictures of the ocean but I jus cant believe it. How can it be like that Duke?"

"Just is." I tell her. "Lissen." I say. "Lu Ann. You dont have to go all that way to San Francisco to see the ocean. We got an ocean right here."

"Where we got an ocean right here?" She sit up she get all excited.

"Got an ocean out at Coney Island." I say. "You can get there on the subway."

"Get on the subway and it take me to the ocean? Duke you gassin me?"

"Truth Lu Ann."

"Lissen Duke." She say. "You take me out to the ocean first thing tomorra hear? I pay you way too."

"I take you Sunday. Cant go tomorra."

"That a promise Duke?" I tell her sure I take her Sunday. She say. "I never be able to sleep now knowin you have an ocean an I goin to see it Sunday."

"Where you from Lu Ann you dont know about the ocean out at Coney?"

She say. "Now Man you aint gassin me you really got an ocean you can get to on the subway?"

"You see it for you self Sunday."

Finely she went to sleep an when I woke up it was still dark but gettin light. I took off my close then an set by the winda and smoked a cigarette. They a little wind that time of night. Lu Ann layin on her side with her head on her hands like a baby. Where she from? I wonder. An whut will happen to her whut will become of her? When it get light I go inta the kitchen an make some coffee. Lu Ann got a pot an a can of coffee. When I go thru Little Mans old room I hold my breath an not look at any thing.

WE GO TO CONEY

Some time I jus dont under stand Lu Ann an how she acts I mean. All the time we in the subway she actin like a scared little kid who aint never been in a subway befor. She keep crowdin up to me an holdin onto my arm an puttin her head on my shoulder. She say. "Oh Duke I dont like this bein under ground like this."

I say. "We be out of it soon."

"When?" She say. "Nex stop Duke? Will we be out of it nex stop?"

People lookin at her the way she huddlin up against me like she cold or somethin an wantin to get warm. I keep tryin to move away a little but the train too crowded. Jammed with people carryin bags fulla bathinsuits an sanwiches & carryin portable radios an even portable fonografs. Babys cryin and kids yellin an 1 old man sittin there readin a newspaper with funny printin on it like he all by him self. Lu Ann keep lookin at this old man with the long white beard.

She say. "Whuts that crazy printin he readin off that newspaper?"

"Look like Chineese to me." I tell her.

"You gassin me Duke?"

"It could be Chineese." I tell her. "An stop crowdin me."

"I dont like it down here Duke."

"Well aint nothin I can do about it Lu Ann. You want to see the goddam ocean this the way how you got to go to get there." I say to her an pull my arm away from where she clutchin at it.

She hunch her self an say. "Dont be

mean to me Duke." An then she sit there like she goin to cry. I never see her like that befor. Next stop she clutch my arm again an then I notice like you know evry time the train stop at a stop she grab my arm. She thought I was gonna run out on her.

Lu Ann sit thru the whole rest of the ride with out she sayin a word an not takin her eyes off the old man with the white beard readin the newspaper. Evry once in a while he make his hand into like a komb and komb his beard but keep on readin that crazy newspaper an never raisin his eyes from it.

Lu Ann say. "Is it the nex stop yet Duke?" An I swear to it whut happen then. The old man never lift his eyes but he like knew. He started foldin his paper. He folded it into a square like it was a handkercheef and stuck it in his pocket. An just the second he finish doin it the train came out of the ground an the sun come in! Lu Ann look at me. That old man knew right to the second! Lu Ann never took her eyes off him an I kep lookin at him. When we got out the train he was right in front of us wearin this crazy black coat an hat even in all that hot wether. An then he jus disapeer. Goin down the steps. Suddenly he gone an no where though we look aroun evry where.

When we get to the bottom of the steps Lu Ann take my arm ahold so tight I stop an look at her. She lookin at me her eyes all round like she jus found money. She say. "You know who that was Duke?"

"Who?"

"The old man." She say. I knew she ment the old man. I say. "I know the old man. Who is he?" An she say. "Duke he must be GOD that old man."

"Oh Man." I say an hit my for head to show her how crazy an wild she is.

"No now Duke lissen Man." She say. "He got that beard like GOD dont he? An he readin that crazy print no body know how to read. An he knew when we was comin out from under ground dint he? Knew it befor any body an with out even lookin up. Now aint that all true Duke?"

I say yeh I guess that all true.

Lu An say. "Well then. He GOD all right. No body else he could be."

"Oh Man you really wild." I say. "You been smokin too much Lu Ann."

"He GOD." She say. "I tellin you Duke an I know it. Man that old man is GOD."

I say to her. "So if he GOD you tell me whut he doin here on a hot day like this ridin the train to Coney." Is whut I say to her.

"May be he come out to see the ocean." She say.

I take her arm an start walkin her again. "You real wild Lu Ann. He invent the ocean so why would he come all this way to see it?"

She say. "How I know why he come all this way. Man jus cause he invent it dont mean he dont ever want to see it. Duke Man whuts that crazy smell?"

I tell her. "Thats the ocean you smellin. We almost to it now. That the board walk up ahead. We go up on the board walk an you can see it."

She start takin long deep breathes like she smokin an tryn to get it in to her blood streem. "Smell like fish." She say. "Smell like cold fish and salt."

"That whut the ocean is." I tell her. "Fulla salt an fish."

"You gassin me Duke?"

"Oh Man." I say.

We walk up this like little rise an on up to the board walk. Jammed with people. I take Lu Anns arm an snake our way thru till we up against the rails on the other side. "Well they it is Lu Ann. I promise you an I keep my promise now look at it."

She look at it. "Oh Man." She say. "It always movin like that Duke all the time? It never stop? Duke Man I wanta get down there close to it."

I take her under the board walk an out on the sand. Soon she stop an take off her shoes an we go walkin aroun all the people layin out tryin to get black on towels. Lu Ann hurryin ahead like she forgot all about me an I tryin to keep up with her without I step on some body. We get to the part of the beech where the sand damp an Lu Ann keep walkin till the ocean come in an wet her feet. "That water cold." She say. Nex wave come by she stick her hand in it an taste the stuff. "Man you wasnt gassin me." She say. "That salt all right." She stand there I dont know how long lookin out an lettin them little waves scutter over her ankels.

She say. "Duke whut happen when you

get out there to where it end? Out to where that line is Duke."

"Thats Europe out that way." I tell her.

She look at me like she goin crazy. "An which way to Africa Man?" She ask me.

"Well you go out a ways an then you head south." I dont know for sure about that but I figure it hot in Africa so it prolly south. Lu Ann stand there lookin out like she gonna see both them countries any minit. She say. "Duke when I look down at my feet when the ocean come in it look like I goin out. Hold onto me Duke."

"You aint goin no where. That jus the tide pullin at you." I say.

Two little Negro kids whut have been in swimmin a boy an a girl maybe 7 year old come walkin in holdin hands an Lu Ann say to them. "Childern do you know thats Europe an Africa out there?"

The little boy say. "Sure we know that." An they keep on walkin.

I gettin tired of standin an my shoes full of sand. I say. "Lu Ann I tired of standin. Lets go get a hot dog an take some rides."

"I dont want to go yet." She say.

"We gonna come back." I say. "Come on now. We get some hot dogs and go on some rides."

Finely she come with me talkin all the time about the ocean an Europe out there an all that. We eat some hot dogs Lu Ann payin an then I took her on some rides. We went on the whip an rode risin horses on the merry go round an all like that. The big ones Lu Ann aint much intrested in them. So after a while an it was gettin late I sit her down on a bench an tell her to wait I have to find the toilets.

When I come back she gone. I sit down an wait. I figure she prolly went to find the toilets too. I wait a long time an then I think she prolly down on the beach standin in the ocean again so I go down to look for her.

I look all up and down that beech for her an callin her name. Woman say to me, "Boy you lookin for a little girl?" I say yes an she say. "Well they was a little lost girl an the cop took her to the station. About 7–8 year old?" She say. I tell her no that aint the one I lookin for.

Then when it get dark I walk up an down the board walk an even went thru the fun house an the tunnel of love. I stand out side the shows an the horror museums an lookin for her evry where till near mid night it was. I knowed she would never find her way home with out me. But I never find her.

I wait for her all night in the front room at Little Mans. Two or 3 time in the night I think I hear her comin. "Lu Ann." I say. "Lu Ann. That you Lu Ann?"

But in the morning she wasnt there an the nex day an the nex day neither. So finely I know she aint comin back an that she lost for good. She had her pocket book with her an I guess all the money she made. I dont know whut even happen to her. May be she go to San Francisco. No body I know of ever see her again.

Vietnam #4
CLARENCE MAJOR

a cat said
on the corner

the other day
dig man

how come so many
of us
niggers

are dying over there
in that white
man's war

they say more of us
are dying

than them peckerwoods
& it just
          don't make sense
unless it's true
that the honkeys

are trying to kill us out
with the same stone

they killing them other cats
with

you know, he said
two birds with one stone

The three pieces which follow are, essentially, about one another. Mailer wrote his remarkably prophetic essay, "The White Negro," in 1957. Baldwin's response (really an attack on the styles and sensibilities of the "Beat" writers— Kerouac, Corso, Ferlinghetti, etc.—and those aspects of Mailer's essay which he believes resemble them) to Mailer's existential interpretation of the relationship between black America and the social phenomenon of rising antagonism on the part of young whites to middle-class ideals was published in *Esquire* in 1961. Cleaver's essay, which appeared in 1967, discusses Baldwin and Mailer, and, to complete the circle, itself *exemplifies* in its rhetoric the phenomenon on which Mailer bases his theory. It also illustrates a phenomenon frequently observed in such writing— the shifting of focus from one "ism" (racism in this case) to another (sexism— Baldwin's sex life becomes the focus of the attack).

So we have here a kind of public correspondence, spanning an essential decade, which deals with some of the most inflammatory issues of our time— racial sexual myths, especially— presented in the highly personal voices of three of the most talented stylists of post–World War II America.

FROM

Advertisements for Myself
NORMAN MAILER

THE WHITE NEGRO

Superficial Reflections on the Hipster

Our search for the rebels of the generation led us to the hipster. The hipster is an enfant terrible *turned inside out. In character with his time, he is trying to get back at the conformists by lying low. . . . You can't interview a hipster because his main goal is to keep out of a society which, he thinks, is trying to make everyone over in its own image. He takes marijuana because it supplies him with experiences that can't be shared with "squares." He may affect a broad-brimmed hat or a zoot suit, but usually he prefers to skulk unmarked. The hipster may be a jazz musician; he is rarely an artist, almost never a writer. He may earn his living as a petty criminal, a hobo, a carnival roustabout or a free-lance moving*

man in Greenwich Village, but some hipsters have found a safe refuge in the upper income brackets as television comics or movie actors. (The late James Dean, for one, was a hipster hero.) . . . It is tempting to describe the hipster in psychiatric terms as infantile, but the style of his infantilism is a sign of the times. He does not try to enforce his will on others, Napoleon-fashion, but contents himself with a magical omnipotence never disproved because never tested. . . . As the only extreme nonconformist of his generation, he exercises a powerful if underground appeal for conformists through newspaper accounts of his delinquencies, his structureless jazz, and his emotive grunt worlds.
     —*"Born 1930: The Unlost Generation"*
                    by Caroline Bird
          Harper's Bazaar, February 1957

The Second World War presented a mirror to the human condition which blinded anyone who looked into it. For if tens of millions were killed in concentration camps out of the inexorable agonies and contractions of superstates founded upon the always insoluble contradictions of injustice, one was then obliged also to see that no matter how crippled and perverted an image of man was the society he had created, it was nonetheless his creation, his collective creation (at least his collective creation from the past) and if society was so murderous, then who could ignore the most hideous of questions about his own nature?

Worse. One could hardly maintain the courage to be individual, to speak with one's own voice, for the years in which one could complacently accept oneself as part of an elite by being a radical were forever gone. A man knew that when he dissented, he gave a note upon his life which could be called in any year of overt crisis. No wonder then that these have been the years of conformity and depression. A stench of fear has come out of every pore of American life, and we suffer from a collective failure of nerve. The only courage, with rare exceptions, that we have been witness to, has been the isolated courage of isolated people.

It is on this bleak scene that a phenomenon has appeared: the American existentialist—the hipster, the man who knows that if our collective condition is to live with instant death by atomic war, relatively quick death by the State as *l'univers concentrationnaire,* or with a slow death by conformity with every creative and rebellious instinct stifled (at what damage to the mind and the heart and the liver and the nerves no research foundation for cancer will discover in a hurry), if the fate of twentieth-century man is to live with death from adolescence to premature senescence, why then the only life-giving answer is to accept the terms of death, to live with death as immediate danger, to divorce oneself from society, to exist without roots, to set out on that uncharted journey into the rebellious imperatives of the self. In short, whether the life is criminal or not, the decision is to encourage the psychopath in oneself, to explore that domain of experience where security is boredom and therefore sickness, and one exists in the present, in that enormous present which is without past or future, memory or planned intention, the life where a man must go until he is beat, where he must gamble with his energies through all those small or large crises of courage and unforeseen situations which beset his day, where he must be with it or doomed not to swing. The unstated essence of Hip, its psychopathic brilliance, quivers with the knowledge that new kinds of victories increase one's power for new kinds of perception; and defeats, the wrong kind of defeats, attack the body and imprison one's energy until one is jailed in the prison air of other people's habits, other people's defeats, boredom, quiet desperation, and muted icy self-destroying rage. One is Hip or one is Square (the alternative which each new generation coming into American life is beginning to feel), one is a rebel or one conforms, one is a frontiersman in the Wild West of American night life, or else a Square cell, trapped in the totalitarian issues of American society, doomed willy-nilly to conform if one is to succeed. . . .

So no wonder that in certain cities of America, in New York of course, and New Orleans, in Chicago and San Francisco and Los Angeles, in such American cities as Paris and Mexico, D.F., this particular part of a generation was attracted to what the Negro had to offer. In such places as Greenwich Village, a ménage-à-trois was completed—the bohemian and the juvenile delinquent came face-to-face with the Negro, and the hipster was a fact in American life. If marijuana was the wedding ring, the child was the language of Hip for its argot gave expression to abstract states of feeling which all could share, at least all who were Hip. And in this wedding of the white and the black it was the Negro who brought the cultural dowry. Any Negro who wishes to live must live with danger from his first day, and no experience can ever be casual to him, no Negro can saunter down a street with any real certainty that violence will not visit him on his walk. The cameos of security for the average white: mother and the home, job and the family, are not even a mockery to millions of Negroes; they are impossible. The Negro has the simplest of alternatives: live a life of constant humility or ever-threatening danger. In such a pass where paranoia is as vital to survival as blood, the Negro had stayed alive and begun to grow by following the need of his body where he could. Knowing in the cells of his existence that life was war, nothing but war, the Negro (all exceptions admitted) could rarely afford the sophisticated inhibitions of civilization, and so he kept for his survival the art of the primitive, he lived in the enormous present, he subsisted for his Saturday night kicks, relinquishing the pleasures of the mind for the more obligatory pleasures of the body, and in his music he gave voice to the character and quality of his existence, to his rage and the infinite variations of joy, lust, languor, growl, cramp, pinch, scream, and despair of his orgasm. For jazz is orgasm, it is the music of orgasm, good orgasm and bad, and so it spoke across a nation, it had the communication of art even where it was watered, perverted, corrupted, and almost killed, it spoke in no matter what laundered popular way of instantaneous existential states to which some whites could respond, it was indeed a communication by art because it said, "I feel this, and now you do too."

So there was a new breed of adventurers, urban adventurers who drifted out at night looking for action with a black man's code to fit their facts. The hipster had absorbed the existentialist synapses of the Negro, and for practical purposes could be considered a white Negro. . . .

It may be fruitful to consider the hipster a philosophical psychopath, a man interested not only in the dangerous imperatives of his psychopathy but in codifying, at least for himself, the suppositions on which his inner universe is constructed. . . .

Before one can say more about the hipster, there is obviously much to be said about the psychic state of the psychopath — or, clinically, the psychopathic personality. Now, for reasons which may be more curious than the similarity of the words, even many people with a psychoanalytical orientation often confuse the psychopath with the psychotic. Yet the terms are polar. The psychotic is legally insane, the psychopath is not; the psychotic is almost always incapable of discharging in physical acts the rage of his frustration, while the psychopath at his extreme is virtually as incapable of restraining his violence. The psychotic lives in so misty a world that what is happening at each moment of his life is not very real to him whereas the psychopath seldom knows any reality greater than the face, the voice, the being of the particular people among whom he may find himself at any moment. Sheldon and Eleanor Glueck describe him as follows:

The psychopath . . . can be distinguished from the person sliding into or clambering out of a "true psychotic" state by the long tough persistence of his anti-social attitude and behaviour and the absence of hallucinations, delusions, manic flight of ideas, confusion, disorientation, and other dramatic signs of psychosis.

The late Robert Lindner, one of the few experts on the subject, in his book *Rebel Without a Cause — The Hypno-analysis of a Criminal Psychopath* presented part of his definition in this way:

. . . the psychopath is a rebel without a cause, an agitator without a slogan, a revolutionary without a program: in other words, his rebelliousness is aimed to achieve goals satisfactory to himself alone; he is incapable of exertions for the sake of others. All his efforts, hidden under no matter what disguise, represent investments designed to satisfy his immediate wishes and desires. . . . The psychopath, like the child, cannot delay the pleasures of gratification; and this trait is one of his underlying, universal characteristics. He cannot wait upon erotic gratification which convention demands should be preceded by the chase before the kill: he must rape. He cannot wait upon the development of prestige in society: his egoistic ambitions lead him to leap into headlines by daring performances. Like a red thread the predominance of this mechanism for immediate satisfaction runs through the history of every psychopath. It explains not only his behaviour but also the violent nature of his acts.

Yet even Lindner who was the most imaginative and most sympathetic of the psychoanalysts who have studied the psychopathic personality was not ready to project himself into the essential sympathy — which is that the psychopath may indeed be the perverted and dangerous front-runner of a new kind of personality which could become the central expression of human nature before the twentieth century is over. For the psychopath is better adapted to dominate those mutually contradictory inhibitions upon violence and love which civilization has exacted of us, and if it be remembered that not every psychopath is an extreme case, and that the condition of psychopathy is present in a host of people including many politicians, professional soldiers, newspaper columnists, entertainers, artists, jazz musicians, call-girls, promiscuous homosexuals, and half the executives of Hollywood, television, and advertising, it can be seen that there are aspects of psychopathy which already exert considerable cultural influence.

What characterizes almost every psychopath and part-psychopath is that they are trying to create a new nervous system for themselves. . . .

The psychopath is notoriously difficult

to analyze because the fundamental decision of his nature is to try to live the infantile fantasy, and in this decision (given the dreary alternative of psychoanalysis) there may be a certain instinctive wisdom. For there is a dialectic to changing one's nature, the dialectic which underlies all psychoanalytic method: it is the knowledge that if one is to change one's habits, one must go back to the source of their creation, and so the psychopath exploring backward along the road of the homosexual, the orgiast, the drug-addict, the rapist, the robber, and the murderer seeks to find those violent parallels to the violent and often hopeless contradictions he knew as an infant and as a child. For if he has the courage to meet the parallel situation at the moment when he is ready, then he has a chance to act as he has never acted before, and in satisfying the frustration — if he can succeed — he may then pass by symbolic substitute through the locks of incest. In thus giving expression to the buried infant in himself, he can lessen the tension of those infantile desires and so free himself to remake a bit of his nervous system. Like the neurotic he is looking for the opportunity to grow up a second time, but the psychopath knows instinctively that to express a forbidden impulse actively is far more beneficial to him than merely to confess the desire in the safety of a doctor's room. The psychopath is inordinately ambitious, too ambitious ever to trade his warped brilliant conception of his possible victories in life for the grim if peaceful attrition of the analyst's couch. So his associational journey into the past is lived out in the theater of the present, and he exists for those charged situations where his senses are so alive that he can be aware actively (as the analysand is aware passively) of what his habits are, and how he can change them. . . .

At bottom, the drama of the psychopath is that he seeks love. Not love as the search for a mate, but love as the search for an orgasm more apocalyptic than the one which preceded it. Orgasm is his therapy — he knows at the seed of his being that good orgasm opens his possibilities and bad orgasm imprisons him. But in this search, the psychopath becomes an embodiment

of the extreme contradictions of the society which formed his character, and the apocalyptic orgasm often remains as remote as the Holy Grail, for there are clusters and nests and ambushes of violence in his own necessities and in the imperatives and retaliations of the men and women among whom he lives his life, so that even as he drains his hatred in one act or another, so the conditions of his life create it anew in him until the drama of his movements bears a sardonic resemblance to the frog who climbed a few feet in the well only to drop back again.

Yet there is this to be said for the search after the good orgasm: when one lives in a civilized world and still can enjoy none of the cultural nectar of such a world because the paradoxes on which civilization is built demand that there remain a cultureless and alienated bottom of exploitable human material, then the logic of becoming a sexual outlaw (if one's psychological roots are bedded in the bottom) is that one has at least a running competitive chance to be physically healthy so long as one stays alive. It is therefore no accident that psychopathy is most prevalent with the Negro. Hated from outside and therefore hating himself, the Negro was forced into the position of exploring all those moral wildernesses of civilized life which the Square automatically condemns as delinquent or evil or immature or morbid or self-destructive or corrupt. (Actually the terms have equal weight. Depending on the telescope of the cultural clique from which the Square surveys the universe, "evil" or "immature" are equally strong terms of condemnation.) But the Negro, not being privileged to gratify his self-esteem with the heady satisfactions of categorical condemnation, chose to move instead in that other direction where all situations are equally valid, and in the worst of perversion, promiscuity, pimpery, drug addiction, rape, razor-slash, bottle-break, what-have-you, the Negro discovered and elaborated a morality of the bottom, an ethical differentiation between the good and the bad in every human activity from the go-getter pimp (as opposed to the lazy one) to the relatively dependable pusher or prostitute. Add to this, the cunning of their language, the abstract ambiguous alternatives in which from the danger of their oppression they learned to speak ("Well, now, man, like I'm looking for a cat to turn me on . . ."), add even more the profound sensitivity of the Negro jazzman who was the cultural mentor of a people, and it is not too difficult to believe that the language of Hip which evolved was an artful language, tested and shaped by an intense experience and therefore different in kind from white slang, as different as the special obscenity of the soldier which, in its emphasis upon "ass" as the soul and "shit" as circumstance, was able to express the existential states of the enlisted man. What makes Hip a special language is that it cannot really be taught—if one shares none of the experiences of elation and exhaustion which it is equipped to describe, then it seems merely arch or vulgar or irritating. It is a pictorial language, but pictorial like non-objective art, imbued with the dialectic of small but intense change, a language for the microcosm, in this case, man, for it takes the immediate experiences of any passing man and magnifies the dynamic of his movements, not specifically but abstractly so that he is seen more as a vector in a network of forces than as a static character in a crystallized field. (Which latter is the practical view of the snob.) For example, there is real difficulty in trying to find a Hip substitute for "stubborn." The best possibility I can come up with is: "That cat will never come off his groove, dad." But groove implies movement, narrow movement but motion nonetheless. There is really no way to describe someone who does not move at all. Even a creep does move—if at a pace exasperatingly more slow than the pace of the cool cats.

Like children, hipsters are fighting for the sweet, and their language is a set of subtle indications of their success or failure in the competition for pleasure. Unstated but obvious is the social sense that there is not nearly enough sweet for everyone. And so the sweet goes only to the victor, the best, the most, the man who knows the most about how to find his

energy and how not to lose it. The emphasis is on energy because the psychopath and the hipster are nothing without it since they do not have the protection of a position or a class to rely on when they have overextended themselves. So the language of Hip is a language of energy, how it is found, how it is lost.

But let us see. I have jotted down perhaps a dozen words, the Hip perhaps most in use and most likely to last with the minimum of variation. The words are man, go, put down, make, beat, cool, swing, with it, crazy, dig, flip, creep, hip, square. They serve a variety of purposes, and the nuance of the voice uses the nuance of the situation to convey the subtle contextual difference. If the hipster moves through his life on a constant search with glimpses of Mecca in many a turn of his experience (Mecca being the apocalyptic orgasm) and if everyone in the civilized world is at least in some small degree a sexual cripple, the hipster lives with the knowledge of how he is sexually crippled and where he is sexually alive, and the faces of experience which life presents to him each day are engaged, dismissed, or avoided as his need directs and his lifemanship makes possible. For life is a contest between people in which the victor generally recuperates quickly and the loser takes long to mend, a perpetual competition of colliding explorers in which one must grow or else pay more for remaining the same (pay in sickness, or depression, or anguish for the lost opportunity), but pay or grow.

Therefore one finds words like go, and make it, and with it, and swing: "Go" with its sense that after hours or days or months or years of monotony, boredom, and depression one has finally had one's chance, one has amassed enough energy to meet an exciting opportunity with all one's present talents for the flip (up or down) and so one is ready to go, ready to gamble. Movement is always to be preferred to inaction. In motion a man has a chance, his body is warm, his instincts are quick, and when the crisis comes, whether of love or violence, he can make it, he can win, he can release a little more energy for himself since he hates himself a little less, he can make a little better nervous system, make it a little more possible to go again, to go faster next time and so make more and thus find more people with whom he can swing. For to swing is to communicate, is to convey the rhythms of one's own being to a lover, a friend, or an audience, and—equally necessary—be able to feel the rhythms of their response. To swing with the rhythms of another is to enrich oneself—the conception of the learning process as dug by Hip is that one cannot really learn until one contains within oneself the implicit rhythm of the subject or the person. As an example, I remember once hearing a Negro friend have an intellectual discussion at a party for half an hour with a white girl who was a few years out of college. The Negro literally could not read or write, but he had an extraordinary ear and a fine sense of mimicry. So as the girl spoke, he would detect the particular formal uncertainties in her argument, and in a pleasant (if slightly Southern) English accent, he would respond to one or another facet of her doubts. When she would finish what she felt was a particularly well-articulated idea, he would smile privately and say, "Other-direction . . . do you really believe in that?"

"Well . . . No," the girl would stammer, "now that you get down to it, there is something disgusting about it to me," and she would be off again for five more minutes.

Of course the Negro was not learning anything about the merits and demerits of the argument, but he was learning a great deal about a type of girl he had never met before, and that was what he wanted. Being unable to read or write, he could hardly be interested in ideas nearly as much as in lifemanship, and so he eschewed any attempt to obey the precision or lack of precision in the girl's language, and instead sensed her character (and the values of her social type) by swinging with the nuances of her voice.

So to swing is to be able to learn, and by learning take a step toward making it, toward creating. What is to be created is not nearly so important as the hipster's belief that when he really makes it, he will be able to turn his hand to anything, even to self-discipline. What he must do before

that is find his courage at the moment of violence, or equally make it in the act of love find a little more between his woman and himself, or indeed between his mate and himself (since many hipsters are bisexual), but paramount, imperative, is the necessity to make it because in making it, one is making the new habit, unearthing the new talent which the old frustration denied.

Whereas if you goof (the ugliest word in Hip), if you lapse back into being a frightened stupid child, or if you flip, if you lose your control, reveal the buried weaker more feminine part of your nature, then it is more difficult to swing the next time; your ear is less alive, your bad and energy-wasting habits are further confirmed, you are farther away from being with it. But to be with it is to have grace, is to be closer to the secrets of that inner unconscious life which will nourish you if you can hear it, for you are then nearer to that God which every hipster believes is located in the senses of his body, that trapped, mutilated, and nonetheless megalomaniacal God who is It, who is energy, life, sex, force, the Yoga's *prana,* the Reichian's orgone, Lawrence's "blood," Hemingway's "good," the Shavian life-force; "It"; God; not the God of the churches but the unachievable whisper of mystery within the sex, the paradise of limitless energy and perception just beyond the next wave of the next orgasm.

To which a cool cat might reply, "Crazy, man!"

Because, after all, what I have offered above is an hypothesis, no more, and there is not the hipster alive who is not absorbed in his own tumultuous hypotheses. Mine is interesting, mine is way out (on the avenue of the mystery along the road to "It"), but still I am just one cat in a world of cool cats, and everything interesting is crazy, or at least so the Squares who do not know how to swing would say.

(And yet crazy is also the self-protective irony of the hipster. Living with questions and not with answers, he is so different in his isolation and in the far reach of his imagination from almost everyone with whom he deals in the outer world of the Square, and meets generally so much enmity, competition, and hatred in the world of Hip, that his isolation is always in danger of turning upon itself, and leaving him indeed just that, crazy).

If, however, you agree with my hypothesis, if you as a cat are way out too, and we are in the same groove (the universe now being glimpsed as a series of ever-extending radii from the center), why then you say simply, "I dig," because neither knowledge nor imagination comes easily, it is buried in the pain of one's forgotten experience, and so one must work to find it, one must occasionally exhaust oneself by digging into the self in order to perceive the outside. And indeed it is essential to dig the most, for if you do not dig you lose your superiority over the Square, and so you are less likely to be cool (to be in control of a situation because you have swung where the Square has not, or because you have allowed to come to consciousness a pain, a guilt, a shame or a desire which the other has not had the courage to face). To be cool is to be equipped, and if you are equipped it is more difficult for the next cat who comes along to put you down. And of course one can hardly afford to be put down too often, or one is beat, one has lost one's confidence, one has lost one's will, one is impotent in the world of action and so closer to the demeaning flip of becoming a queer, or indeed closer to dying, and therefore it is even more difficult to recover enough energy to try to make it again, because once a cat is beat he has nothing to give, and no one is interested any longer in making it with him. This is the terror of the hipster—to be beat—because once the sweet of sex has deserted him, he still cannot give up the search. It is not granted to the hipster to grow old gracefully—he has been captured too early by the oldest dream of power, the gold fountain of Ponce de León, the fountain of youth where the gold is in the orgasm.

To be beat is therefore a flip, it is a situation beyond one's experience, impossible to anticipate—which indeed in the circular vocabulary of Hip is still another meaning for flip, but then I have given just a few of the connotations of these words. Like most primitive vocabularies each word is a prime symbol

and serves a dozen or a hundred functions of communication in the instinctive dialectic through which the hipster perceives his experience, that dialectic of the instantaneous differentials of existence in which one is forever moving forward into more or retreating into less.

It is impossible to conceive a new philosophy until one creates a new language, but a new popular language (while it must implicitly contain a new philosophy) does not necessarily present its philosophy overtly. It can be asked then what really is unique in the life-view of Hip which raises its argot above the passing verbal whimsies of the bohemian or the lumpenproletariat.

The answer would be in the psychopathic element of Hip which has almost no interest in viewing human nature, or better, in judging human nature, from a set of standards conceived a priori to the experience, standards inherited from the past. Since Hip sees every answer as posing immediately a new alternative, a new question, its emphasis is on complexity rather than simplicity (such complexity that its language without the illumination of the voice and the articulation of the face and body remains hopelessly incommunicative). Given its emphasis on complexity, Hip abdicates from any conventional moral responsibility because it would argue that the results of our actions are unforeseeable, and so we cannot know if we do good or bad, we cannot even know (in the Joycean sense of the good and the bad) whether we have given energy to another, and indeed if we could, there would still be no idea of what ultimately the other would do with it.

Therefore, men are not seen as good or bad (that they are good-and-bad is taken for granted) but rather each man is glimpsed as a collection of possibilities, some more possible than others (the view of character implicit in Hip) and some humans are considered more capable than others of reaching more possibilities within themselves in less time, provided, and this is the dynamic, provided the particular character can swing at the right time. And here arises the sense of context which differentiates Hip from a Square view of character. Hip sees the context as generally dominating the man, dominating him because his character is less significant than the context in which he must function. Since it is arbitrarily five times more demanding of one's energy to accomplish even an inconsequential action in an unfavorable context than a favorable one, man is then not only his character but his context, since the success or failure of an action in a given context reacts upon the character and therefore affects what the character will be in the next context. What dominates both character and context is the energy available at the moment of intense context.

Character being thus seen as perpetually ambivalent and dynamic enters then into an absolute relativity where there are no truths other than the isolated truths of what each observer feels at each instant of his existence. To take a perhaps unjustified metaphysical extrapolation, it is as if the universe, which has usually existed conceptually as a Fact (even if the Fact were Berkeley's God) but a Fact which it was the aim of all science and philosophy to reveal, becomes instead a changing reality whose laws are remade at each instant by everything living, but most particularly man, man raised to a neo-medieval summit where the truth is not what one has felt yesterday or what one expects to feel tomorrow but rather truth is no more nor less than what one feels at each instant in the perpetual climax of the present.

What is consequent therefore is the divorce of man from his values, the liberation of the self from the Super-Ego of society. The only Hip morality (but of course it is an ever-present morality) is to do what one feels whenever and wherever it is possible, and—this is how the war of the Hip and the Square begins—to be engaged in one primal battle: to open the limits of the possible for onself, for oneself alone, because that is one's need. Yet in widening the arena of the possible, one widens it reciprocally for others as well, so that the nihilistic fulfillment of each man's desire contains its antithesis of human cooperation.

If the ethic reduces to Know Thyself and Be Thyself, what makes it radically different from Socratic moderation with its stern conservative respect for the experience of the past is that the Hip ethic is immoderation, childlike in its adoration of the present (and indeed to respect the past means that one must also respect such ugly consequences of the past as the collective murders of the State). It is this adoration of the present which contains the affirmation of Hip, because its ultimate logic surpasses even the unforgettable solution of the Marquis de Sade to sex, private property, and the family, that all men and women have absolute but temporary rights over the bodies of all other men and women—the nihilism of Hip proposes as its final tendency that every social restraint and category be removed, and the affirmation implicit in the proposal is that man would then prove to be more creative than murderous and so would not destroy himself. Which is exactly what separates Hip from the authoritarian philosophies which now appeal to the conservative and liberal temper—what haunts the middle of the twentieth century is that faith in man has been lost, and the appeal of authority has been that it would restrain us from ourselves. Hip, which would return us to ourselves, at no matter what price in individual violence, is the affirmation of the barbarian, for it requires a primitive passion about human nature to believe that individual acts of violence are always to be preferred to the collective violence of the State; it takes literal faith in the creative possibilities of the human being to envisage acts of violence as the catharsis which prepares growth.

Whether the hipster's desire for absolute sexual freedom contains any genuinely radical conception of a different world is of course another matter, and it is possible, since the hipster lives with his hatred, that many of them are the material for an elite of storm troopers ready to follow the first truly magnetic leader whose view of mass murder is phrased in a language which reaches their emotions. But given the desperation of his condition as a psychic outlaw, the hipster is equally a candidate for the most reactionary and most radical of movements, and so it is just as possible that many hipsters will come—if the crisis deepens—to a radical comprehension of the horror of society, for even as the radical has had his incommunicable dissent confirmed in his experience by precisely the frustration, the denied opportunities, and the bitter years which his ideas have cost him, so the sexual adventurer deflected from his goal by the implacable animosity of a society constructed to deny the sexual radical as well may yet come to an equally bitter comprehension of the slow relentless inhumanity of the conservative power which controls him from without and from within. And in being so controlled, denied, and starved into the attrition of conformity, indeed the hipster may come to see that his condition is no more than an exaggeration of the human condition, and if he would be free, then everyone must be free. Yes, this is possible too, for the heart of Hip is its emphasis upon courage at the moment of crisis, and it is pleasant to think that courage contains within itself (as the explanation of its existence) some glimpse of the necessity of life to become more than it has been.

It is obviously not very possible to speculate with sharp focus on the future of the hipster. Certain possibilities must be evident, however, and the most central is that the organic growth of Hip depends on whether the Negro emerges as a dominating force in American life. Since the Negro knows more about the ugliness and danger of life than the white, it is probable that if the Negro can win his equality, he will possess a potential superiority, a superiority so feared that the fear itself has become the underground drama of domestic politics. Like all conservative political fear it is the fear of unforeseeable consequences, for the Negro's equality would tear a profound shift into the psychology, the sexuality, and the moral imagination of every white alive.

With this possible emergence of the Negro, Hip may erupt as a psychically armed rebellion whose sexual impetus may rebound against the antisexual foundation of every organized power in America, and bring into the air such animosities, antipathies, and new conflicts of interest that the mean empty hypocrisies of mass conformity will no longer work. A time of violence, new hysteria, confusion and rebellion will then be likely to replace the time of conformity. At that time, if the liberal should prove realistic in his belief that there is peaceful room for every tendency in American life, then Hip would end by being absorbed as a colorful figure in the tapestry. But if this is not the reality, and the economic, the social, the psychological, and finally the moral crises accompanying the rise of the Negro should prove insupportable, then a time is coming when every political guidepost will be gone, and millions of liberals will be faced with political dilemmas they have so far succeeded in evading, and with a view of human nature they do not wish to accept. To take the desegregation of the schools in the South as an example, it is quite likely that the reactionary sees the reality more closely than the liberal when he argues that the deeper issue is not desegregation but miscegenation. (As a radical I am of course facing in the opposite direction from the White Citizen's Councils—obviously I believe it is the absolute human right of the Negro to mate with the white, and matings there will undoubtedly be, for there will be Negro high school boys brave enough to chance their lives.) But for the average liberal whose mind has been dulled by the committee-ish cant of the professional liberal, miscegenation is not an issue because he has been told that the Negro does not desire it. So, when it comes, miscegenation will be a terror, comparable perhaps to the derangement of the American Communists when the icons to Stalin came tumbling down. The average American Communist held to the myth of Stalin for reasons which had little to do with the political evidence and everything to do with their psychic necessities. In this sense it is equally a psychic necessity for the liberal to believe that the Negro and even the reactionary Southern white are eventually and fundamentally people like himself, capable of becoming good liberals too if only they can be reached by good liberal reason. What the liberal cannot bear to admit is the hatred beneath the skin of a society so unjust that the amount of collective violence buried in the people is perhaps incapable of being contained, and therefore if one wants a better world one does well to hold one's breath, for a worse world is bound to come first, and the dilemma may well be this: given such hatred, it must either vent itself nihilistically or become turned into the cold murderous liquidations of the totalitarian state.

FROM

Nobody Knows My Name
JAMES BALDWIN

THE BLACK BOY LOOKS AT
THE WHITE BOY

*I walked and I walked
Till I wore out my shoes.
I can't walk so far, but
Yonder come the blues.*
　　　　　　—Ma Rainey

I first met Norman Mailer about five years ago, in Paris, at the home of Jean Malaquais. Let me bring in at once the theme that will repeat itself over and over throughout this love letter: I was then (and I have not changed much) a very tight, tense, lean, abnormally ambitious, abnormally intelligent, and hungry black cat. It is important that I admit that, at the time I met Norman, I was extremely worried about my career; and a writer who is worried about his career is also fighting for his life. I was approaching the end of a love affair, and I was not taking it very well. Norman and I are alike in this, that we both tend to suspect others of putting us down, and we strike before we're struck. Only, our styles are very different: I am a black boy from the Harlem streets, and Norman is a middle-class Jew. I am not dragging my personal history into this gratuitously, and I hope I do not need to say that no sneer is implied in the above description of Norman. But these are the facts and in my own relationship to Norman they are crucial facts.

Also, I have no right to talk about Norman without risking a distinctly chilling self-exposure. I take him very seriously, he is very dear to me. And I think I know something about his journey from my black boy's point of view because my own journey is not really so very different, and also because I have spent most of my life, after all, watching white people and outwitting them, so that I might survive. I think that I know something about the American masculinity which most men of my generation do not know because they have not been menaced by it in the way that I have been. It is still true, alas, that to be an American Negro male is also to be a kind of walking phallic symbol: which means that one pays, in one's own personality, for the sexual insecurity of others. The relationship, therefore, of a black boy to a white boy is a very complex thing.

There is a difference, though, between Norman and myself in that I think he still imagines that he has something to save, whereas I have never had anything to lose. Or, perhaps I ought to put it another way: the things that most white people imagine that they can salvage from the storm of life is really, in sum, their innocence. It was this commodity precisely which I had to get rid of at once, literally, on pain of death. I am afraid that most of the white people I have ever known impressed me as being in the grip of a weird nostalgia, dreaming of a vanished state of security and order, against which dream, unfailingly and unconsciously, they tested and very often lost their lives. It is a terrible thing to say, but I am afraid that for a very long time the troubles of white people failed to impress me as being real trouble. They put me in mind of children crying because the breast has been taken away. Time and love have modified my tough-boy lack of charity, but the attitude sketched above was my first attitude and I am sure that there is a great deal of it left.

To proceed: two lean cats, one white and one black, met in a French living room. I had heard of him, he had heard of me. And here we were, suddenly, circling around each other. We liked each other at once, but each was frightened that the other would pull rank. He could have pulled rank on me because he was more famous and had more money and also because he was white; but I could have pulled rank on him precisely because I was black and knew more about that periphery he so helplessly maligns in *The White Negro* than he could ever hope to know. . . .

Norman and his wife, Adele, along with a Negro jazz musician friend, and myself, met fairly often during the few weeks that found us all in the same city. I think that Norman had come in from Spain, and he was shortly to return to the States, and it was not long after Norman's departure that I left Paris for Corsica. My memory of that time is both blurred and sharp, and, oddly enough, is principally of Norman —confident, boastful, exuberant, and loving—striding through the soft Paris nights like a galdiator. And I think, alas, that I envied him: his success, and his youth, and his love. And this meant that though Norman really wanted to know me, and though I really wanted to know him, I hung back, held fire, danced, and lied. I was not going to come crawling out of my ruined house, all bloody, no, baby, sing no sad songs for *me.* And the great gap between Norman's state and my own had a terrible effect on our relationship, for it inevitably connected, not to say collided, with that myth of the sexuality of Negroes which Norman, like so many others, refuses to give up. The sexual battleground, if I may call it that, is really the same for everyone; and I, at this point, was just about to be carried off the battleground on my shield, if anyone could find it; so how could I play, in any way whatever, the noble savage?

At the same time, my temperament and my experience in this country had led me to expect very little from most American whites, especially, horribly enough, my friends: so it did not seem worthwhile to challenge, in any real way, Norman's views of life on the periphery, or to put him down for them. I was weary, to tell the truth. I had tried, in the States, to convey something of what it felt like to be a Negro and no one had been able to listen: they wanted their romance. And, anyway, the really ghastly thing about trying to convey to a white man the reality of the Negro experience has nothing whatever to do with the fact of color, but has to do with this man's

relationship to his own life. He will face in your life only what he is willing to face in his. Well, this means that one finds oneself tampering with the insides of a stranger, to no purpose, which one probably has no right to do, and I chickened out. And matters were not helped at all by the fact that the Negro jazz musicians, among whom we sometimes found ourselves, who really liked Norman, did not for an instant consider him as being even remotely "hip" and Norman did not know this and I could not tell him. He never broke through to them, at least not as far as I know; and they were far too "hip," if that is the word I want, even to consider breaking through to him. They thought he was a real sweet ofay cat, but a little frantic. . . .

I was not, however, on the scene. I was on the road—not quite, I trust, in the sense that Kerouac's boys are; but I presented, certainly, a moving target. And I was reading Norman Mailer. Before I had met him, I had only read *The Naked and The Dead, The White Negro,* and *Barbary Shore* —I think this is right, though it may be that I only read *The White Negro* later and confuse my reading of that piece with some of my discussions with Norman. Anyway, I could not, with the best will in the world, make any sense out of *The White Negro* and, in fact, it was hard for me to imagine that this essay had been written by the same man who wrote the novels. Both *The Naked and The Dead* and (for the most part) *Barbary Shore* are written in a lean, spare, muscular prose which accomplishes almost exactly what it sets out to do. Even *Barbary Shore,* which loses itself in its last half (and which deserves, by the way, far more serious treatment than it has received) never becomes as downright impenetrable as *The White Negro* does.

Now, much of this, I told myself, had to do with my resistance to the title, and with a kind of fury that so antique a vision of the blacks should, at this late hour, and in so many borrowed heirlooms, be stepping off the A train. But I was also baffled by the passion with which Norman appeared to be imitating so many people inferior to himself, i.e., Kerouac, and all the other Suzuki rhythm boys. From them, indeed, I expected nothing more than their

pablum-clogged cries of *Kicks!* and *Holy!*
It seemed very clear to me that their
glorification of the orgasm was but a way of
avoiding all of the terrors of life and love.
But Norman knew better, had to know
better. *The Naked and The Dead, Barbary
Shore,* and *The Deer Park* proved it. In each
of these novels, there is a toughness and
subtlety of conception, and a sense of the
danger and complexity of human
relationships which one will search for in
vain, not only in the work produced by the
aforementioned coterie, but in most of the
novels produced by Norman's
contemporaries. What in the world, then,
was he doing, slumming so outrageously,
in such a dreary crowd?

For, exactly because he knew better, and
in exactly the same way that no one can
become more lewdly vicious than an
imitation libertine, Norman felt compelled
to carry their *mystique* further than they
had, to be more "hip," or more "beat," to
dominate, in fact, their dreaming field; and
since this *mystique* depended on a total
rejection of life, and insisted on the
fulfillment of an infantile dream of love, the
mystique could only be extended into
violence. No one is more dangerous than
he who imagines himself pure in heart: for
his purity, by definition, is unassailable.

But *why* should it be necessary to borrow
the Depression language of deprived
Negroes, which eventually evolved into
jive and bop talk, in order to justify such a
grim system of delusions? Why malign the
sorely menaced sexuality of Negroes in
order to justify the white man's own sexual
panic? Especially as, in Norman's case,
and as indicated by his work, he has a very
real sense of sexual responsibility, and,
even, odd as it may sound to some, of
sexual morality, and a genuine commitment
to life. None of his people, I beg you to
notice, spend their lives on the road. They
really become entangled with each other,
and with life. They really suffer, they spill
real blood, they have real lives to lose. This
is no small achievement; in fact, it is
absolutely rare. No matter how uneven one
judges Norman's work to be, all of it is
genuine work. No matter how harshly one
judges it, it is the work of a genuine
novelist, and an absolutely first-rate talent.

Which makes the questions I have tried
to raise—or, rather, the questions which
Norman Mailer irresistibly represents—all
the more troubling and terrible. I certainly
do not know the answers, and even if I did,
this is probably not the place to state them.

But I have a few ideas. Here is Kerouac,
ruminating on what I take to be the loss of
the garden of Eden:

*At lilac evening I walked with every muscle
aching among the lights of 27th and Welton
in the Denver colored section, wishing I
were a Negro, feeling that the best the white
world had offered was not enough ecstasy
for me, not enough life, joy, kicks, darkness,
music, not enough night. I wished I were a
Denver Mexican, or even a poor
overworked Jap, anything but what I so
drearily was, a "white man" disillusioned.
All my life I'd had white ambitions. . . . I
passed the dark porches of Mexican and
Negro homes; soft voices were there,
occasionally the dusky knee of some
mysterious sensuous gal; and dark faces of
the men behind rose arbors. Little children
sat like sages in ancient rocking chairs.*

Now, this is absolute nonsense, of
course, objectively considered, and
offensive nonsense at that: I would hate
to be in Kerouac's shoes if he should ever
be mad enough to read this aloud from the
stage of Harlem's Apollo Theater.

And yet there is real pain in it, and real
loss, however thin; and it *is* thin, like soup
too long diluted; thin because it does not
refer to reality, but to a dream. Compare
it, at random, with any old blues:

*Backwater blues done caused me
To pack my things and go.
'Cause my house fell down
And I can't live there no mo'.*

"Man," said a Negro musician to me
once, talking about Norman, "the only
trouble with that cat is that he's white."
This does not mean exactly what it says—or,
rather, it *does* mean exactly what is says,
and not what it might be taken to mean
—and it is a very shrewd observation.
What my friend meant was that to
become a Negro man, let alone a Negro

artist, one had to make oneself up as one went along. This had to be done in the not-at-all-metaphorical teeth of the world's determination to destroy you. The world had prepared no place for you, and if the world had its way, no place would ever exist. Now, this is true for everyone, but, in the case of a Negro, this truth is absolutely naked: if he deludes himself about it, he will die. This is not the way this truth presents itself to white men, who believe the world is theirs and who, albeit unconsciously, expect the world to help them in the achievement of their identity. But the world does not do this—for anyone; the world is not interested in anyone's identity. And, therefore, the anguish which can overtake a white man comes in the middle of his life, when he must make the almost inconceivable effort to divest himself of everything he has ever expected or believed, when he must take himself apart and put himself together again, walking out of the world, into limbo, or into what certainly looks like limbo. This cannot yet happen to any Negro of Norman's age, for the reason that his delusions and defenses are either absolutely impenetrable by this time, or he has failed to survive them. "I want to know how power works," Norman once said to me, "how it really works, in detail." Well, I know how power works, it has worked on me, and if I didn't know how power worked, I would be dead. And it goes without saying, perhaps, that I have simply never been able to afford myself any illusions concerning the manipulation of that power. My revenge, I decided very early, would be to achieve a power which outlasts kingdoms.

FROM
Soul on Ice
ELDRIDGE CLEAVER

NOTES ON A NATIVE SON

After reading a couple of James Baldwin's books, I began experiencing that continuous delight one feels upon discovering a fascinating, brilliant talent on the scene, a talent capable of penetrating so profoundly into one's own little world that one knows oneself to have been unalterably changed and *liberated,* liberated from the frustrating grasp of whatever devils happen to possess one. Being a Negro, I have found this to be a rare and infrequent experience, for few of my black brothers and sisters here in America have achieved the power, which James Baldwin calls his revenge, which outlasts kingdoms: the power of doing whatever cats like Baldwin do when combining the alphabet with the volatile elements of his soul. (And, like it or not, a black man, unless he has become irretrievably "white-minded," responds with an additional dimension of his being to the articulated experience of another black—in spite of the universality of human experience.)

I, as I imagine many others did and still do, lusted for anything that Baldwin had written. It would have been a gas for me to sit on a pillow beneath the womb of Baldwin's typewriter and catch each newborn page as it entered this world of ours. I was delighted that Baldwin, with those great big eyes of his, which one thought to be fixedly focused on the macrocosm, could also pierce the microcosm. And although he was so full of sound, he was not a noisy writer like Ralph Ellison. He placed so much of my own experience, which I thought I had understood, into new perspective.

Gradually, however, I began to feel uncomfortable about something in Baldwin. I was disturbed upon becoming aware of an aversion in my heart to part of the song he sang. Why this was so, I was unable at first to say. Then I read *Another Country,* and I knew why my love for Baldwin's vision had become ambivalent.

Long before, I had become a student of Norman Mailer's *The White Negro,* which seemed to me to be prophetic and penetrating in its understanding of the psychology involved in the accelerating confrontation of black and white in America. I was therefore personally insulted by Baldwin's flippant, schoolmarmish dismissal of *The White*

Negro. Baldwin committed a literary crime by his arrogant repudiation of one of the few gravely important expressions of our time. *The White Negro* may contain an excess of esoteric verbal husk, but one can forgive Mailer for that because of the solid kernel of truth he gave us. After all, it is the baby we want and not the blood of afterbirth. Mailer described, in that incisive essay, the first important chinks in the "mountain of white supremacy"—important because it shows the depth of ferment, on a personal level, in the white world. People are feverishly, and at great psychic and social expense, seeking *fundamental and irrevocable liberation*—and, what is more important, *are succeeding in escaping*—from the big white lies that compose the monolithic myth of White Supremacy/Black Inferiority, in a desperate attempt on the part of a new generation of white Americans to enter into the cosmopolitan egalitarian spirit of the twentieth century. But let us examine the reasoning that lies behind Baldwin's attack on Mailer.

There is in James Baldwin's work the most grueling, agonizing, total hatred of the blacks, particularly of himself, and the most shameful, fanatical, fawning, sycophantic love of the whites that one can find in the writings of any black American writer of note in our time. This is an appalling contradiction and the implications of it are vast.

A rereading of *Nobody Knows My Name* cannot help but convince the most avid of Baldwin's admirers of the hatred for blacks permeating his writings. In the essay "Princes and Powers," Baldwin's antipathy toward the black race is shockingly clear. The essay is Baldwin's interpretation of the Conference of Black Writers and Artists which met in Paris in September 1956. The portrait of Baldwin that comes through his words is that of a mind in unrelenting opposition to the efforts of solemn, dedicated black men who have undertaken the enormous task of rejuvenating and reclaiming the shattered psyches and culture of the black people, a people scattered over the continents of the world and the islands of the seas, where they exist in the mud of the floor of the foul dungeon into which the world has been transformed by the whites.

In his report of the conference, Baldwin, the reluctant black, dragging his feet at every step, could only ridicule the vision and efforts of these great men and heap scorn upon them, reserving his compliments—all of them lefthanded—for the speakers at the conference who were themselves rejected and booed by the other conferees because of their reactionary, sycophantic views. Baldwin felt called upon to pop his cap pistol in a duel with Aimé Césaire, the big gun from Martinique. Indirectly, Baldwin was defending his first love—the white man. But the revulsion which Baldwin felt for the blacks at this conference, who were glorying in their blackness, seeking and showing their pride in Negritude and the African Personality, drives him to self-revealing sortie after sortie, so obvious in "Princes and Powers." Each successive sortie, however, becomes more expensive than the last one, because to score each time he has to go a little farther out on the limb, and it takes him a little longer each time to hustle back to the cover and camouflage of the perfumed smoke screen of his prose. Now and then we catch a glimpse of his little jive ass—his big eyes peering back over his shoulder in the mischievous retreat of a child sneak-thief from a cookie jar.

In the autobiographical notes of *Notes of a Native Son,* Baldwin is frank to confess that, in growing into his version of manhood in Harlem, he discovered that, since his African heritage had been wiped out and was not accessible to him, he would appropriate the white man's heritage and make it his own. This terrible reality, central to the psychic stance of all American Negroes, revealed to Baldwin that he hated and feared white people. Then he says: "This did not mean that I loved black people; on the contrary, I despised them, possibly because they failed to produce Rembrandt." The psychic distance between love and hate could be the mechanical difference between a smile and a sneer, or it could be the journey of a nervous impulse from the depths of one's brain to the tip of one's toes. But this impulse in its path through North American nerves may, if it is honest, find the passage disputed: may find the leap from the fiber of hate to that of love too taxing on its meager store of energy—and so the long trip back may never be completed, may end in a reconnaissance, a compromise, and then a lie.

Self-hatred takes many forms; sometimes it can be detected by no one, not by the keenest observer, not by the self-hater himself, not by his most intimate friends. Ethnic self-hate is even more difficult to detect. But in American Negroes, this ethnic self-hatred often takes the bizarre form of a racial death-wish, with many and elusive manifestations. Ironically, it provides much of the impetus behind the motivations of integration. And the attempt to suppress or deny such drives in one's psyche leads many American Negroes to become ostentatious separationists, Black Muslims, and back-to-Africa advocates. It is no wonder that Elijah Muhammad could conceive of the process of controlling evolution whereby the white race was brought into being. According to Elijah, about 6300 years ago all the people of the earth were Original Blacks. Secluded on the island of Patmos, a mad black scientist by the name of Yacub set up the machinery for grafting whites out of blacks through the operation of a birth-control system. The population on this island of Patmos was 59,999 and whenever a couple on this island wanted to get married they were only allowed to do so if there was a difference in their color, so that by mating black with those in the population of a brownish color and brown with brown—but never black with black— all traces of the black were eventually eliminated; the process was repeated until all the brown was eliminated, leaving only men of the red race; the red was bleached out, leaving only yellow; then the yellow was bleached out, and only white was left. Thus, Yacub, who was long since dead, because this whole process took hundreds of years, had finally succeeded in creating the white devil with the blue eyes of death.

This myth of the creation of the white race, called "Yacub's History," is an inversion of the racial death-wish of American Negroes. Yacub's plan is still being followed by many Negroes today. Quite simply, many Negroes believe, as the principle of assimilation into white America implies, that the race problem in America cannot be settled until all traces of the black race are eliminated. Toward this end, many Negroes loathe the very idea of two very dark Negroes mating. The children, they say, will come out ugly. What they mean is that the children are sure to be black, and this is not desirable. From the widespread use of cosmetics to bleach the black out of one's skin and other concoctions to take Africa out of one's hair, to the extreme, resorted to by more Negroes than one might wish to believe, of undergoing nose-thinning and lip-clipping operations, the racial death-wish of American Negroes—Yacub's goal—takes its terrible toll. What has been happening for the past four hundred years is that the white man, through his access to black women, has been pumping his blood and genes into the blacks, has been diluting the blood and genes of the blacks—i.e., has been fulfilling Yacub's plan and accelerating the Negroes' racial death-wish.

The case of James Baldwin aside for a moment, it seems that many Negro homosexuals, acquiescing in this racial death-wish, are outraged and frustrated because in their sickness they are unable to have a baby by a white man. The cross they have to bear is that, already bending over and touching their toes for the white man, the fruit of their miscegenation is not the little half-white offspring of their dreams but an increase in the unwinding of their nerves—though they redouble their efforts and intake of the white man's sperm.

In this land of dichotomies and disunited opposites, those truly concerned with the resurrection of black Americans have had eternally to deal with black intellectuals who have become their own opposites, taking on all of the behavior patterns of their enemy, vices and virtues, in an effort to aspire to alien standards in all respects. The gulf between an audacious, bootlicking Uncle Tom and an intellectual buckdancer is filled only with sophistication and style. On second thought, Uncle Tom comes off much cleaner here because usually he is just trying to survive, choosing to pretend to be something other than his true self in order to please the white man and thus receive favors. Whereas the intellectual sycophant does not pretend to be other than he actually is, but hates what he is and seeks to redefine himself in the image of his white idols. He becomes a white man in a black body. A self-willed, automated slave, he becomes the white man's most valuable tool in oppressing other blacks.

The black homosexual, when his twist has a racial nexus, is an extreme embodiment of this contradiction. The white man has deprived him of his masculinity, castrated him in the center of his burning skull, and when he submits to this change and takes the white man for his lover as well as Big Daddy, he focuses on "whiteness" all the love in his pent up soul and turns the razor edge of hatred against "blackness"—upon himself, what he is, and all those who look like him, remind him of himself. He may even hate the darkness of night.

The racial death-wish is manifested as the driving force in James Baldwin. His hatred for blacks, even as he pleads what he conceives as their cause, makes him the apotheosis of the dilemma in the ethos of the black bourgeoisie who have completely rejected their African heritage, consider the loss irrevocable, and refuse to look again in that direction. This is the root of Baldwin's violent repudiation of Mailer's *The White Negro.*

To understand what is at stake here, and to understand it in terms of the life of this nation, is to know the central fact that the relationship between black and white in America is a power equation, a power struggle, and that this power stuggle is not only manifested in the aggregate (civil rights, black nationalism, etc.) but also in the interpersonal relationships, actions, and reactions between blacks and whites where taken into account. When those "two lean cats," Baldwin and Mailer, met in a French living room, it was precisely this power equation that was at work.

It is fascinating to read (in *Nobody Knows My Name)* in what terms this power equation was manifested in Baldwin's

immediate reaction to that meeting: "And here we were, suddenly, circling around each other. We liked each other at once, but each was frightened that the other would pull rank. He could have pulled rank on me because he was more famous and *had more money* and also *because he was white;* but I could have pulled rank on him precisely because I was black and knew more about that periphery he so helplessly maligns in *The White Negro* than he could ever hope to know." [Italics added.]

Pulling rank, it would seem, is a very dangerous business, especially when the troops have mutinied and the basis of one's authority, or rank, is devoid of that interdictive power and has become suspect. One would think that for Baldwin, of all people, these hues of black and white were no longer armed with the power to intimidate—and if one thought this, one would be exceedingly wrong: for behind the structure of the thought of Baldwin's quoted above, there lurks the imp of Baldwin's unwinding, of his tension between love and hate—love of the white and hate of the black. And when we dig into this tension we will find that when those "two lean cats" crossed tracks in that French living room, one was a Pussy Cat, the other a Tiger. Baldwin's purr was transmitted magnificently in *The Fire Next Time.* But his work is the fruit of a tree with a poison root. Such succulent fruit, such a painful tree, what a malignant root!

It is ironic, but fascinating for what it reveals about the ferment in the North American soul in our time, that Norman Mailer, the white boy, and James Baldwin, the black boy, encountered each other in the eye of a social storm, traveling in opposite directions; the white boy, with knowledge of white Negroes, was traveling toward a confrontation with the black, with Africa; while the black boy, with a white mind, was on his way to Europe. Baldwin's nose, like the North-seeking needle on a compass, is forever pointed toward his adopted fatherland, Europe, his by intellectual osmosis and in Africa's stead. What he says of Aimé Césaire, one of the greatest black writers of the twentieth century, and intending it as an ironic rebuke, that "he had penetrated into the heart of the great wilderness which was Europe and stolen the sacred fire . . . which . . . was . . . the assurance of his power," seems only too clearly to speak more about Peter than it does about Paul. What Baldwin seems to forget is that Césaire explains that fire, whether sacred or profane, burns. In Baldwin's case, though the fire could not burn the black off his face, it certainly did burn it out of his heart.

I am not interested in denying anything to Baldwin. I, like the entire nation, owe a great debt to him. But throughout the range of his work, from *Go Tell It on the Mountain,* through *Notes of a Native Son, Nobody Knows My Name, Another Country,* to *The Fire Next Time,* all of which I treasure, there is a decisive quirk in Baldwin's vision which corresponds to his relationship to black people and to masculinity. It was this same quirk, in my opinion, that compelled Baldwin to slander Rufus Scott in *Another Country,* venerate André Gide, repudiate *The White Negro,* and drive the blade of Brutus into the corpse of Richard Wright. As Baldwin has said in *Nobody Knows My Name,* "I think that I know something about the American masculinity which most men of my generation do not know because they have not been menaced by it in the way I have been." O.K., Sugar, but isn't it true that Rufus Scott, the weak, craven-hearted ghost of *Another Country,* bears the same relation to Bigger Thomas of *Native Son,* the black rebel of the ghetto and a man, as you yourself bore to the fallen giant, Richard Wright, a rebel and a man?

Somewhere in one of his books, Richard Wright describes an encounter between a ghost and several young Negroes. The young Negroes rejected the homosexual, and this was Wright alluding to a classic, if cruel, example of a ubiquitous phenomenon in the black ghettos of America: the practice by Negro youths of going "punk-hunting." This practice of seeking out homosexuals on the prowl, rolling them, beating them up, seemingly just to satisfy some savage impulse to inflict pain on the specific target selected, the "social outcast," seems to me to be not unrelated, in terms of the psychological mechanisms involved, to the ritualistic

lynchings and castrations inflicted on Southern blacks by Southern whites. This was, as I recall, one of Wright's few comments on the subject of homosexuality.

I think it can safely be said that the men in Wright's books, albeit shackled with a form of impotence, were strongly heterosexual. Their heterosexuality was implied rather than laboriously stated or emphasized; it was taken for granted, as we all take men until something occurs to make us know otherwise. And Bigger Thomas, Wright's greatest creation, was a man in violent, though inept, rebellion against the stifling, murderous, totalitarian white world. There was no trace in Bigger of a Martin Luther King-type self-effacing love for his oppressors. For example, Bigger would have been completely baffled, as most Negroes are today, at Baldwin's advice to his nephew *(The Fire Next Time),* concerning white people: "You must accept them *and accept them with love.* For these innocent people have no other hope." [Italics added.]

Rufus Scott, a pathetic wretch who indulged in the white man's pastime of committing suicide, who let a white bisexual homosexual fuck him in his ass, and who took a Southern Jezebel for his woman, with all that these tortured relationships imply, was the epitome of a black eunuch who has completely submitted to the white man. Yes, Rufus was a psychological freedom rider, turning the ultimate cheek, murmuring like a ghost, *"You took the best so why not take the rest,"* which has absolutely nothing to do with the way Negroes have managed to survive here in the hells of North America! This all becomes very clear from what we learn of Erich, the arch-ghost of *Another Country,* of the depths of his alienation from his body and the source of his need: "And it had taken him almost until this very moment, on the eve of his departure, to begin to recognize that part of Rufus' great power over him had to do with the past which Erich had buried in some deep, dark place; was connected with himself, in Alabama, *when I wasn't nothing but a child;* with the cold white people and the warm black people, warm at least for him. . . ."

So, too, who cannot wonder at the source of such audacious madness as moved Baldwin to make this startling remark about Richard Wright, in his ignoble essay "Alas, Poor Richard": "In my own relations with him, I was always exasperated by his notions of society, politics, and history, for they seemed to me utterly fanciful. I never believed that he had any real sense of how a society is put together."

Richard Wright is dead and Baldwin is alive and with us. Baldwin says that Richard Wright held notions that were utterly fanciful, and Baldwin is an honorable man.

"O judgment; thou art fled to
  brutish beasts,
And men have lost their reason!"

Wright has no need, as Caesar did, or an outraged Antony to plead his cause: his life and his work are his shield against the mellow thrust of Brutus' blade. The good that he did, unlike Caesar's, will not be interred with his bones. It is, on the contrary, only the living who can be harmed by Brutus.

Baldwin says that in Wright's writings violence sits enthroned where sex should be. If this is so, then it is only because in the North American reality hate holds sway in love's true province. And it is only through a rank perversion that the artist, whose duty is to tell us the truth, can turn the two-dollar trick of wedding violence to love and sex to hate—if, to achieve this end, one has basely to transmute rebellion into lamblike submission—*"You took the best,"* sniveled Rufus, *"so why not take the rest?"* Richard Wright was not ghost enough to achieve this cruel distortion. With him, sex, being not a spectator sport or a panacea but the sacred vehicle of life and love, is itself sacred. And the America which Wright knew and which *is,* is not the Garden of Eden but its opposite. Baldwin, embodying in his art the self-flagellating policy of Martin Luther King, and giving out falsely the news that the Day of the Ghost has arrived, pulled it off in *Another Country.*

Of all black American novelists, and indeed of all American novelists of any hue,

Richard Wright reigns supreme for his profound political, economic, and social reference. Wright had the ability, like Dreiser, of harnessing the gigantic, overwhelming environmental forces and focusing them, with pinpoint sharpness, on individuals and their acts as they are caught up in the whirlwind of the savage, anarchistic sweep of life, love, death, and hate, pain, hope, pleasure, and despair across the face of a nation and the world. But, ah! "O masters," it is Baldwin's work which is so void of a political, economic, or even a social reference. His characters all seem to be fucking and sucking in a vacuum. Baldwin has a superb touch when he speaks of human beings, when he is inside of them—especially his homosexuals—but he flounders when he looks beyond the skin; whereas Wright's forte, it seems to me, was in reflecting the intricate mechanisms of a social organization, its functioning as a unit.

Baldwin's essay on Richard Wright reveals that he despised—not Richard Wright, but his masculinity. He cannot confront the stud in others—except that he must either submit to it or destroy it. And he was not about to bow to a *black* man. Wright understood and lived the truth of what Norman Mailer meant when he said ". . . for being a man is the continuing battle of one's life, and one loses a bit of manhood with every stale compromise to the authority of any power in which one does not believe." Baldwin, compromised beyond getting back by the white man's *power,* which is real and which has nothing to do with *authority,* but to which Baldwin has ultimately succumbed psychologically, is totally unable to extricate himself from that horrible pain. It is the scourge of his art, because the only way out for him is psychologically to embrace Africa, the land of his fathers, which he utterly refuses to do. He has instead resorted to a despicable underground guerrilla war, waged on paper, against black masculinity, playing out the racial death-wish of Yacub, reaching, I think, a point where Mailer hits the spot: "Driven into defiance, it is natural if regrettable, that many homosexuals go to the direction of assuming that there is something intrinsically superior in homosexuality, and carried far enough it is a viewpoint which is as stultifying, as ridiculous, and as anti-human as the heterosexual's prejudice."

I, for one, do not think homosexuality is the latest advance over heterosexuality on the scale of human evolution. Homosexuality is a sickness, just as are baby-rape or wanting to become the head of General Motors.

A grave danger faces this nation, of which we are as yet unaware. And it is precisely this danger which Baldwin's work conceals; indeed, leads us away from. We are engaged in the deepest, the most fundamental revolution and reconstruction which men have ever been called upon to make in their lives, and which they absolutely cannot escape or avoid except at the peril of the very continued existence of human life on this planet. The time of the sham is over, and the cheek of the suffering saint must no longer be turned twice to the brute. The titillation of the guilt complexes of bored white liberals leads to doom. The grotesque hideousness of what is happening to us is reflected in this remark by Murray Kempton, quoted in *The Realist:* "When I was a boy Stepin Fetchit was the only Negro actor who worked regularly in the movies. . . . The fashion changes, but I sometimes think that Malcolm X and, to a degree even James Baldwin, are *our* Stepin Fetchits."

Yes, the fashion does change. "Will the machinegunners please step forward," said LeRoi Jones in a poem. "The machine gun on the corner," wrote Richard Wright, "is the symbol of the twentieth century." The embryonic spirit of kamikaze, real and alive, grows each day in the black man's heart and there are dreams of Nat Turner's legacy. The ghost of John Brown is creeping through suburbia. And I wonder if James Chaney said, as Andrew Goodman and Michael Schwerner stood helplessly watching, as the grizzly dogs crushed his bones with savage blows of chains—did poor James say, after Rufus Scott—*"You took the best, so why not take the rest?"* Or did he turn to his white brothers, seeing their plight, and say, after Baldwin, "That's your problem, baby!"

I say, after Mailer, "There's a shit-storm coming."

What We Want
STOKELY CARMICHAEL

One of the tragedies of the struggle against racism is that up to now there has been no national organization which could speak to the growing militancy of young black people in the urban ghetto. There has been only a civil rights movement, whose tone of voice was adapted to an audience of liberal whites. It served as a sort of buffer zone between them and angry young blacks. None of its so-called leaders could go into a rioting community and be listened to. In a sense, I blame ourselves—together with the mass media—for what has happened in Watts, Harlem, Chicago, Cleveland, Omaha. Each time the people in those cities saw Martin Luther King get slapped, they became angry; when they saw four little black girls bombed to death, they were angrier; and when nothing happened, they were steaming. We had nothing to offer that they could see, except to go out and be beaten again. We helped to build their frustration.

For too many years, black Americans marched and had their heads broken and got shot. They were saying to the country, "Look, you guys are supposed to be nice guys and we are only going to do what we are supposed to do—why do you beat us up, why don't you give us what we ask, why don't you straighten yourselves out?" After years of this, we are at almost the same point—because we demonstrated from a position of weakness. We cannot be expected any longer to march and have our heads broken in order to say to whites: come on, you're nice guys. For you are not nice guys. We have found you out.

An organization which claims to speak for the needs of a community—as does the Student Nonviolent Coordinating Committee—must speak in the tone of that community, not as somebody else's buffer zone. This is the significance of black power as a slogan. For once, black people are going to use the words they want to use, not just the words whites want to hear. And they will do this no matter how often the press tries to stop the use of the slogan by equating it with racism or separatism.

An organization which claims to be working for the needs of a community —as SNCC does—must work to provide that community with a position of strength from which to make its voice heard. This is the significance of black power beyond the slogan.

Black power can be clearly defined for those who do not attach the fears of white America to their questions about it. We should begin with the basic fact that black Americans have two problems: they are poor and they are black. All other problems arise from this two-sided reality: lack of education, the so-called apathy of black men. Any program to end racism must address itself to that double reality.

Almost from its beginning, SNCC sought to address itself to both conditions with a program aimed at winning political power for impoverished Southern blacks. We had to begin with politics because black Americans are a propertyless people in a country where property is valued above all. We had to work for power, because this country does not function by morality, love, and nonviolence, but by power. Thus we determined to win political power, with the idea of moving on from there into activity that would have economic effects. With power, the masses could *make or participate in making* the decisions which govern their destinies, and thus create basic change in their day-to-day lives.

But if political power seemed to be the key to self-determination, it was also obvious that the key had been thrown down a deep well many years earlier. Disenfranchisement, maintained by racist terror, makes it impossible to talk about organizing for political power in 1960. The right to vote had to be won, and SNCC workers devoted their energies to this from 1961 to 1965. They set up voter registration drives in the Deep South. They created pressure for the vote by holding mock

elections in Mississippi in 1963 and by helping to establish the Mississippi Freedom Democratic Party (MFDP) in 1964. That struggle was eased, though not won, with the passage of the 1965 Voting Rights Act. SNCC workers could then address themselves to the question: "Who can we vote for, to have our needs met —how do we make our vote meaningful?"

SNCC had already gone to Atlantic City for recognition of the Mississippi Freedom Democratic Party by the Democratic convention and been rejected; it had gone with the MFDP to Washington for recognition by Congress and been rejected. In Arkansas, SNCC helped thirty Negroes to run for school board elections; all but one were defeated, and there was evidence of fraud and intimidation sufficient to cause their defeat. In Atlanta, Julian Bond ran for the state legislature and was elected—twice —and unseated—twice. In several states, black farmers ran in elections for agricultural committees which make crucial decisions concerning land use, loans, etc. Although they won places on a number of committees, they never gained the majorities needed to control them.

All of the efforts were attempts to win black power. Then, in Alabama, the opportunity came to see how blacks could be organized on an independent party basis. An unusual Alabama law provides that any group of citizens can nominate candidates for county office and, if they win 20 per cent of the vote, may be recognized as a county political party. The same then applies on a state level. SNCC went to organize in several counties such as Lowndes, where black people—who form 80 percent of the population and have an average annual income of $943—felt they could accomplish nothing within the framework of the Alabama Democratic Party because of its racism and because the qualifying fee for this year's elections was raised from $50 to $500 in order to prevent most Negroes from becoming candidates. On May 3, five new county "freedom organizations" convened and nominated candidates for the offices of sheriff, tax assessor, members of the school boards. These men and women are up for election in November—if they live until then. Their ballot symbol is the black panther: a bold, beautiful animal, representing the strength and dignity of black demands today. A man needs a black panther on his side when he and his family must endure—as hundreds of Alabamians have endured —loss of job, eviction, starvation, and sometimes death, for political activity. He may also need a gun and SNCC reaffirms the right of black men everywhere to defend themselves when threatened or attacked. As for initiating the use of violence, we hope that such programs as ours will make that unnecessary; but it is not for us to tell black communities whether they can or cannot use any particular form of action to resolve their problems. Responsibility for the use of violence by black men, whether in self defense or initiated by them, lies with the white community.

This is the specific historical experience from which SNCC's call for "black power" emerged on the Mississippi march last July. But the concept of "black power" is not a recent or isolated phenomenon: it has grown out of the ferment of agitation and activity by different people and organizations in many black communities over the years. Our last year of work in Alabama added a new concrete possibility. In Lowndes county, for example, black power will mean that if a Negro is elected sheriff, he can end police brutality. If a black man is elected tax assessor, he can collect and channel funds for the building of better roads and schools serving black people—thus advancing the move from political power into the economic arena. In such areas as Lowndes, where black men have a majority, they will attempt to use it to exercise control. This is what they seek: control. Where Negroes lack a majority, black power means proper representation and sharing of control. It means the creation of power bases from which black people can work to change statewide or nationwide patterns of oppression through pressure from strength—instead of weakness. Politically, black power means what it has always meant to SNCC: the coming-together of black people to elect representatives and

to force those representatives to speak to their needs. He does not mean merely putting black faces into office. A man or woman who is black and from the slums cannot be automatically expected to speak to the needs of black people. Most of the black politicians we see around the country today are not what SNCC means by black power. The power must be that of a community, and emanate from there.

SNCC today is working in both North and South on programs of voter registration and independent political organizing. In some places, such as Alabama, Los Angeles, New York, Philadelphia, and New Jersey, independent organizing under the black panther symbol is in progress. The creation of a national "black panther party" must come about; it will take time to build, and it is much too early to predict its success. We have no infallible master plan and we make no claim to exclusive knowledge of how to end racism; different groups will work in their own different ways. SNCC cannot spell out the full logistics of self-determination but it can address itself to the problem by helping black communities define their needs, realize their strength, and go into action along a variety of lines which they must choose for themselves. Without knowing all the answers, it can address itself to the basic problem of poverty; to the fact that in Lowndes County, 86 white families own 90 per cent of the land. What are black people in that county going to do for jobs, where are they going to get money? There must be reallocation of land, of money.

Ultimately, the economic foundations of this country must be shaken if black people are to control their lives. The colonies of the United States—and this includes the black ghettoes within its borders, north and south—must be liberated. For a century, this nation has been like an octopus of exploitation, its tentacles stretching from Mississippi and Harlem to South America, the Middle East, southern Africa, and Vietnam; the form of exploitation varies from area to area but the essential result has been the same—a powerful few have been maintained and enriched at the expense of the poor and voiceless colored masses. This pattern must be broken. As its grip loosens here and there around the world, the hopes of black Americans become more realistic. For racism to die, a totally different America must be born.

This is what the white society does not wish to face; this is why that society prefers to talk about integration. But integration speaks not at all to the problem of poverty, only to the problem of blackness. Integration today means the man who "makes it," leaving his black brothers behind in the ghetto as fast as his new sports car will take him. It has no relevance to the Harlem wino or to the cottonpicker making three dollars a day. As a lady I know in Alabama once said, "The food that Ralph Bunche eats doesn't fill my stomach."

Integration, moreover, speaks to the problem of blackness in a despicable way. As a goal, it has been based on complete acceptance of the fact that *in order to have* a decent house or education, blacks must move into a white neighborhood or send their children to a white school. This reinforces, among both black and white, the idea that "white" is automatically better and "black" is by definition inferior. This is why integration is a subterfuge for the maintenance of white supremacy. It allows the nation to focus on a handful of Southern children who get into white schools, at great price, and to ignore the 94 per cent who are left behind in unimproved all-black schools. Such situations will not change until black people have power—to control their own school boards, in this case. Then Negroes become equal in a way that means something, and integration ceases to be a one-way street. Then integration doesn't mean draining skills and energies from the ghetto into white neighborhoods; then it can mean white people moving from Beverly Hills into Watts, white people joining the Lowndes County Freedom Organization. Then integration becomes relevant.

Last April, before the furor over black power, Christopher Jencks wrote in a *New Republic* article on white Mississippi's manipulation of the anti-poverty program:

The war on poverty has been predicated on the notion that there is such a thing as a community which can be defined geographically and mobilized for a collective effort to help the poor. This theory has no relationship to reality in the Deep South. In every Mississippi county there are two communities. Despite all the pious platitudes of the moderates on both sides, these two communities habitually see their interests in terms of conflict rather than cooperation. Only when the Negro community can muster enough political, economic and professional strength to compete on somewhat equal terms, will Negroes believe in the possibility of true cooperation and whites accept its necessity. En route to integration, the Negro community needs to develop greater independence—a chance to run its own affairs and not cave in whenever "the man" barks. . . . Or so it seems to me, and to most of the knowledgeable people with whom I talked in Mississippi. To OEO, this judgment may sound like black nationalism. . . .

Mr. Jencks, a white reporter, perceived the reason why America's anti-poverty program has been a sick farce in both North and South. In the South, it is clearly racism which prevents the poor from running their own programs; in the North, it more often seems to be politicking and bureaucracy. But the results are not so different: In the North, non-whites make up 42 per cent of all families in metropolitan "poverty areas" and only 6 per cent of families in areas classified as not poor. SNCC has been working with local residents in Arkansas, Alabama, and Mississippi to achieve control by the poor of the program and its funds; it has also been working with groups in the North, and the struggle is no less difficult. Behind it all is a federal government which cares far more about winning the war on the Vietnamese than the war on poverty; which has put the poverty program in the hands of self-serving politicians and bureaucrats rather than the poor themselves; which is unwilling to curb the misuse of white power but quick to condemn black power.

To most whites, black power seems to mean that the Mau Mau are coming to the suburbs at night. The Mau Mau are coming, and whites must stop them. Articles appear about plots to "get whitey," creating an atmosphere in which "law and order must be maintained." Once again, responsibility is shifted from the oppressor to the oppressed. Other whites chide, "Don't forget—you're only 10 per cent of the population; if you get too smart, we'll wipe you out." If they are liberals, they complain, "What about me?—don't you want my help any more?" These are people supposedly concerned about black Americans, but today they think first of themselves, of their feelings of rejection. Or they admonish, "You can't get anywhere without coalitions," when there is in fact no group at present with whom to form a coalition in which blacks will not be absorbed and betrayed. Or they accuse us of "polarizing the races" by our calls for black unity, when the true responsibility for polarization lies with whites who will not accept their responsibility as the majority power for making the democratic process work.

White America will not face the problem of color, the reality of it. The well-intended say: "We're all human, everybody is really decent, we must forget color." But color cannot be "forgotten" until its weight is recognized and dealt with. White America will not acknowledge that the ways in which this country sees itself are contradicted by being black—and always have been. Whereas most of the people who settled this country came here for freedom or for economic opportunity, blacks were brought here to be slaves. When the Lowndes County Freedom Organization chose the black panther as its symbol, it was christened by the press "the Black Panther Party"—but the Alabama Democratic Party, whose symbol is a rooster, has never been called the White Cock Party. No one ever talked about "white power" because power in this country *is* white. All this adds up to more than merely identifying a group phenomenon by some catchy name or adjective. The furor over that black panther reveals the problems that white America has with color and sex; the furor over

"black power" reveals how deep racism runs and the great fear which is attached to it.

Whites will not see that I, for example, as a person oppressed because of my blackness, have common cause with other blacks who are oppressed because of blackness. This is not to say that there are no white people who see things as I do, but that it is black people I must speak to first. It must be the oppressed to whom SNCC addresses itself primarily, not to friends from the oppressing group.

From birth, black people are told a set of lies about themselves. We are told that we are lazy—yet I drive through the Delta area of Mississippi and watch black people picking cotton in the hot sun for fourteen hours. We are told, "If you work hard, you'll succeed"—but if that were true, black people would own this country. We are oppressed because we are black—not because we are ignorant, not because we are lazy, not because we're stupid (and got good rhythm), but because we're black.

I remember that when I was a boy, I used to go to see Tarzan movies on Saturday. White Tarzan used to beat up the black natives. I would sit there yelling, "Kill the beasts, kill the savages, kill 'em!" I was saying: Kill *me*. It was as if a Jewish boy watched Nazis taking Jews off to concentration camps and cheered them on. Today, I want the chief to beat hell out of Tarzan and send him back to Europe. But it takes time to become free of the lies and their shaming effect on black minds. It takes time to reject the most important lie: that black people inherently can't do the same things white people can do, unless white people help them.

The need for psychological equality is the reason why SNCC today believes that blacks must organize in the black community. Only black people can convey the revolutionary idea that black people are able to do things themselves. Only they can help create in the community an aroused and continuing black consciousness that will provide the basis for political strength. In the past, white allies have furthered white supremacy without the whites involved realizing it—or wanting it, I think. Black people must do things for themselves; they must get poverty money they will control and spend themselves, they must conduct tutorial programs themselves so that black children can identify with black people. This is one reason Africa has such importance: The reality of black men ruling their own natives gives blacks elsewhere a sense of possibility, of power, which they do not now have.

This does not mean we don't welcome help, or friends. But we want the right to decide whether anyone is, in fact, our friend. In the past, black Americans have been almost the only people whom everybody and his momma could jump up and call their friends. We have been tokens, symbols, objects—as I was in high school to many young whites, who liked having "a Negro friend." We want to decide who is our friend, and we will not accept someone who comes to us and says: "If you do X, Y, and Z, then I'll help you." We will not be told whom we should choose as allies. We will not be isolated from any group or nation except by our own choice. We cannot have the oppressors telling the oppressed how to rid themselves of the oppressor.

I have said that most liberal whites react to "black power" with the question, What about me? rather than saying: Tell me what you want me to do and I'll see if I can do it. There are answers to the right question. One of the most disturbing things about almost all white supporters of the movement has been that they are afraid to go into their own communities—which is where the racism exists—and work to get rid of it. They want to run from Berkeley to tell us what to do in Mississippi; let them look instead at Berkeley. They admonish blacks to be nonviolent; let them preach nonviolence in the white community. They come to teach me Negro history; let them go to the suburbs and open up freedom schools for whites. Let them work to stop America's racist foreign policy; let them press this government to cease supporting the economy of South Africa.

There is a vital job to be done among poor whites. We hope to see, eventually, a coalition between poor blacks and poor whites. That is the only coalition which

seems acceptable to us, and we see such a coalition as the major internal instrument of change in American society. SNCC has tried several times to organize poor whites; we are trying again now, with an initial training program in Tennessee. It is purely academic today to talk about bringing poor blacks and whites together, but the job of creating a poor-white power bloc must be attempted. The main responsibility for it falls upon whites. Black and white can work together in the white community where possible; it is not possible, however, to go into a poor Southern town and talk about integration. Poor whites everywhere are becoming more hostile—not less—partly because they see the nation's attention focussed on black poverty and nobody coming to them. Too many young middle-class Americans, like some sort of Pepsi generation, have wanted to come alive through the black community; they've wanted to be where the action is—and the action has been in the black community.

Black people do not want to "take over" this country. They don't want to "get whitey"; they just want to get him off their backs, as the saying goes. It was for example the exploitation by Jewish landlords and merchants which first created black resentment toward Jews—not Judaism. The white man is irrelevant to blacks, except as an oppressive force. Blacks want to be in his place, yes, but not in order to terrorize and lynch and starve him. They want to be in his place because that is where a decent life can be had.

But our vision is not merely of a society in which all black men have enough to buy the good things of life. When we urge that black money go into black pockets, we mean the communal pocket. We want to see money go back into the community and used to benefit it. We want to see the cooperative concept applied in business and banking. We want to see black ghetto residents demand that an exploiting store keeper sell them, at minimal cost, a building or a shop that they will own and improve cooperatively; they can back their demand with a rent strike, or a boycott, and a community so unified behind them that no one else will move into the building or buy at the store. The society we seek to build among black people, then, is not a capitalist one. It is a society in which the spirit of community and humanistic love prevail. The word love is suspect; black expectations of what it might produce have been betrayed too often. But those were expectations of a response from the white community, which failed us. The love we seek to encourage is within the black community, the only American community where men call each other "brother" when they meet. We can build a community of love only where we have the ability and power to do so: among blacks.

As for white America, perhaps it can stop crying out against "black supremacy," "black nationalism," "racism in reverse," and begin facing reality. The reality is that this nation, from top to bottom, is racist; that racism is not primarily a problem of "human relations" but of an exploitation maintained — either actively or through silence — by the society as a whole. Camus and Sartre have asked, Can a man condemn himself? Can whites, particularly liberal whites, condemn themselves? Can they stop blaming us, and blame their own system? Are they capable of the shame which might become a revolutionary emotion?

We have found that they usually cannot condemn themselves, and so we have done it. But the rebuilding of this society, if at all possible, is basically the responsibility of whites — not blacks. We won't fight to save the present society, in Vietnam or anywhere else. We are just going to work, in the way *we* see fit, and on goals *we* define, not for civil rights but for all our human rights.

AMERICA, AMERIKA

One camp in our divided country faithfully believes that America has fulfilled the promise that Whitman detected, its "manifest destiny" of carrying freedom and democracy, the "American way of life," throughout North America and ultimately the world. The other camp—the Yippies, the SDS, the Black Panthers, and assorted "moderates" as well—sees the America of Whitman as Amerika (the German spelling after the novel of Kafka), a "fascist" state at home controlled by the whims of the military-industrial complex, an imperialist force abroad laboring in the interest of Coca Cola capitalism. Indirectly, of course, almost every piece in this volume relates to these antithetical states of mind, as does most of the strife in our society.

The following selections focus on a related, in fact, disturbingly parallel, phenomenon: the split between the large cosmopolitan, ethnically heterogeneous cities (especially on the East coast and in Northern California, which are considered politically "liberal") and the surrounding middle-class suburbs and less urban states of "Middle America." Back in the 1940s, the New Yorker magazine published a "New Yorker's

View of America," a map which made Mercator's distortion miniscule by comparison. The Eastern one-third of the nation was taken up entirely by New York City with a little space for Boston. Chicago occupied roughly the area of the state of Missouri; that is, it formed the northern border of New Orleans. The West was divided almost equally between Los Angeles and San Francisco, with the advantage to the latter. Such a vision of America has more, not less, currency now. We live in an age in which suburbanites and city dwellers can barely speak to one another; in which the "simple" folk of middle America believe that life in the city can lead only to rape and ruin, probably perpetrated by the different, "colored" races. Easy Rider, one of the most popular movies of recent years among the young and the urban-hip, shows three young Americans being senselessly slaughtered in the rural South because they looked different. The scene, by the way, is said to be regularly applauded in some towns.

These selections deal with controversy relevant to the urban young, with certain urban writers' visions of what it's like "out there." And, basic to each piece, certainly, is the question of how America has lived up to the ideals of its early years.

PART EIGHT

I Hear America Singing
WALT WHITMAN

I hear America singing, the varied carols I hear,
Those of mechanics, each one singing his as it should be blithe
    and strong,
The carpenter singing his as he measures his plank or beam,
The mason singing his as he makes ready for work, or leaves
    off work,
The boatman singing what belongs to him in his boat, the
    deckhand singing on the steamboat deck,
The shoemaker singing as he sits on his bench, the hatter
    singing as he stands,
The wood-cutter's song, the plowboy's on his way in the
    morning, or at noon intermission or at sundown,
The delicious singing of the mother, or of the young wife at
    work, or of the girl sewing or washing,
Each singing what belongs to him or her and to none else,
The day what belongs to the day—at night the party of youn
    fellows, robust, friendly,
Singing with open mouths their strong melodious songs.

Monster
JOHN KAY AND JERRY EDMONTON

Once the religious, the hunted and weary
Chasing the promise of freedom and hope
Came to this country to build a new vision
Far from the reaches of Kingdom and pope

Like good Christians some would burn the witches
Later some bought slaves to gather riches

And still from near and far to seek America
They came by thousands, to court the wild
But she patiently smiled, and then bore them a child
To be their spirit and guiding light.

And when the ties with the crown had been broken
Westward in saddle and wagon it went
And till the railroad linked ocean to ocean
Many the lives which had come to an end

While we bullied, stole and bought our homeland
We began the slaughter of the red man

But still from near and far to seek America
They came by thousands, to court the wild

"Monster," by John Kay and Jerry Edmonton,
reprinted by permission of Steppenwolf, Inc.

Photograph by Judith Mallinson.

But she patiently smiled and bore them a child
To be their spirit and guiding light.

The Blue and Grey they stomped it
They kicked it just like a dog
And when the war was over
They stuffed it just like a hog

But though the past has its share of injustice
Kind was the spirit in many a way

But its protectors and friends have been sleeping
Now it's a monster and will not obey.

The spirit was freedom and justice
Its keepers seemed generous and kind
Its leaders were supposed to serve the country
Now they don't pay it no mind
Cause the people got fat and grew lazy
Now their vote is a meaningless joke
They babble about law and 'bout order
But it's just the echo of what they've been told.

Yes a monster's on the loose.
It's put our heads into the noose.
And just sits there watching
The cities have turned into jungles
And corruption is strangling the land

The police force is watching the people
And the people just can't understand
We don't know how to mind our own business
The whole world has to be just like us
Now we are fighting a war over there
No matter who's the owner we can't pay the cost

Yes a monster's on the loose
It's put our heads in a noose
And just sits there watching.

America where are you now
Don't you care about your sons and daughters
Don't you know we need you now
We can't fight alone against the monster.

FROM

Cannibals and Christians
NORMAN MAILER

For a century now the best of the White
Protestants have been going from the farm
to the town, leaving the small city for the
larger one, transferring from Shaker
Heights High to Lawrenceville, from
Missouri State Teacher's to Smith, from
Roast Turkey to Cordon Rouge, off
rectitude onto wickedness, out of
monogamy into *Les Liaisons Dangereuses,*
from *Jane Eyre* to *Candy;* it's a long trip
from the American Legion's Annual Ball
to the bust-outs of Southampton. There's
the unheard cry of a wounded coyote in all
the minor leagues of the Junior League,
in all the tacky doings of each small town,
the grinding rasp of envy rubs the liver of

each big frog in his small pond, no hatred
like hatred for the East in the hearts of those
who were left behind: the horror in the
heart of social life in America is that one
never knows whether one is snubbed for
too much or too little, whether one was too
fine or not fine enough, too graceless or
too possessed of special grace, too hungry
for power or not ambitious enough — the
questions are burning and never answered
because the Establishment of the East
rarely rejects, it merely yields or ignores,
it promises and forgets, it offers to
attend your daughter's party and somehow
does not quite show up, or comes that
fraction too late which is designed to spoil
the high anticipation of the night. (Or worse,
leaves a fraction too early.) The Wasps who
were for Goldwater were the social culls
of that Eastern Society which ran the land,
yes, the Goldwater Wasps were the old

doctors of Pasadena with their millions in stock and their grip on the A.M.A., the small-town newspaper editors, the president of the second most important bank, the wives of Texas oil, yes the wives and family of all the prominent and prosperous who had a fatal touch of the hick, all the Western ladies who did the Merengue at El Morocco on a trip to New York, and did it not quite well enough, you could just hear the giggles in the throat of Archie or Lightning Dick or Sad One-Eye, the Haitian and/or Jamaican who had taught them how. Yes the memory of those social failures is the saliva of intellectual violence. The old Goldwater Wasps, the ones who had been sitting in the hotel lobbies, had an insane sting to their ideas — they were for birching America's bare bottom where Come-you-nisms collected: white and Negro equality; sexual excess; Jew ideas; dirty linen, muddled thinking, lack of respect for the Constitution. The Right in America had an impacted consistency of constipation to their metaphor. Small wonder they dreamed of a Republican purge. The Wasps were full of psychic wastes they could not quit — they had moved into the Middle West and settled the West, they had won the country, and now they were losing it to the immigrants who had come after and the descendants of slaves. They had watched as their culture was adulterated,

transported, converted into some surrealist mélange of public piety *cum* rock and roll, product of the movies and television, of the mass media where sons of immigrants were so often king, yes the Wasps did not understand what was going on, they were not so ready after all to listen to those of their ministers who would argue that America had a heritage of sin and greed vis-à-vis the Negro, and those sins of the blood must be paid; they were not at all ready to listen to the argument that America's industry had been built out of the hardworking hard-used flesh of five generations of immigrants, no, they were Christian but they did not want to hear any more about the rights of others, they suffered from the private fear they were not as good, not as tough, not as brave as their great-grandfathers, they suffered from the intolerable fear that they were not nearly so good nor so tough as those other Christians close to two thousand years ago who faced Romans, so they were now afraid of the East which had dominated the fashion and style of their life, they were ready to murder the East, the promiscuous adulterous East — in a good fast nuclear war they might allow the Russians a fair crack at New York — yes they were loaded with one hatred: the Eastern Establishment was not going to win again, this time Main Street was going to take Wall Street.

A Supermarket in California
ALLEN GINSBERG

What thoughts I have of you tonight, Walt Whitman, for I walked down the sidestreets under the trees with a headache self-conscious looking at the full moon.

In my hungry fatigue, and shopping for images, I went into the neon fruit supermarket, dreaming of your enumerations!

What peaches and what penumbras! Whole families shopping at night! Aisles full of husbands! Wives in the avocados, babies in the tomatoes! — and you, Garcia Lorca, what were you doing down by the watermelons?

I saw you, Walt Whitman, childless, lonely old grubber, poking among the meats in the refrigerator and eyeing the grocery boys.

I heard you asking questions of each: Who killed the pork chops? What price bananas? Are you my Angel?

I wandered in and out of the brilliant stacks of cans following you, and followed in my imagination by the store detective.

We strode down the open corridors together in our solitary fancy tasting artichokes, possessing every frozen delicacy, and never passing the cashier.

Where are we going, Walt Whitman? The doors close in an hour. Which way does your beard point tonight?

(I touch your book and dream of our odyssey in the supermarket and feel absurd.)

Will we walk all night through solitary streets? The trees add shade to shade, lights out in the houses, we'll both be lonely.

Will we stroll dreaming of the lost America of love past blue automobiles in driveways, home to our silent cottage?

Ah, dear father, graybeard, lonely old courage-teacher, what America did you have when Charon quit poling his ferry and you got out on a smoking bank and stood watching the boat disappear on the black waters of Lethe?

California: A State of Excitement
FROM *TIME* MAGAZINE

If an earthquake were somehow to tear California off the continent and set it afloat in the sea, the island state might survive. But could the rest of the U.S.? California is virtually a nation unto itself, but it holds a strange hope, a sense of excitement — and some terror — for Americans. As most of them see it, the good, godless, gregarious pursuit of pleasure is what California is all about. The citizens of lotusland seem forever to be lolling around swimming pools, sautéing in the sun, packing across the Sierra, frolicking nude on the beaches, getting taller each year, plucking money off the trees, romping around topless, tramping through the redwoods and — when they stop to catch their breath — preening themselves on-camera before the rest of an envious world. "I have seen the future," says the newly returned visitor from California, "and it plays."

It is widely believed that this El Dorado is the mirror of America as it will become, or at least the hothouse for its most rousing fads, fashions, trends and ideas.

California clothes, architecture, arts, business ventures, topless/bottomless, parks, table wines, liberated leisure styles, cults, think tanks and Disneylands seem to be spreading everywhere. California's people have created their own atmosphere, like astronauts. Yet it could be that the state is not really so different from the rest of the U.S. as it seems: that it is, in fact, a microcosm of modern American life, with all its problems and promises — only vastly exaggerated.

In California everything seems intensified to the point of excess. If excellence and beauty are nowhere more excellent and beautiful than in California, it is also true that nowhere else is the bad so ugly and the ugly so bad. It is full of dramatic contrasts, but what is the essence behind them? It is changing at a dizzying rate, but where are the changes taking it? What is it that people do to California — or California to them? One way to find out is to be born there. Another is to play a latter-day Candide — an innocent in the West of all possible worlds. TIME Correspondent Tim Tyler, 28, born in New York City and based in Los Angeles for the past 22 months, played that role recently. In effect, Tyler became a camera, zooming in on the human-natural scene, searching

for something like the soul of the state.
His report:

CANDIDE CAMERA:
IN SEARCH OF THE SOUL

I start by driving up the shore from Santa
Monica to Malibu just because I like the
drive. That area, along the shore, is my
idea of California. It has the free
impermanence of the place. The beach
houses stand wall to wall on the sand,
weather-beaten dwellings right next to
opulent villas. The cliff on the other side
is raw, crumbling dirt, and it periodically
dumps its houses right down on the road.
I get the feeling that the whole state may
subside into the ocean some day.

I follow an old Volkswagen bus north to
Malibu, where it U-turns and pauses at the
water's edge. Four surfboards on top, four
kids with long hair inside. I ask the nearest
surfer on the beach, "Why do you do it?"
Terry Sinclair, a college boy with long dark
hair, answers: "Because I wrecked my leg
motorcycle racing."

Back on the highway, I am distracted not
by traffic, but by birds. In bathing suits these
are not just any girls. California Girls. There
is a difference. Maybe it's the orange juice.
Or the incessant sunshine. Or the surfing
and the skiing. But there is something
transporting about a California Girl; the legs
are longer, the eyes clearer, the skin more
exuberant. Maybe an out-of-towner can
become a California Girl if she comes here
early—say at about age three. After that,
it's too late. She can be beautiful. And
healthy. And sexy. But she can never quite
be that combination of maximum looks and
minimum restraint, that tranquil body and
restive psyche that is the California Girl!
As difficult as it is to be a California Girl,
it is harder still to stay one—even for the
natives. Hence the amount of time she
spends fending wrinkles, pounds and
ennui.

CUT TO: BEVERLY HILLS HEALTH CLUB
FOR WOMEN   This is a salon for the whole
body—and the whole day. The exercise
room, carpeted in gold and orange, has
25 California ladies lying in it, most of them
gray and hefty, in variegated pastel tights,
slowly moving their limbs through the air
in time with an instructress.

A young married woman, only 20 pounds
away from being a California Girl, comes
up. "I spend the whole day here. They have
a lot of things to keep you busy—
electrologist, beauty parlor, masseuse,
steam room, baths, pool, coffee shop.
You never have to leave. I've learned to
use cocoa butter for my skin, take
vitamin A for my hair, cuticle cream for my
nails, and I've bought a new wig. It's a
whole way of life. Except some of these
older ladies here don't really lose any
weight. . ."

Then why do they pay $200 a year to be
members?

"It's a way to spend the day. When you're
naked in the steam room, there's no
façades. Some of them spend eight hours
a day in here; this place is their whole life."

CUT TO: FULLERTON   I go to see the
head of a California conglomerate. I expect
a Western version of controlled optimism,
with touches of anxiety around the edges.
Company men out here are always
mentioning "the rising tide of Pacific
business," the giant market in Asia barely
tapped—"1 out of 18 jobs in the state is
linked to foreign trade," one executive says.
And the domestic market promises even
more. By 1975, personal income in
California will have soared to $110
billion! But David Mahoney, young and
relaxed at 46, turns out to be 180° from
the kind of executives I know back East.
He sits behind a modern oval desk in a
palatial three-room suite of offices that
he has taken over as board chairman of
Norton Simon, Inc., a year-and-a-half-old
concern formed from Canada Dry, Hunt
Foods, McCall's and other companies.
The place is plush—driftwood walls, deep-
pile carpet. The whole bit. He smiles and
says, "Let's go outside." I follow him into
the Norton Simon garden, and he takes
off his jacket and we walk among the sunlit
ferns and flowers. "Why aren't you
behaving like an executive?" I ask. "Haven't
you heard of status?"

"Out here, the business executives think
they're younger. They feel that all New York
businesses are part of one big

Establishment. And in a way, they are. In New York all different kinds of industries — Wall Street, Madison Avenue, all of it — are interlocking. They all depend on the big New York banks. Out here, the industries are mostly smaller, and they're independent of one another. It's less stifling."

I watch him saunter around, loose-limbed and relaxed, and I believe the sales talk. "You know, a lot of board chairmen are here not because of the job, but because they want to live in California. Some top executives live here but commute to New York for five days a week. In fact, the speed of travel and communications today has ended the inferiority complex the California businessman used to have. The California industrialist is liberated from that old provincial feeling. And he shows it. He is tanned, he swims a lot, he is healthy — people are interested in the body out here. The California businessman is a rounded guy." I watch Mahoney stroll through the ferns and I wonder . . . maybe his bottom drawer really is free of Gelusils and Miltown. But what about the executives on the lower level? Are they quite as ulcer-and-anxiety free? Where, after all, do California psychiatrists find their patients?

CUT TO: SOUTH-CENTRAL LOS ANGELES   Celes King is director of the Los Angeles Rumor Control and Information Center, which serves as a switchboard for the black and Mexican minority organizations. King, a chunky brown man in his 40s, sits in a storefront office on a cheap vinyl couch. I ask him if the blacks are happy. King laughs bitterly. He points out that juvenile unemployment in the black community is 25% to 30%; adult unemployment is 12% to 15%. Transportation is a big part of the problem. Los Angeles is a horizontal city, and it's huge. Most industrial jobs are ten to 20 miles or more from the black ghettos. Angelenos own 3,000,000 cars. But 31% of the black families don't have a car, so how can they get to work? "Then," says King, "there is housing. There are other problems too. The city's going to have to make some substantial moves fast before it decays. The colonies — that's what they

are, colonies — are on the threshold of exploding."

CUT TO: BLACK LOS ANGELES
Saturday night. Watts. Like an anthill. Gaggles of black people gathered and gabbing everywhere — on sidewalks, front steps, bars, service-station lots. Sergeant Warren Larson, white, cool and 30, drives through the gloom. "Shooting at 2024½ W. Florence Avenue," barks Larson's radio. "Any unit that can handle please identify."

Larson finds the victim, a 35-year-old man, sitting on the sidewalk with a groove in his head where one bullet grazed him, and a hole in one leg. The sergeant goes up to talk to the assailant in a two-room apartment. The man is wearing socks and a T shirt. He tells Larson: "You damn right I shot him. I shot at him twice. He tried to break down the door. He had two Molotov cocktails in his hands all set to go. Hey, did I hit him? Where's he hit?" They lead the firebomber, drunk and bleeding, to an ambulance. They leave the man who shot him sitting on his bed alone.

CUT TO: THE *BARRIOS* OF L.A.   Half of the 2,000,000 Mexicans in Southern California no longer call themselves Mexican Americans. They use the tougher name *Chicanos,* and they are renaming their political organization, United Mexican-American Students, MECHA — which means fuse. They are getting mad.

Sal Castro, a slight, handsome *Chicano* leader, walks with me through the broken, crumbling *barrios* of East Los Angeles and tells me: "We have a new nationalism now. There is no more Tio Taco, which is our version of Uncle Tom. We may be a few years behind the blacks in our militance, but we are getting there very fast.

"Our unemployment is three times that of the whites in Los Angeles. Our economic situation is so bad that less than half of us are able to finish high school. That means we can't even break the language barrier with the whites, so we can't even begin to get the jobs we need — it's a vicious circle, but we'll break it any way we can. We have the leadership now, you know. Suddenly, our people are getting educations. In 1967 only 350 Mexicans were going to U.C.L.A.; now there are a thousand. This can make a revolution. We are demanding Mexican cultural studies in grade schools and high schools, and bilingual education. We are demanding better housing and jobs now. We will fight and picket and sit-in until we get them. And we will have our confrontations with the police, too, and they will be worse than those of the blacks because there are 2,000,000 of us here."

CUT TO: VAN NUYS SHOPPING CENTER On my way to the center, a pretty girl (California bred, obviously) stands behind a table. "Exercise your constitutional rights," she urges. How can I resist? "I'm with the people's lobby," she explains. "We fill up petitions on contract for different kinds of groups. In California you can get most kinds of laws passed by the people without going near the legislature. The Clean-Air Council and a group called Write for Your Life are behind this one, but there are other smog groups, one called The Right to Clean Air, another called Stamp Out Smog—S.O.S.—and one called People Pledged to Clean Air. In that one, you pledge not to buy an internal-combustion car after 1975. Right now, there are 10,000 people in the state getting petitions signed against smog. The people of Southern California are madder than hell."

CUT TO: SAN FERNANDO VALLEY A lady I will call Joan Adkins lives in Mission Hills. On her color television set is a bowl of water with a statuette of Jesus submerged in it. She turns out to be the extreme in the antismog movement. "The smog here is very bad," she tells me. "I've been fighting it for twelve years. I have to put cream in my nasal passages, but sometimes my nose swells up anyway, and I chew gum. They say that helps. And I have to keep washing out my eyes. You know, they say that smog can affect your mental outlook, damage the brain.

"I've written to everybody about smog," she continues. "First I wrote my representatives; then I wrote the county supervisors and I wrote to Lyndon Johnson; and then I read where Nixon was gonna declare war on pollution, so I

wrote him. I wrote Ronald Reagan and I wrote Mayor Yorty. I wrote the airlines, the car manufacturers and J. Edgar Hoover. Sometimes I picket. We had a couple of breathe-ins downtown; we wore health masks into the county supervisors' offices. There isn't much time left. We make more smog, inside our houses, you know, from all those jet cans: beer cans, shaving cream, hair spray. I often wonder if there's any Communist payoffs behind the smog."

CUT TO: THE FREEWAY NORTH Zap— the green farmland changes to brown, fields of burned grass roll gleaming up the mountains from the sea. If someone turned off the irrigation faucet for a week, green Southern California would be a dust bowl. I switch to an inland freeway heading north. The concrete knifes through raw-earth hills with drainage pipes running down the sides to keep the hills from washing away. A hundred miles north, the land is flat and planted in cotton and grapes and fruit trees. I head for Yosemite, and make it by dusk, 7 o'clock.

Joe Cody, who's camping next to me under the tall cedars, has driven here with his wife and child in a Camper bus all the way from New Hampshire, just to climb around on these rocks. He has degrees in chemistry, biochemistry and physics that could be bringing him at least $15,000 if he worked—but he would rather climb mountains. "Every climber in the world aspires to come to this valley," he says. "This is the best. El Capitan, the high rock with the sharp nose that you passed on your way in, is the most famous climbing rock in the world. We may try to find a house somewhere near Yosemite. Every kid who climbs dreams of coming here."

CUT TO: THE THINK TANK I head out to the Rand Corp., dominant think tank of Southern California—and probably of the world. Here at Santa Monica, with the glittering Pacific in view, everything is in the future tense—very tense. Nobody bothers me when I park in the lot, but when I enter the sun-washed flower-pot-pink cement two-story building, I am met by a uniformed guard. Employees no longer have to wear badges; but visitors do. The atmosphere seems antiseptic, full of right angles, and suffocatingly quiet. But it's not quite as uptight as it appears. This is, after all, California and the deepthinkers are dressed in California motley— everything from shirtsleeves to Brooks Bros. suits. One man, an administrator no less, has been known to pull into the parking lot on a motorcycle and in a black leather jacket. The guard leaves me, and all formality falls away as I greet Anthony Pascal, a 36-year-old mental machine with a great, comical handlebar moustache and electric curls shooting out all over his head. He sits down and says, "Name the topic, and I'll tell you what'll happen."

I think, and say "Riots." He shoots back: "Rioting could well re-emerge. In the '70s, with fewer jobs available, employers will exercise their prejudice more; there will be more minority unrest, and more trouble."

"Education," I say, warming to this cosmic one-sided game of pingpong, and he says: "There will be more and more private money in education in the '70s, because education is getting too expensive for the taxpayers to bear any more of the burden. You may see the Government issue vouchers to people, worth so much for private education. This system would spawn a whole new generation of private schools, which in turn will leave the way open for far more innovative teaching methods than we've seen."

Guaranteed wage? "It will come. And when it does, it will pull the poor and the lower-middle class back together, because it will help remove the stigma of unemployment."

Leisure time? "The 30-hour work week will not come. People will enter the labor market later and later as educations grows. And they may retire earlier, but they will continue to take their benefits in the form of money rather than a shorter week."

Marijuana? "It will be legalized. It has to be, once Nixon reduces the penalty. Without the motivation of a stiff penalty, the law becomes impossible to enforce, like a law against scratching your nose in your own house."

Religion? "A whole new religious movement is beginning. We will see the further decline of organized Protestant denominations; more and more Eastern-religious and pseudoreligious movements will take hold."

I leave, located somewhere in the future, and when my feet meet the pavement outside, I return to the present with a jarring thud. I make the adjustment in a microsecond. California is billed as a now scene. But the fact is, everyone living here has one foot in now and another in tomorrow. Here, you get the feeling, is the authentic international dateline. Here the future begins. As I walk away from Rand, the prospect seems kind of pleasing after all.

CUT TO: FARMLAND SOUTHEAST OF SAN FRANCISCO   The old Victorian farmhouse is a wreck. It is bare wood now, so you can hardly tell it was ever painted. The yard is all high weeds, covered with dog droppings, buzzing with flies. A radio plays through the broken screen door. I can't raise anybody so I go around back, where I find Bill McCorry and Bill McCorry Jr., the owners. The old man wears a cowboy hat and boots, the son has a flattop and cowboy boots, but a city shirt. I ask the son how he's making out.

"Oh, we're gettin' by. We got 5,000 acres here, some rented, some owned. We got 300 heada Hereford, and some hogs. We raise a little barley. Dad an' me do most of the work, but we got two men who help us part time." One of the ranch hands materializes at his side like a movie extra and sharpens his knife on a pocket stone. It is 100° in the yard. "There's not much money in ranchin' around here," continues McCorry. "One trouble is the rain. In a year we don't get but ten, eleven inches. We get a lot of fires. A fire last year burned 9,000 acres around here. But we get green grass in November; it lasts till spring."

"What I like about ranchin' is you're not workin' with the public; you're not all boxed in, crowded in. An' listen, we have some fun. My wife and I go to Vegas every year. You get hooked on farmin', really, I'm the third generation on this farm; my grandfather came here from Ireland in 1882—he had a family of ten. You know, I'd hate to see even one field sold away from the ranch."

CUT TO: DOWNTOWN SAN JOSE   A young man, Dennis, sits on the front porch in a floorlength white robe, with blond hair flowing past his shoulders. "Why are you wearing a dress?" I ask. "I'm a witch," he answers. "In fact, you're just in time to see one of my ceremonies. Come on upstairs." I follow. "Don't worry, I'm not a black witch, I'm a white witch. Most of us are. Our powers diminish when we use them selfishly." We come into a room draped with silk cloths. A dozen people— housewives, girls, young men—are sitting in a circle on the floor. Lying in the middle is a blonde, Leslie, around 20. Dennis joins the circle, all 13 witches join hands, and Dennis chants, "Spring equinox, golden son of the mountains, illumine the land!" The blonde, whose name is Leslie, says, "Little things are going wrong, and I know it can't be just bad luck." "Leslie's karma has been messed up," Dennis explains. "We have to locate the spirit." The whole group slides closer to Leslie, and all place hands on her body. "Where do you feel it?" he asks. "In my stomach and thighs," says Leslie. "Oh, boy!" says Dennis. "I want you to just breathe in and out, really hard." Everybody presses down on Leslie. "You're hurting my stomach," she groans. Finally the spirit is out; the group brushes it away with ostrich plumes. "All you have to do now is live, Leslie," says Dennis. She limps downstairs, and he smiles: "It works every time."

CUT TO: CHINATOWN IN SAN FRANCISCO   Steep, narrow streets, wrinkled old Chinese selling vegetables, white matrons walking with their arms full of laundry, families of tourists admiring the shops and looking for a Chinese restaurant. People smile, stop and talk on the street; it is predictably peaceful. But in Portsmouth Square 200 people mill around a rostrum. On the platform are an army bugler, a line of speakers and a big sign that says MEMORIAL SERVICE FOR OUR COMPATRIOTS MASSACRED BY THE CHINESE COMMUNISTS.

A dozen red flags are waving in the air. A young Chinese woman grabs my arm. "The Red Guard," she says, and leads me away. "This is not a good place to be. I knew there would be trouble. All of Chinatown is divided." Divided? "Yes." We walk up the hill toward Grant Avenue. A young Chinese with long hair, George Woo, joins us. The year before, he helped start a radical youth movement called Wah Ching in Chinatown.

"Chinatown is a whore!" he yells. "The Gray Line tours are pimps, and the tourists are customers. This is the only ghetto in the world with tours. Most Chinese live in miserable apartments. The average Chinese over 25 has had 1.7 years of education. We won't take it any more. Now, for the first time, we demonstrate. And we sue the city."

CUT TO: LAGUNA HILLS RETIREMENT VILLAGE   They come from all over the country to Ross Cortese's Leisure World, where you can play tennis and golf and sit by the pool all year round: 7,000 homes, everything they could ever need, and it's all walled in.

The old men sit in the sun. Their skin is brown and pebblegrained like a football. Harry Weiss, in black knee socks, blue shorts and pink shirt, comes by the pool and says, "It's heaven on earth. I got more friends here in four months than I had in L.A. in 24 years." Near by, in the clay-modeling shop, Mrs. Margaret L. Saulino, a big lady from Warwick, R.I., sits making a vase. "Tuesday morning is sewing, Tuesday afternoon is knitting," she says. "I used to take Spanish lessons too, but I didn't want to tie myself down." Her glasses hang from a pearl chain. "The only thing I miss is October. You know, when the leaves turn."

LABORATORY IN THE SUN:
THE PAST AS FUTURE

Thus a camera view of California. The surfing boys and leggy girls, the hikers and farmers and futurists, the kooks and the activists are all part of the scene— arbitrarily chosen parts, some more valid than others, but all typical and yet unique. The force that binds them together, the soul of California, is the search for a better life carried on by 20 million individuals, a tenth of the U.S. population. The will-o'-the-wisp—Californism—propels the matron to the massage parlor, impels the petitioner or protester to demonstrate against smog or close a campus in the name of students' rights. It fuels the rage of the blacks and the *Chicanos* and the newly militant Chinese, who are all more conscious than minorities anywhere else of deprivation in the midst of fantastic plenty. It is the fear of losing their place in the sun that leads middle-class Californians to vote for a Ronald Reagan or a Sam Yorty.

Most of the trends that have recently and radically changed California life are familiar in the other America—though many first came to prominence in California. They include the hippie movement, the pop-drug culture, widespread sexual permissiveness, campus revolt and, since the Watts explosion in 1965, more virulent ghetto riots. They also include, in reaction to much of this, a political swing to the right. Not to mention pollution of all kinds and the resulting concern for salvaging the threatened environment.

A thousand Americans a day become Californians. They come West with high expectations that the wealth, the welcoming land, the easy ambience, the astonishing diversity of opportunity will all provide something far different from the dull sublunary routine of most mortals. To many of them, indeed, the new setting does mean an end to the grim struggle for existence, the beginning of a life that frees emotional energies for the pursuit of self.

Once they arrive—hardly anyone "settles" —no familial or community traditions bind them. "That's why we have so many nuts out here," says Los Angeles Pollster Don Muchmore. "People come and do things here that they wouldn't normally do back home because such behavior is unacceptable. They don't want to answer to the neighbors. They want the independence of being who they are and what they are, when they want to. It's a sort of Paradise situation."

Officially, Paradise opened for business in July, 1769, when Father Junipero Serra, alias Charlton Heston, planted the Cross at San Diego, establishing California's first mission. This year the state is celebrating its bicentennial with dutiful if lackluster civic ceremonies. Fortunately, perhaps, most Californians are too busy having fun to pause for renditions of their state song:

I love you California,
You're the greatest state of all;
I love you in the winter,
Summer, spring and in the fall.

The men who followed Serra to California were lusty freebooters (Puritans, for some reason, had little zest for El Dorado). The trait they shared was an ability to build what Historian Arthur M. Schlesinger, Sr. approvingly called "a special brand of democracy, one based on the notion that the best good of all was served by everyone looking out for himself."

They created what is still today virtually regarded as four different states. In the rugged but temperate north, they built San Francisco, a swashbuckling port city that reflected equally the liberal influence of Europe and the Eastern Seaboard of the U.S.; hence the light touch of cosmopolitanism that suffuses the town. Those who populated the rolling, semitropical south—especially in the years during and following World War II—were mostly the staid Midwesterners and Southerners who came to buy so many square feet of sunshine, and the blue-collar workers who filled the factories; hence the heavy strain of conservatism that characterizes the region. The third state, running the length of inland California, is largely agricultural and might as well be East Texas with mountains. The fourth state, defying all maps and imagination, is Hollywood.

In the two pieces that follow, Warner describes an antiwar protest, in Honolulu, which he helped organize, from the point of view of one who is inside something that is happening *now.* Boyle approaches the same "sanctuary," and accompanying Hawaiian phenomena, as an outsider, with the possible benefit of hindsight.

'Sanctuary'
REVEREND ROBERT WARNER

On Wednesday, August 6, 1969, Hiroshima Day, Airman Louis "Buffy" Parry announced his decision to seek sanctuary with the Hawaii Resistance at Crossroads Church. His historic move, echoing the action of Tom Met and Gary Gray, Kaneohe Marines, has begun the largest sanctuary community in the country and potentially one of the most significant examples of non-cooperation with military injustice in U.S. history. From one serviceman's act of conscience, from one serviceman's commitment to peace and love, a movement has grown, the likes of which Hawaii has never seen.

On the following Sunday, August 10, 1969, we of the Resistance Sanctuary celebrated humanity in a service of worship at Crossroads Church. Then, 400 strong, we followed Buffy, as he openly defied arrest, in a march through the streets of Waikiki to Ala Moana Park for a rally. There five more servicemen announced their revulsion toward military dehumanization and courageously joined the sanctuary community. Since Sunday, our numbers have grown steadily to fifteen "actively retired" servicemen and a supporting group of 200 civilians.

Our action is having nationwide repercussions, including countrywide TV and magazine coverage. Our support is mushrooming. Money, food, clothing, supplies, professional and technical services, concerned inquiries, even songs and poetry, are pouring in from all over the country.

More and more citizens who are fed up with the war in Vietnam and servicemen who are sick of the inhuman life style of the military are finding that the Crossroads Sanctuary experience is an effective and meaningful way to express their protest.

Our days are spent devouring huge home-cooked meals and organizing and carrying on the work necessary to spread the good news of the community. Time is spent dancing to the music of live rock bands; singing and jamming in various groups; tossing footballs and frisbees; and writing songs, poetry, and short stories. We talk intensely with each other and with numerous servicemen who visit each day to show support, ask questions, express specific needs and wrestle with other alternatives to military service. A library has been started and a reading room is set up. Some of us are working with the children of Crossroads experimental "New Kind of School". Laughter fills the air often. Free school seminars are being offered by University of Hawaii professors.

Perhaps most significantly, the sanctuary has become a depth community experience in which many different kinds of people have developed profound personal relationships with each other and in which an amazing spirit of solidarity and, yes, of love has taken over. And the men do not stand alone; there are sisters from the movement here day and night working in the kitchen, in the office and generally talking with and supporting these men in a way only a woman can do. The excitement, enthusiasm and joy here at Crossroads are boundless. We can truly say that we are *celebrating* our acts of conscience.

If our spirit is one of celebration, it is also that of *determination*. We consider what we are doing is so crucial to the history of mankind that we have vowed to stand firmly behind our ideals.

When in conscience we break unjust laws, we are actually making a truly ethical commitment to living rather than killing, to concerned critique rather than apathetic conformity, to deep-feeling and persons rather than callous systems and machines. Though police authorities and other people in power may consider our action illegal, we know that there are moments in history when the only truly ethical action will be resistance to unjust authority.

We will resist any attempt to squash our movement. Neither will we cooperate with action to arrest us; rather we will use any means of non-violent action necessary to resist attempts to halt our witness. And if an arrest comes, we will fight our cases all the way to the U.S. Supreme Court. The Crossroads sanctuary has just begun. People of many persuasions are rapidly swelling our ranks — people who care. We are not *military,* but our love is certainly *militant.* Although we will not injure, we will fight. Armed with the disarming weapons of love, we are moving out. We will never give up. If some of us are taken to jail, others will surely spring up in our places. Our sanctuary will last until military injustice is ended and life is made safe for children and for men.

Manifest Destiny
THOMAS F. BOYLE

I   THE CHURCH

As does its name, much about the Church of the Crossroads in Honolulu, Hawaii, is representative of the happy (to the Tourist Bureau mentality) paradox of the 50th State. Here is the "meeting of East and West," though of course not what Kipling meant, but a kind of mixed marriage between industrial Japan and California. The ample grounds are full of palms, banana plants and flowers. There is a hint of the long rolling surf and blue horizon off Waikiki, Diamond Head (a super Ben Bulben) to the East, and the sun, hot in the close sky, almost always shining. Yet it stands near the noise and smoke of the Lunalillo Expressway, which separates commercial Honolulu from the hibiscus and orchid ringed mansions and the new high rises on the mountain before the Pali Pass; and it is overlooked by the towering, modern, Bank Building which looks like a white, round, toy tractor tread turned on its side and given windows. The Church belongs to the United Church of Christ which smacks, to the Celtic or Mediterranean Eastern American, of tight-lipped and high collared conformity, yet its bulletin boards espouse underground newspapers instead of Biblical exegeses, organic food replaces bread and wine.

The physical plant continues the analogy. The grounds are enclosed in a triangular approximation of Japanese Buddhist temple construction, a sort of open lanai. The two equal sides are red shingled roofs over open passageways, lending themselves to the beauty and clear air of the surroundings. The American Protestant asserts itself, however, in the severity of the chapel's interior at the apex (tightly packed rows of folding funeral chairs attached by a common footrail — no statuary, a plain pulpit and choir seats) and the functionality of the complex of offices, auditorium, and kitchen which comprise the base.

There are 50 or 60 people on the grounds, most of them young, many listless in the afternoon heat. A few of the adults (still, by and large, young) stride about with a sense of purpose. A robust 14 year old girl in bikini top and slacks wrestles with her boyfriend and a young German Shepherd over a football. In the shade of the passageways, hurried whispered conferences take place. Rock music is heard from inside. All of the males are shirtless; no one wears shoes. The sense is that of a summer camp between activities, the counselors muttering, "What do we do with them now?" Directors striding about with clipboards. It is startling to hear, in the quiet rest break, shouts of "Kill! Kill" and childish screams of pain come from the auditorium, (there is a rehearsal of "Viet Rock" going on), and perplexing, to the outsider, to see in front of the chapel a great jerry-built sign, of the sort one remembers from World War II "drives" in small towns, with a large #11 above the scrawled letters: "IN SANCTUARY" and the names:

BUFFY
DANNY
ERIC
JOHN
VINCE
HOWARD
BOB
BOB
LOU
CURT
RON

It is August 12, 1969, and The Church of the Crossroads has become the largest public-church haven in the country's history for young men who have chosen to risk 5 years at hard labor rather than continue serving the military. And it isn't even half-way to its peak. In ten days 23 GI's, Army, Air Force, Navy, Marines, will have taken refuge there.

Rising above the sign and chapel, yet hardly noticeable, like a shrinking flower of the machine age, is a metal pole not much larger than a TV aerial, with a battered and rusty cross dangling from it at, as it were, half-mast.

In spite of his rhetoric and euphemism (which we will discuss later) what the Rev. Warner says is essentially accurate, especially in that it communicates the spirit of youth, of "love" and "peace" which prevails. And Bob Warner himself is a considerable part of it. A local paper had described him on the day after the march as looking like "a younger Dylan Thomas," but he hardly lives up, or down, to it. Instead, dressed in green Dacron pants, black vestment top, and a full Roman collar, (of course, barefoot), he looked like David Nelson with his hair frizzed out: very WASP, blonde, strong nose and chin, flared nostrils, late twenties.

"Is it I to whom you wish to speak?" he asked an interviewer, in his best mild Princeton Theological accent. He seemed relaxed and open, though he had certainly been through the same recitations numberless times that week. He was consistently interrupted by a procession of children needing direction, ("It's in my car, the blue Ford Fairlane with the surfrack.") to graduate-student types who prodded him seriously with his duties and their communal importance.

"Remember, Bob, it's the news at 6."

"Don't you think we should eat early tomorrow so we can see Viet Rock?"

"Those two guys aren't spies. They're stringers from *Time* (triumphant note here)."

"The most important thing," Warner said, "is the *sharing* of Community Existence—learning responsibilities. . ." After this he launches, dreamfully, into a catalogue of responsibilities almost lost in the cacophony of the community rising from its siesta.

The Viet Rock rehearsal (which had been sponsored then 'busted' by another church and had to move to the Crossroads) had broken up, and a score of teeny-boppers exploded onto the lawn. The air *was* full of flying frisbees and footballs, although the writing of songs, poetry, and short stories was not apparent. A Japanese girl in a MuuMuu undulated with a hula hoop while three dogs leaped and snapped at it in play. The sanctuaried GI's became evident as they filtered from the offices and cool crannies of the buildings. A rock band tuned up.

"High level strategy meeting . . ." Warner was saying, ". . . Resistance steering committee. . . ."

The most obvious distinction between GI and civilian was the color of skin, and it had nothing to do with race: The GI's were all "white Americans" and the civilians were at least 80% haole (white Mainland derivation). It was simple: the GI's had a submarine pallor from collar bone to waist and bicep to wristwatch; the civilians were deeply, healthily tan. Long-haired, mostly blonde surfboard heads of California and Hawaii. If one made a simple recitation of their eccentricities of dress and hair-style, the reader would find it difficult to distinguish them from the children of St. Mark's Place or The Haight. But in their eyes and bodies there is something different, a spring, a physical spark. "Head," no matter their drug habits, is the wrong term: try body and vitamin C and forget rationalizing. An inland or Eastern kid becomes a freaky scarecrow beside him, even if each is hirsute, Robin Hood hat, leather vest, barefoot.

A group formed in a corner of the lawn in a sort of semi-upright football huddle (maybe 8 guys and 3 girls, the standard percentage), arms around shoulders.

"It's a hug-in," someone yelled.

"A love-in," chirped a beautiful Polynesian teenybop.

Warner had just answered the reporter's last question: "Resistance will use whatever tactics and harassment necessary short of violence in order to protect servicemen in Sanctuary." He sauntered over to the hug-in which soon degenerated into a giggling free-for-all.

Through it all the GI's, happily, seemed to integrate themselves, not isolating into any one group. A couple indulged in the hug-in; one danced an anachronistic semi-twist; two more drank Budweisers on the grass with their feet up on the chapel steps. Most of them sat quietly with groups who were listening to the music, looking a bit mystified to find themselves, with their short hair, grey plastic spectacles and baggy small-town gabardines, sitting here barefoot, barechested (as was Warner, having divested himself of collar and shirt for the free-for-all) among the Children of Paradise in, yes, the word was right: IN SANCTUARY. A cry went up: "6 o'clock news. We're on TV!" And everyone rushed into the chapel.

II   THE HOUSE: THE ESCAPE

Over the mountains from Honolulu, over the wind-tunnel ravines and desperate vistas of the Pali Pass, where the soft, fragrant *ambience* of Hawaiian seaside with its warm water and mild summer surf turns rough and striking as Wales or Mexico, is Oahu's Windward Side. Isolated until a few years back, a new highway has turned it into a burgeoning suburbia of rambling beach houses and California-style developments with their attendant drive-in culture. There is a house there, low and spacious, separated from a fine, uncluttered beach only by a protective wind-bent jungle of tropical evergreen and brush, which is particularly pertinent to our subject because one of the leaders of the Resistance-Sanctuary, Curtis McClane, was living there, and because I was a guest there, of a member of the absent owner's family, for most of the month of August. My presence during this period of intense political activity was inadvertant (as was the intensity of the activity). No one expected the Sanctuary to be so successful. My credentials would hardly recommend me as an accomplished activist: I had poll-watched for Lindsay, marched in a couple of Peace parades, quietly supported Cleaver and Mailer early on in the disaster of November, 1968. Once I had attempted to organize my Army Reserve Unit into not cashing their Dept.

of the Army paychecks, but instead sending them to a "worthy cause." Of course, everyone was willing to not cash the checks, but no one was willing to agree on one place to send them. The "movement" folded, as Captain Jack Boyle phrased it, in a state of chassis. Thus my political involvement.

One the afternoon of August 11, the day before, I was sitting at that house in my favorite white wing chair, drinking beer, pretending to work on notes for a book. I was really indulging myself in the brew, the breeze from the beach, the wraparound view of the bay. The occasional scudding of a tiny cloud from left to right would shift the color of the water from deep blue to a glassy green. These complacencies of brisk air and mottled sunshine (How these *fin de siècle* cliches renew themselves when we return to primitive environments.) were disturbed by a racket in the driveway. I dropped my book and went out to investigate.

Curt McClane, lean, Jim Morrison hair, 20 years old, was circling a white compact car, opening and slamming doors, looking in the trunk, under the hood, stalking all the while as a man whose time is too important to be wasted by such triviality. He was being watched by two young women, one a flashy blonde, the other stocky and pregnant, and three rather scruffy teenage boys whom I recognized as being part of a floating population of self-designated "runaways" who, with McClane's approval, inhabited tents in the narrow swarth of jungle between beach and house. Finally, McClane darted into the back seat (close-set eyes, strong nose and teeth) like a mongoose after a rat and began, in a kind of frenzy, to tear the seat out.

The phone rang. He dashed out of the car and into the house. Muffled conversation. He came back slowly: "Well, we're in for it now. He's in the phone booth at the Service Club. Says he can't go back to the barracks and he thinks a couple of M.P.'s are looking him over. We have to go in."

"Maybe he's a plant . . . uh . . . a decoy?" suggested his girlfriend, another member of the household.

Curt's mouth twitched dramatically. His gray pale eyes looked beyond the horizon.

It was an expression one has seen in a hundred bad films: Making A Decision. "No," he said, "he's OK. I can sense it." Hmmm. Indian Making Decision.

The decision concerned this: Louis Jones, a Marine Corporal, stationed at the nearby Kaneohe Marine Base (it is on the same bay as the house), a Vietnam veteran and about to return, has decided to go AWOL. Since there had been a race riot on the base the night before (one white reported killed. Affirmed by Jones. Denied by Marines.), all passes have been pulled. Jones clams that his opposition to the war and intentions of going over the hill are suspected by his superiors. Therefore, pass or not, he must get out by tonight.

His first move was to call the Resistance at the church. He explained that he had witnessed the march on Sunday and had spoken to some of the people involved. They had dispatched the two women to the house as a kind of jumping off post. The pregnant one, whom we shall call Noreen, was essential to the plan as, being a Resistance member married to a GI (stationed in Southeast Asia), she was the only available person with a military sticker on her car, and who, therefore, would have ready access to the base.

The blonde, Bridget Overstreet, was the wife of Danny Overstreet, one of the first, and most articulate, GIs in Sanctuary. She had been spending "R&R" with him in Honolulu when he decided not to go back to Vietnam. They had been living in hotels since July 3, and the Sanctuary offered an escape from the pressures of the fugitive existence. She seemed to have been sent along as "company" for Noreen.

When I discovered McClane trying to yank out the back seat, the girls had already been inside Kaneohe once.

"Jeez!" Noreen said, "We kept trying to go around a corner . . . y'know all them barracks look the same . . . we had him in the back seat already . . . and stick him in the trunk. And every time we stopped, there was a damn M.P. looking at us. We was finally so scared and tired of going around the corners that looked the same that we just dropped him off where we picked him up and come back here to start a new plan. We got his suitcase, though."

"Now he's at the phone at the Service Club with those goddam pig M.P.'s following him" elaborated McClane.

"How did you get in," I asked, "if the Post is restricted?"

"Oh, you mean about the colored. . . ." began Noreen, when Bridget stepped forward, like a little girl in a play, and chirped:

"We told them we were going to the PX, but I think they were suspicious. They stared and stared."

I too was staring at her. She is a striking blonde, looking a bit older than her twenty years. She's a lot closer to Vegas than the upper East Side—but so, spiritually, is the suburb of Detroit from which she and her husband hail. One recalls, reluctantly, 1940's comic book slang like "gams" and "stems" to describe her legs. She wore a brief beach shift which displayed her rather wonderful, goldenbrown breasts. One would have pegged her as definitely Southern California (or is it that all girls who seem to be developing into Playboy Bunnies are moved by their mothers to Southern California for maximum exposure?). Her heavy eye make-up, which succeeded in giving the orbs a remarkable brilliance, tended, at the same time, to question the brilliance of what was behind them. I attributed the staring of the MPs to other characteristics than their suspicious natures.

Curt had renewed his attack on the back seat. Soon he judged the project a success: if the girls could get Corporal Jones in the car unobserved, and if he was no larger than Curt (they weren't sure), and as agile as a gymnast, he should be able to remove the back seat, scramble into the trunk; and remain there, the seat replaced, until they were off base.

Bridget objected: "But we have to wait until the shift changes at 8. They'll recognize us."

McClane countered, "You can go in disguise." I had an idea, not entirely unkind, that one of us was soon to turn into James Mason . . . Checkpoint Charley . . .

"They'll recognize the car," snorted the realistic Noreen. So we waited.

"Why don't *you* take the car?" asked one of the girls.

"Because my hair's too long, stupid. That's just what they're looking for. Besides, I'm *known.*" It was true that his name was known anyway. He had received a call threatening his life before the March Sunday.

So we settled in the living room, a soldier's wife, a sailor's wife, two female members of the owner's family, three teenage runaways, and I, tourist, stranger, New Yorker, hell, *oldster.* I was born *before* the war. This crowd ran from post WW II to Korean. I had been perspicacious enough in 1955 to choose Chuck Berry and the Clovers over the Gaylords and Eddie Fisher, and even manage to spend an evening now and then at the Fillmore East; but here I was out of my element. Yet it was OK; it was, after all, a strange island and I was, after all, where the action was. It was exciting.

Two jarring elements, which I dismissed at the time: Mrs. Overstreet's primary interest in the Sanctuary seemed to be that she was sure to be interviewed on TV, at which time she would "get her say" about the army and, as the radio news announced that the Chicago Cubs had acquired knuckleballer Ken Johnson from the New York Mets, Curt's girlfriend exclaimed, "Oh, what have those pig Chicago cops done now!"

At 8, Jones called. He was told the girls would leave immediately and pick him up on a specific corner near the Service Club.

At 8:15 they were back. "They wouldn't let us in. Base closed," Noreen called from the car. "Now we have to get back to town." I suspected a note of relief in her voice. I was disappointed but I couldn't blame her.

So we sat down to our spaghetti, having picked as much of the meat out as possible: McClane and his girlfriend had recently converted to vegetarianism. I was to find later that almost everyone in Hawaii who considered himself anti-establishment and was not heavily into drugs, spent most of his time talking of growing his own organic food on Maui, (a relatively underdeveloped Hawaiian Island), and getting closer to God. The tone was not unlike that in which New Yorkers speak of Truro or Easthampton. The runaways had washed and wetted their

locks down and seemed cheered and carefree at their inclusion in the 'big house' dinner. The rest of us had Lou Jones gnawing at our consciences.

The phone rang.

"It's him," Curt shouted, "Wow, it's him— he walked down to the water and climbed under the fence."

Two hours later Lou Jones, showered and comfortable in his civvies, relaxed with a beer and talked about the war in Vietnam. He was from near Charleston, S.C., and looked it: a narrow head, jugeared, slight, pale, impenetrable blue eyes, the kind of jaw one expects to chew tobacco. He was surprisingly articulate, in a trite way, and confessed to having two years of college and a penchant for speaking in public.

"Well, mostly I'm worried about people getting killed. The GI's don't care about the Vietnamese people. Hell, most chances they get, they rape 'em or anyway harass them . . .

"Man, and the South Vietnamese; when you're surrounded, the enemy gives the South Vietnamese troops a chance to surrender . . . and they do!

"The VC are just little farmers during the day and at night they just . . . well, I guess they do it pretty well . . . they leave mines and . . . and, you know, harass . . ."

In reply to most questions, he returned to his central theme: a defiant, "I've got something to say, and I want the opportunity to say it." The fact, of course, was that he had nothing new to say, nothing that hadn't been uttered before in hundreds of different accents. But this little guy was appealing in spite of the cliches and the platitudes which would have hung heavy on the tongue of an ideologue. (And his was a tale of bravery too. The next day we were to read of roving bands of black and white toughs who were beating up anyone the wrong color. Thus the double security MP's. When he was sneaking along the fence, he was in No Man's Land—between the Law and the Lawless. He was stopped by a guard whom he told he had left the barracks to get out of a fight.) The point was, he wasn't an eccentric or a sermonizer. He was my bunkmate in basic training at Fort Jackson, he was everybody's first "regular" southerner. And here he was, going over the hill "on principle." After he left, I determined to spend more time at the Sanctuary. Thus it was that, when, on the next afternoon, the members of the Resistance and Sanctuary group rushed to see themselves (i.e., Lou Jones) on TV, I was among them, and, in my fashion, just as enthusiastic.

It was in the chapel that I first smelled the rat.

In spite of the rush to the door, the group became orderly inside, like children going to a Procession rehearsal. We divided evenly between two TV's, both of which were on the altar. The one on the left was placed on the pulpit and was, appropriately, in the charge of Warner. The other was being controlled by a bearded aide who, I later found out, was awaiting trial for refusing military service.

There were two news programs running simultaneously, so each TV was set to a different channel. The channel on Warner's side used as its lead story the Kaneohe Marine Base race riots; but after panning over the base, when the cameras shifted to a press conference of white officers and black noncoms, the cry went up from the other side: "It's on! It's on!" and Warner rather clumsily switched to the other channel where we saw a long shot of children playing frisbee at the church and then a close-up interview with Lou Jones. He repeated essentially what he had said the night before, adding, (naturally, I supposed, for the circumstances) bits of rhetoric: of the definitive sort ("inhumane and unjust war"); and the Johnson-Nixon Presidential fluff variety (". . . peace . . . life, joy, and the pursuit of happiness for everyone.") The interviewer then apprised the audience of the growth in numbers, three more that day, and signed off. The picture shifted to Kaneohe. An interviewer was asking a black sergeant: "Just what do you think are the immediate moves necessary to grant the Negro the equality he demands in the U.S. Armed Services . . .?" Before the sergeant could answer the shout went up again on the other side

of the chapel: "Hey, we're on the other station now!" Warner vaulted back up to the set and changed it. We watched Lou Jones again and heard that three more men had joined the Sanctuary. One small voice (an art professor at the University, an older movement member) protested. No one paid attention. When the spot on the Church was over, everyone filtered back outside. The Axe Undervault began tuning up again, and an enormous dinner of fried chicken and rice was served. I noted, sardonically, that some of the servicemen had slipped out of the news early (or hadn't gone in) and were already standing at the head of the chow line.

III THE KIDS ON THE BEACH: HUCK FINN AS ACID HEAD

"Far Out!" exclaimed Arjay Flyte in a rush of breath after sucking in deeply on a very fat marijuana cigarette. I had just asked him what he thought of the Resistance Sanctuary.

"What do you mean," I persisted. "The social scene or the idea of it?"

"O man! The whole thing. It's so beautiful so . . ."

"Together!" supplied Jerry Rolland.

"That's *right!*" affirmed Arjay, and occupied himself again with the joint which had gone round the circle and returned to him. Sitting in the entrance to the tent, with his feet up on a disused surfboard, eyes closed, the hot, burning, semi-roach held delicately between his fingers, head inclined back, he was a contemporary caricature of pre-Raphaelite ecstasy. He was 13 years old, and the ecstasy was not assumed. He and his friends were on their third joint of *ganja* that morning. They were happy to have it. The Nixon-engineered shutdown of the Mexican border had left the stuff in short supply and they, their cronies, and the GI's and tourists they occasionally "dealt" with had had to be satisfied with LSD, DMT, Mescaline, Psilocybin or Methedrine, which drugs, it appears, the administration prefers its citizens to use. They were happy that some grass had got through.

"It's nice, you know," said Arjay, "a

couple of tokes of good shit and you're fine. This is probably local stuff, and it takes a bit more. Acid, though I dig it, should be, you know, for special occasions . . ."

"Sunshine!" interjected Matt, a rangy 16, his shoulder-length hair flopping in and out of his eyes.

"Purple tabs! Orange tabs!" exclaimed Arjay, stretching his arms wide.

"Mesc," added Jerry quietly. He is alternating between drawling a psychedelic Medusa on the back of a photocopy of the Declaration of Independence distributed by the Resistance, and playing with the tent kitten, who is tiny, smoky grey, and named Ganja. "Mesc is like religious."

"Far out!"

The context in which Arjay, Jerry, and their friends exist would be virtually unrecognizable to the most cosmopolitan citizen of, say, 1960. It combines Mark Twain with Timothy Leary, straddling the boundaries of 19th century about-to-be-abused innocence and today's mind-bending enormous present. Even those aspects of life generally accepted as "reality" have achieved strange dimensions: like waking in the morning. To the warming Pacific breeze in a tent amidst the chaos of tangled mosquito netting, psychedelic posters, a toppled strobe candle, the air itchy with mattress stuffing, surrounded by endless boxes of candy bars. Smoke a joint. A plunge in the surf. Baked beans over a fire. Another joint. Pockets stuffed with candy bars, they drive back over the pass to Honolulu (car overheating at least once), where they alternate between a mild form of hustling at the unofficial drug Bourse which convenes daily outside Waikiki's tourist-filled International Market Place, and, of course, The Church of the Crossroads.

One day I hitched a ride with them and some friends in a 1959 Ford convertible painted with flowers, beasty face (unconsciously parodying the tiger-faced fighter planes of World War II, which is madness?), Resistance and peace symbols, tangled locks riding on the breeze. I felt a flow of vibrations from pedestrians and other motorists unlike anything generated by the hot rods, and nosed, decked,

lowered, chopped and channeled flame jobs I had known in the past. We were saluted with a V sign of support by a group of Japanese kindergarten kids and threatened by a fist-waving gang of crew-cut marine lifers outside a bar. A carful of "mokes" (so far as I can determine, a pejorative term for working class, brown skinned Polynesians, roughly equivalent to "townies") were equally divided between greeting us with the V sign and the erect middle finger. Your living breathing baby boy, Mother, has become the symbol, the Rorshach battlefield, over which ignorant armies clash day and night.

Nevertheless, to describe them all as "alienated" or "runaways" is imprecise. Two of them were in fact on their own: Tim, a 15 year old Hawaiian boy, who had been sent to the Juvenile Detention Home before I arrived on a complaint from his father (an ex-Army Sergeant who didn't care if he came home or not, but objected to his lifestyle); and Jerry, who had refused to accompany his Naval parents when they were transferred to Europe.

The remainder kept some kind of contact with home. Matt's mother showed up frequently with donations of food, not a few tears in her eyes, and sad invitations to all the sundry to "come home and have a good steak."

Arjay spoke often of his family: mother, sister, and grandmother. There seemed to be no men in his life. "What do you think of your mother?" I once asked him. "What do you think," he responded with his usual twinkle, "she's a Black Belt in Karate." His charm was infectious, especially, like so many children raised by women, with the ladies. Like Antoine in *The 400 Blows:* worldly but cuddly, deep, confused. He is "one-quarter pure Hawaiian and three quarters some kind of English," and he's not really more than politely interested in New York or Paris which, he had been advised, would be his proper *metier.*

"We'll take you up to the Green Valley, man. That's where it's at!"

"Yeh!" agreed Matt, "we'll take you hurtling. There are these little fast moving streams up there, going downhill, real steep. You just get in one and it hurtles you along. Like surfing, only better."

"Wi-i-i-ipe o-u-u-u-t," screams Arjay.

A girl, Nancy, seemed to go home only to manufacture an excuse to return. She was 12 or 13 and never wore anything but the same bikini top and jeans, close to falling off. Jail bait. She told her parents she was staying with a girlfriend, the old standard, but it was difficult to see how they could believe her, since she usually stayed at the tent for four or five day stretches and never washed. It was doubtful that she ever took her clothes off. "We'd rape her," Matt once said, "but she's too greasy." And she was. She was, also, easily the best mechanic in the communal operations performed on Jerry's twenty dollar Simca, whose battery inevitably gave out in the driveway. Nancy's chief asset, besides of course, her nymphettishness, was a little cow bell she wore around her neck and which announced her presence whether they were returning from town at night or raiding the ice box of guava juice in the morning.

Typical teenage stuff except for two things: drugs and not going home at night. The Huck Finns of the Acid Generation.

Jerry is the serious one; and with the end of summer, he had some serious problems to face: food, shelter, and school. He was recently 18 and had just burnt his draft card, but his aspect, short and stocky, scruffy beard, horn-rimmed glasses with a cracked lens, was that of a middle-aged eccentric. When he smoked grass, he somehow hunched his entire body around the joint, drawing on it with an intensity (and tolerance for heat and smoke) belied by his mild manner.

His aims were in fact solidly sensible. He wanted to finish his last year of high school and go to college, and he wanted to do it independently. It wasn't easy because, in order to go to school full time in the day session, he had to find a foster home. At the end of August, he still hadn't found one, and the pressure was heavy from his parents to join them. His situation with them seemed representative of what I heard from most of the disaffected young people to whom I spoke.

Towards the end of the month, he received a long wire from his father, in what seemed to be conciliatory terms, with instructions as to how Jerry should pick up his tickets to fly and join them. Jerry had shown it to me, but didn't comment when I finished it. Later I found the wire discarded in the middle of the floor. "Why don't you go?" I asked him. "Hell, you've never been to Europe, and if you have to freak out or go on the road, there's no better place to do it."

"First of all, it didn't say so in the wire, but there are conditions he's laid on me. First, he says I have to get my hair cut, which is OK up to a point. Then he says no drugs, which . . ." he looked up at me hesitantly. Jerry speaks slowly and deliberately, and his conversation is sprinkled with long looks and pauses, "I agreed to. Then he said I had to go to the school on base, which means with all military kids, which I don't like. Finally he wants say on my friends. He wants to pick them. I won't go along with that."

Later, he showed me a draft of a letter he was sending his father. It meandered politely along, a tortuous course of erasures and marginal additions, until finally he had written, "Dad, I just can't take all this bullshit, the military, the rules, all of it! Why can't we love and do our own thing?"

Later, Arjay spoke of the situation. "Parents," he said, "are mostly a bummer."

Their enthusiasm for day-to-day life was difficult to dampen, however. They went to the garbage dump to scrounge food. "You wouldn't believe what some people throw away," one of them said. "One day we met a guy who had a whole carload of frozen food. Their electricity had gone off for, like, only a *half an hour* and his wife decided everything was spoiled. We got about a month's worth of eats that way. I used to work at this candy factory. They throw away all the chocolate bars made before a certain date. Too old, they say. Hell, we got a few bushels of them. Nothing wrong with them at all."

An interesting, if somewhat romantic, solution to the housing problem was found on a day we drove up to the North Shore to see the Green Valley and Sunset and Waimea beaches, whose thirty feet surf was made famous in *Endless Summer*. They had been told to clean up and vacate the front yard of the house before the end of the month because the owner was returning in early September.

"Hey," said Arjay, "my Granny lives along here and she says that during the war they had all these pillboxes to protect against an invasion."

All the way along the highway they spotted pillboxes.

"You'd be like Stephan Dedalus and Buck Mulligan in the Martello tower," I made the mistake of saying.

"Huh?"

"They're characters in this book, *Ulysses,* based on what the author really did when he was . . ." The mention of a book turned them off, as it had before. Arjay sat up on the back of the seat of the open convertible.

"Blow your mind, man. We could drop acid and spot submarines from pillboxes. Rat-tat-tat." He was a machine gun.

The mainlander in Hawaii early acquires three local customs. He takes his shoes off before entering a house; he forgets about surnames, which are dismissed almost entirely at the social level; and he pretends to lose his curiosity about other people's occupations. Thus, with some restraint on my part, the fact that I made my living as a teacher didn't come up in the first three weeks of conversation with the kids. One day, Arjay said, "Hey, you're a teacher, aintcha?"

"That's right."

"You know, I don't much like school . . . ," and, confessionally, "or do that good except in History."

"Why History?"

"Oh, because it's after lunch hour, man, and I used to turn on at lunch hour. Wow, that teacher really thought I was something. I'd get so stoned, not like I was going to crash though, but just so all those pictures of those cats in the funny uniforms looked *so groovy,* and I'd ask such crazy questions. Far out."

It is difficult to be of one mind about Arjay and his friends. Their freedom, affirmation, the innocent *cool* were undeniably appealing, like those fashionably arty quick-cut commercials of beautiful youth romping through a park. I thought of an idea for a short story: aging Madison Avenue executive vacations in Hawaii, meets kids, turns on, decides not to leave, moves into tent and starts eyeing Nancy with her cowbell and sweet little butt: "If only she weren't so greasy," he laughs to himself. Their use of drugs, shocking with statistical distance, disturbing as it contributes to the continuance of their special brand of blissful ignorance, can seem harmless, even funny, there in the open context of fresh air and organic food.

IV   SHADOW AND SUBSTANCE: THE VAST CIRCLE JERK

Back at the Sanctuary, as a penumbral gloom began to dim the glow of inspiration, a few good moments remained.

Two GIs stagger into the kitchen under a heavy sack: "Fifty pounds of vegetables, Ma'am. Liberated from the Kaneohe Marine Air Base."

A stranger on a guitar leads a midnight jam (including Arjay's gang on mouth organ and jugs) in *Eve of Destruction, Season of the Witch.* Teeny bop chicks with tambourines fill a break with a swaying, free-form, *Hare Krishna.* Becomes *Marijuana* halfway through.

A black sailor, sweat gleaming on his broad nose, like Floyd Patterson before the Liston fights, outwardly discusses his fear of combat for the first time.

A kid from the Church stares straight at the FBI spies in the Bank Building with his *own* binoculars.

But there was something wrong. It could be *felt* in the atmosphere around the middle class revolutionaries and their pale, now-unshaven charges. I was not alone in feeling it. Older Movement people, and some of the younger veterans, without detectable rancor or jealousy, could only cluck tongues, shake heads. The revolution this wasn't, and what it was could be mighty horrifying to behold.

For instance, when the guitarist had turned everyone on to *Season of the Witch,* the Resistance aides began whispering, disappearing, and arriving with bongos, etc. — like kindergarten teachers. "We've got them interested! Take advantage!" Then much of the love-communication and community-touch action I observed resembled nothing so much as "copping a feel." And, if I was not myself entirely without sin, I was still repulsed by its pretense here—like watching one of those fat Scoutmaster pederasts goosing the cubs in the name of Freedom.

It wasn't precisely that. It was heterosexual (predominantly, anyhow: one heard persistant rumors about late night Men's Room activity, and one of the Resistance Cadre minced and lisped deliciously after certain of the enlisted men like a mother hen); the participants were by-and-large attractive and young; it was directed by a man of the cloth (Warner was described to me by one Resistance member as 'the preacher with the constant erection'); thus did he "wrestle with alternatives to the military," and its *raison d'etre* was its function in the advancement of a larger Cause. It was while pondering the question of commitment to this cause that a voice, admittedly conservative, a kind of atavism of the Hemingway mood of the last generation, whispered: "What is this? An effective protest against War, against Viet Nam, or a vast circle jerk in love beads?"

Disturbing images occurred and recurred: the sullen look in the eyes of a lonely GI who has been flirted with, or seduced, by a Resistance honey only to find in the morning that he had been an experiment in Peace and Freedom and not the Love object, in the old stud sense, he considered himself. Or McClane's girlfriend, pretty, with vacuous blue-grey eyes and the painfully diffident manner of the True Disciple, talking to visitors when the least pleasant of the AWOLs, aspect of the barracks leech, slinks by and passes his hand lingeringly over her buttocks. "Oh dear," she says, "it's such a shame. There just aren't enough girls to go around . . . I've tried calling some of my friends but . . ." She looks off into space, abstracted by the logistical problems of Supply, of giving happiness to the deprived rest of the world.

And *give* is the operative word. The ultimate aura, which subsumed the comparisons made before—Boy Scout, Summer Camp, etc.—was the awful sense that every action on the part of the Resistance Sanctuary Committee presumed a moral, intellectual, Christ!

sensual inferiority on the part of the GI's. The Church of the Crossroads had become the great isosceles triangle of the spiritual handout.

The gifts being dispensed were body and soul of the superficial side of the New Generation: beads (remember the Indians!), dope (One GI who had been having "emotional" problems was taken to a private apartment and *given* some LSD as "therapy." Bad trip. Much gnashing of teeth back at the Chapel.); sex; and "counseling," that great catch-all of condescension. They interfered with those very gut matters which are the last existential province of the private citizen, how we get high and how we make love. No chickenshit Lieutenant or hardass DI ever presumed to interfere to such a degree with a "troop."

This masquerade, complacent superiority posing as communal Love, had, of course, been the source of the bad vibrations in the air. It was not only anti-Revolutionary, it was Medieval, elitist. I had noted, early on, that not 10% of the GIs would have had the opportunity or the inclination to consort with such as the Resistance people on the "outside." Now, it became an evil statistic. They were basically lower-middle or working class and uneducated, victims of the inequitable draft system now being exploited by those who could afford to evade it.

This complacency was the worm in the intestine of Bob Warner's rhetoric: "Our days are spent devouring huge home-cooked meals and organizing and carrying on the work necessary to spread the good news of the community."

"We are not *military* but our love is certainly *militant.* Although we will not injure, we will fight. Armed with the disarming weapons of love we are moving out." Lyndon Johnson's banality lives!

Sleazy innuendo: "There are sisters from the Movement here day night working in the kitchen, in the office and generally talking with and supporting these men in a way only a woman can do."

Or, "The excitement, enthusiasm, and joy here are boundless. We can truly say that we are *celebrating* our acts of conscience." But what of the guy facing the choice between 5 years in Leavenworth or getting his ass shot off in Viet Nam? How *boundless* is his joy?

Certainly, this was the blindness in the heart of Curt McClane's crusading spirit. He insisted, all the time I was there, that he had well in hand the disposition of Tim, the runaway who was being held in the Detention Home. Curt had a solemn luncheon at the house for a YMCA board member, and a hilarious evening meeting with a tough Job Corps advisor from Brooklyn: neither understood a word the other said. Then he moved to the Church and assumed his heavy duties as roommate of Warner and Danny Overstreet (and their ladies), general aide de camp, and official photographer. After the kid had been in the lock-up for a month, Curt was asked what he intended to do about it. The kids in the tent, and, presumably, Timmy, had boundless faith in his power to overcome the authorities.

"I'm getting him released in my custody," he said.

"But," someone replied, "You're only twenty years old, you have no income and no place of your own to live."

"That's OK," snorted Curt, dismissing the matter.

When I left, Tim was still in the Detention Home.

His next project, after the Sanctuary was over, was to open a "new kind of school."

"It'll be revolutionary," he said. "We'll give the kids love and freedom—dispense with the artificial structures of society. Get them away from their parents' values. It'll teach love to everybody and when these kids become adults, they'll change society."

"How are you going to finance it?"

"Well, for a start, I guess we'll just be able to take rich kids. We'll have to charge an *awful* lot."

I participated in endless discussions as to how Warner's self-indulgence and McClane's stupidity (which are, I guess, the same thing) could be so pervasive in the Sanctuary. There *were* Resistance leaders, notably John Witeck, who was awaiting trial for refusing induction himself, who seemed intelligent and aware of things, though perhaps a bit overcome by

circumstances. One person suggested the Lotus-eating irrelevance of a Surfing-Tourist society; another attributed it to Hawaiian "time-lag": everything gets to Hawaii 6 months after it is judged passé or irrelevant on the mainland. Some insiders claimed that the fragmentation of the Resistance by the defection of a Third World Wing had left the regular, white, middle class wing grasping for straws of self-assertion and publicity.

By the time I left, things had quieted down considerably. Bad publicity had driven the Church members to call a meeting which restricted activities and cut down on the use of the place as a crash pad. A Unitarian Church had accepted a few of the GIs (and, I understand, this annex was run on a low key, the future of the AWOLs being of primary consideration.) And, as the Army had anticipated—by not making a bust just yet—a few turned themselves in. One of them, Vincent Ventimiglia was picked up gangster-Judas style while having dinner with his parents who had come from Brooklyn to see him at a restaurant. They had notified the MPs themselves.

Overstreet, who often seemed the most self-aware and mature of the bunch, conferred with a lawyer one Saturday (he was advised to cop a plea on a back injury) and was gone Sunday morning. He left no note for the Resistance Committee, nor for his wife, who had seemed to be actually enjoying the Sanctuary.

Later, in New York I was to see Lou Jones and Buffy Parry on the Walter Cronkite Show. They had been flown to an Episcopal convention at Notre Dame to make a plea for general sanctuary for draft resisters by the Church.

On September 13, 1969, this article appeared in the *New York Times:*

Honolulu, Sept. 12
Military Policemen raided three churches today and seized a dozen antiwar servicemen who had taken "sanctuary" within the last six weeks.

Scores of uniformed men moved into the churches at dawn and quickly took the AWOL-servicemen into custody. They offered no resistance.

The MP's broke down a door in one of

*the churches to get into locked offices.
They were searching for several other
anti-Vietnam war soldiers and sailors who
had taken sanctuary.*

*A military spokesman said the other
eight or nine men had not been arrested
because "they weren't around." But
arresting officers promised they would
be back.*

What of the "other eight or nine?" What
of the *principle* of sanctuary, of loyalty, of
commitment to the public statement of
opposition to the war and unified passive
resistance to the authorities? *Resistance
Notes,* the Movement newsletter, clarified
the issue, and with characteristic
rationalization, destroyed the last vestige
of respect one might have had for them:

*We find we must speak for several men who
are not in a position to speak for themselves
at this point, in a reply to a Star-Bulletin
editorial (Honolulu establishment daily)
accusing them of cowardice. As the papers
have reported, a number of men once in
sanctuary have been picked up at Honolulu
International Airport. These men were on
their way to mainland rendezvous to spread
the word of resistance to military injustice
on the mainland. They were not running
away from their stated commitment of
opposing the inhumanity of military
existence. There are things happening.
Sanctuary is not dead, it's simply gone
underground until an opportunity arises
for it to surface effectively.*

On one of my last nights in Hawaii, I
stopped by the church. A TV crew was
there, the cameraman trying to pack a
group together so they could appear,
laughing and talking, on the next day's
news. A woman standing next to me began
to scream: "Clare, Clare!"

A TV man and Warner's serious graduate
student aide hurried over to shush her.
She wouldn't shut up. "Goddammit Clare,
get out of there. You *promised* me you
wouldn't get on television." The spot was
finished. She walked away, shaking her
head. "That girl. She always has to be in
the middle of everything."

It was very quiet. The Church members
were having a meeting to discuss the
problem of the Sanctuary. They could be
heard singing, "Oh, God, Our Help in Ages
Past." I decided to sneak around to an
open window to hear what they were
saying, being technically uninvolved and,
I guess, guiltless. As I rounded the corner,
I discovered Curtis McClane curled into
a corner, his ear against the wall. He started.

"Well," I said jovially, "we've caught one
another spying." He grunted and pushed
past me, his head down. I lingered for just
a moment, the congregation was just as
boring as one might expect, and walked
back across the triangle of lawn. The night
was quite dark and, with the relative quiet
and official drone emitting from the chapel,
the place for a moment actually felt like a
church, a monastery, perhaps, with the
monks sneaking cigarettes in the shadows.
There was a bulletin board I hadn't seen
before. It was full of Duty Rosters, even
a guard Duty chart, not so much to watch
for a bust as to protect against hostile local
elements. The military efficiency of the
board made me realize what had always
disturbed me about McClane: he was a
perfect example of the sort of fellow who
volunteers for squad leader in Basic
Training, the Eagle Scout. The fact was,
I thought, that at the Sanctuary he had
displayed precisely those talents he should
in principle have despised, those of a small-
time military gent: a taste for petty
bureaucracy, an uncritical enthusiasm
for any undertaking endorsed from higher
up, a profound belief that he was absolutely
essential to the movement's success, a total
lack of a sense of humor concerning
himself or it (which were, to him, essentially
the same: *L'état c'est moi*). Momentarily,
I conceived of a fantasy: the church
becomes a barracks; two of the GI's about
to go on guard duty are polishing their
boots.

"If," says one, "we ever get into combat,
I'm gonna shoot that motherfucking Lt.
Warner in the back of the head."

"Nah," drawls the other, "it's not his
doin' that we got stuck with duty again.
It's that dude, Sgt. McClane. If Ah ever see
him at the beer hall or out on a pass, Ah'm
gonna put my E-3 low quarter up his E-5
ass."

But it's not really funny. The guys who were standing up to the military were getting hurt. And the shadow of fatuity which dominated on their horizon was reflected in a poem signed by McClane and tacked to the bulletin board:

On the 6th there was only one
        & a few good friends
On the tenth we marched   hundreds
That night there were 7, 8
        and many good friends
Over the fence came number 9
Ten, a few minutes later
    Tomorrow?
Now we groove together   a community
There is peace
      Now
        at Crossroads
And with every minute it looks better
Eat, rap, sing and dance, time to think
A community
But some don't know   they put us down
And all they need is love
I love you

V   DEPARTURE: PRESSED VERONICA PLUS . . .

The Honolulu International Center is one of those white-and-silver domed performing arts and sports centers common to newly expanding cities. I should imagine Virginia Beach has one and Phoenix at least two. The long-awaited Blind Faith concert, the last on their tour, took place there a few hours before I was to fly to the mainland. I had frequented the Hershey (Pa.) Arena in the days of the first big Rock shows (c.1955), had teetered in the balcony for Alan Freed's midnight shows at the Brooklyn Fox, and, as I've said, visited the Fillmore East. They had nothing on the Honolulu International Center that night.

The dome is encircled by an open air corridor, which is separated from the outside by a moat. All through the evening before the show, bands of bare-chested long-haired boys and bikini-topped, slender girl-children roved around the center. Occasionally one or two would leap into the moat and try to wade into the corridor area. A cop would detach himself from his post at the door and knock the kids back into the moat. Then someone would open

as many doors as possible from the inside while the cop was distracted (Nancy of the Cowbell liberated at least two doors successfully. Even that night she looked like she'd been playing in the dirt.), and hordes of kids would pour through the door until the cop could regain his position. Pandemonium, as they say, reigned.

Inside, as Winwood, Grech, Clapton, and Baker begin, kids seem to be tripping all over the arena. Joints are passed from plastic seat to plastic seat through the air-conditioned darkness. Figures flit by, convulsed in macabre, solo dances. One boy cartwheels down to the arena on the side of the stage where I am standing. A cop grabs him and throws him against the wall, off which he rebounds like a slightly deflated basketball off a backboard, cartwheeling away. A few moments later he is standing precariously on someone's shoulders directly in front of Clapton. Ginger Baker begins "Do What You Like."

Veering in and out of traffic on the road to the airport in a station wagon big as a pullman car with eight stoned teenagers, my head is still full of the sweatless pale British working class face of Ginger Baker. It has been pressed on my mind like a Veronica of one of those plaster dying Christs found in impoverished Catholic churches. His trousers had been rolled up, exposing bone-thin calves incessantly pumping. Drumsticks.

Around the bard, like a massive halo, are the shaking, rocking heads of the children of paradise. Even the groupies behind the electronic equipment are strangely subdued by this frantic interaction of Baker's beatitude and these superb bodies. These children, I think, may be invulnerable, without liver, spleen . . .

Now, after the concert we have found a gas station. Three girls are singing Country Joe's "Feel Like I'm Fixin' To Die-Rag" in the back of the wagon:

"One-two-three, what are we fighting for,
Don't ask me, I don't give a damn,
Next stop is Vietnam . . ."

The car behind pulls alongside us at the pump. The driver comes over, shoulders his way past the attendant and leans into Matt's window. After a whispered conference, he strides away. They peel off down the road, V signs out of all the windows.

"What did he want?" Matt was asked.

"He wanted to sell me some Magic Mushroom," he bends over, giggling uncontrollably. "And *I* tried to sell him some *acid!*" V signs aloft, we spin out ourselves, winging it to the airport. The child's chorus resumes, shouting over the 60 mile-an-hour wind-roar of powerful cars on the Lunalillo Expressway:

"Come on, Mothers, throughout the land
Pack your boys off to Viet-Nam
Come on Fathers, don't hesitate,
Send 'em on before it's too late.
Be the first one on your block
To have your boy come home in a box . . ."

I remember what Arjay had said he was going to do with "the ten dollars my mommy laid on me."

"I'm going to buy a ticket to the concert, get a tab of acid, and *blow my mind,* man . . ." He looked down at the beach and played with some sand, his head nodding with a sense of nostalgia, of loss. "After that, I . . . I guess . . . it's . . . all over . . ."

Summer, that was.

Another Week on the Concord and Merrimack Rivers
RAY MUNGO

FOR STEVE LERNER, WHEREVER LOVE MAY FIND HIM

> *God help us,*
> *refugees in winter dress*
> *Skating home on thin ice*
> *from the Apocalypse.*
> Verandah Porche

To one who habitually endeavors to contemplate the true state of things, the political state can hardly be said to have any existence whatever. It is unreal, incredible, and insignificant to him, and for him to endeavor to extract the truth from such lean material is like making sugar from linen rags, when sugar-cane may be had. Generally speaking, the political news, whether domestic or foreign, might be written to-day for the next ten years with

sufficient accuracy. Most revolutions in society have not power to interest, still less alarm us; but tell me that our rivers are drying up, or the genus pine dying out in the country, and I might attend.
Henry D. Thoreau
A Week on the Concord and Merrimack Rivers

FRIDAY: PORTSMOUTH, N.H.

The farm in Vermont had fooled us, just as we hoped it would when we moved there in early '68; it had tricked even battle-scarred former youth militants into seeing the world as bright clusters of Day-Glo orange and red forest, rolling open meadows, sparkling brooks and streams. I had lived in industrial, eastern New England all my life, though, as well as worse places like New York and Washington, D.C., so I might have known better. But Vermont had blurred my memory, and when we finally left the farm for Portsmouth, I was all Thoreau and Frost, October up North, ain't life grand, all fresh and eager to begin rowing up the Concord and Merrimack rivers in the vanished footsteps of Henry D. himself. Verandah Porche, queen of the Bay State Poets for Peace, packed the failing '59 VW, and we went tearing down the mountain, kicking up good earth from the dirt road and barely slowing down for the eighteenth-century graveyard and all manner of wild animals now madly racing for shelter against the sharp winds of autumn in these hills. The frost was on the pumpkin, it was our second autumn together, and warm vibrations made the yellow farmhouse fairly glow in the dying daylight as we pointed east, over the Connecticut River, heading for our rendezvous with what *he* called "the placid current of our dreams." Knockout October day in 1969 in Vermont. All the trees had dropped acid.

The idea had come to me in a dream. It was one of those nights after Steve brought the Sunshine (wotta drug) when I'd wake up and sit bolt upright, alarmed at a sudden capacity, or *power,* I had acquired to *see far.* I could see eternity in the vast darkness outside my window and inside my head, and I remembered feeling that way when but an infant. In my dream, I was floating silently downstream in a birchbark canoe, speechless me watching vistas of bright New England autumn open up with each bend, slipping unnoticed between crimson mountains, blessing the warm sun by day and sleeping on beds of fresh leaves under a canary harvest moon by night. I was on the road to no special place, but no interstate highway with Savarinettes and Sunoco for this kid; I was, in my dream, on a natural highway through the planet, the ever-lovin' me-sustainin' planet that never lets you down. Said Henry: "I have not yet put my foot through it."

It was the farm that allowed me the luxury of this vision, for the farm had given me the insulation from America which the peace movement promised but cruelly denied. When we lived in Boston, Chicago, San Francisco, Washington (you name it, we lived there; some of us still live there), we dreamed of a New Age born of violent insurrection. We danced on the graves of war dead in Vietnam, every corpse was ammunition for Our Side; we set up a countergovernment down there in Washington, had marches, rallies, & meetings; tried to fight fire with fire. Then Johnson resigned, yes, and the universities began to fall, the best and oldest ones first, and by God, every thirteen-year-old in the suburbs was smoking dope and our numbers multiplying into the millions. But I woke up in the spring of 1968 and said, "This is not what I had in mind," because the movement had become my enemy; the movement was not flowers and doves and spontaneity, but another vicious system, the seed of a heartless bureaucracy, a minority party vying for power rather than peace. It was then that we put away the schedule for the revolution, gathered together our dear ones and all our resources, and set off to Vermont in search of the New Age.

The New Age we were looking for proved to be very old indeed, and I've often wondered aloud at my luck for being twenty-three years old in a time and place in which only the past offers hope and inspiration; the future offers only artifice and blight. I travel now in a society of friends who heat their houses with hand-cut wood and eliminate in outhouses, who cut pine shingles with drawknives and haul maple-sugar sap on sleds, who weed potatoes with their university-trained hands, pushing long hair out of their way and thus marking their foreheads with beautiful penitent dust. We till the soil to atone for our fathers' destruction of it. We smell. We live far from the marketplaces in America by our own volition, and the powerful men left behind are happy to have us out of their way. They do not yet realize that their heirs will refuse to inhabit their hollow cities, will find them poisonous and lethal, will run back to the Stone Age if necessary for survival and peace.

Yet this canoe trip had to be made because there was adventure out there. We expected to find the Concord and Merrimack rivers polluted but still beautiful, and to witness firsthand the startling juxtaposition of old New England, land and water and mountain, and new America, factories and highways and dams; and thus to educate ourselves further in the works of God and man. We pushed on relentlessly, top speed 50 mph, in our eggshell Volkswagen (Hitler's manifestly correct conception of the common man's car), 100 miles to the sea. The week following, the week we'd spend in our canoe, was the very week when our countrymen would celebrate Columbus Day (anniversary of the European discovery of Americans), the New York Mets in the World (American) Series, and the National Moratorium to demand an "early end to the war." Since we mourn the ruthless extinction of the natives, have outgrown baseball, and long ago commenced our own total Moratorium on constructive participation in this society, our presence and support were irrelevant to all of these national pastimes. We hoped only to paddle silently through the world, searching for traces of what has been lost.

Portsmouth was in an uproar.

George and Martha Dodge are the parents of the revolution as well as of seven sons, all of whom have now come home to Portsmouth, one of the oldest ports on the Atlantic side and of some importance to the United States Armed Forces. Gus, as he is nicknamed, is a respected physician in the city; Martha was a Nichols and still fries her own October doughnuts. Both are descendants of the oldest New England families, both old-fashioned, hospitable, warm, full of common sense, both admirers of Eldridge Cleaver and passionately involved, almost racked, in attempts to right some of the American wrongs. In short, they are good candidates for an old homestead in Vermont, and yet themselves the most attractive natural resource left in Portsmouth. Another feature of the town is its extraordinary number (and quality) of seventeenth-century and eighteenth-century houses, built with virgin lumber which has yet to begin rotting or even chipping, but many of these houses are being stupidly and arbitrarily destroyed. (More about this in a moment.) Their sons, youngest first, are Peter, fourteen, who claims he can drive a motorcycle; Hovey, sixteen, who puts together electronic systems, including piecemeal stereo systems capable of blasting out "Goddamn the Pusher Man" and other hits from *Easy Rider* at astonishing volume and fidelity; Frank, nineteen, an accomplished cellist; Mark, twenty-two, a soulful painter; Laurie, twenty-five, a New Age carpenter; David, twenty-seven, a man of many pursuits, who at the moment is restoring his house on South Street; and Buzzy, the oldest but no particular age, who can do anything.

It was Buzzy we had come to get, for Buzzy was our Native Indian Guide to the Concord & Merrimack Rivers, and Buzzy could do anything. Had not Buzzy camped out at 60 below zero in Alaska? Wasn't it Buzzy who ran the rapids of the Pemigewasset? Didn't Buzzy fix the freezer with a clothespin or something? Buzzy can build a fire out of wet pine, sleep in a hollow log, make a shed into a mansion, or scale a snow-peaked mountainside. If you are thinking of some perilous undertaking, my friend, my advice is to take Buzzy along. He is gifted with a calm and intelligent temperament, and a general all-around competence which is nothing less than astounding, particularly to half-freaked former militants trying gamely to live the life and discover what the planet is made up of.

We went over to the main house, the Dodge Commune I called it, where the canoe was waiting for us, stored in the garage alongside children's bicycles, rakes, spare parts, nuts-and-bolts jar, the accumulation of seven sons' childhoods in Portsmouth by the sea. Our old friend Laurie, who lived with us in Vermont before the inexplicable magnet of Portsmouth drew him away, took us aside for a long walk through the Desolation Row of fine old buildings scheduled for demolition by Portsmouth Urban Renewal, and he showed us these houses from a carpenter's careful perspective. We touched the beams fourteen inchs thick, the planks wider than an arm-span, and gingerly stepped over broken glass where vandals had wrecked and robbed after the tenants of these buildings were forced to leave. There had been no protest over the demolition of the seventeenth century in Portsmouth, not more than a whimper really, and I felt my long-dormant sense of outrage beginning to rekindle, and I knew I had to split. For outrage leads to action, and action leads . . . where? Usually into a morass. It was strange, though, my outrage reborn not over some plan for future progressive society, but over concern for preservation of ancient hoary stuff from way back. That kind of stuff, I had always thought, is for Historical Society ladies. But when the whole world becomes one McDonald's hamburger stand after another, you too will cry out for even a scrap of integrity.

Back at the Dodge Manse, everything was in healthy chaos as the entire family readied for a trip to Martha's mother's farm in Sturbridge, Mass. The driveway was lined with vehicles which showed the scars of their years of heavy use. Laurie's red pickup was chosen to carry the canoe, first to Sturbridge, then back to Boston (Cambridge), from which it would be driven on a friendly Volvo station wagon to Concord, Mass., where the river trip would begin. Laurie danced in his boots as he painted OCTOBER 15 in big black letters on the sides of the upturned canoe; good advertising for the Moratorium, he said.

Porche and I hadn't counted on a Dodge excursion, and we found ourselves with two days to kill as Saturday dawned. To stay in Portsmouth with the Dodges all gone would have been too depressing, we agreed, so we repacked camping gear and artifacts of outdoor living into aforementioned VW, and decided to wait it out in old college hangouts, blast from the past, in Cambridge.

We split the map south along the green line designated as the Atlantic, uncomplicated by route numbers and little Esso markers, went to hole up in of all places Cambridge.

SUNDAY: CAMBRIDGE, MASS.

I was reading the Boston Sunday *Globe* financial section for lack of other employment or reading matter when I came upon a news account of the spectacular success of a chain of artsie-fartsie shops called Cambridge Spice and Tea Exporters (or something close to that). These shops sell ornaments for the home, bamboo dingdongs to hang over the window, incense, colorful but useless items of all sorts; and the proprietor was there quoted to the effect that the word "Cambridge" on the shops gives them a magic quality which brings in the bread right quick. And of course! Funny I never realized it before, but Cambridge is the home base, one of the centers at least, of useless conceits for the affluent American, including the long-haired variety. Harvard University, if I may say so, could vanish tomorrow (in fact it *may*) with no appreciable loss to the physical or intellectual health of the nation. Those who wished to study Catullus would continue to do so; and those whose lives are considerably less earnest would doubtless find some other occupation, perhaps more rewarding, than hanging out in the Yard.

The great irony of Cambridge is that despite its vaunted status as a center of the arts, education, technology, and political wisdom, it is in reality a Bore. It stultifies, rather than encourages, productive thought and employment, by throwing up countless insuperable obstacles to peace of mind and simple locomotion from one place to another. Why, if all the creative energy expended in Cambridge on paying telephone bills, signing documents, finding a cab, buying a milk shake, bitching at the landlord, and shoplifting from the Harvard Coop could be channeled into writing, playing, loving, and working, the results would probably be stupendous. At the moment, it is simply a marketplace of fatuous ideas and implements for those who seek to amuse themselves while Babylon falls around them. Thoreau on Boston: "I see a great many barrels and fig-drums—piles of wood for umbrella-sticks—blocks of granite and ice—great heaps of goods, and the means of packing and conveying them—much wrapping-paper and twine—many crates and hogsheads and trucks—and that is Boston. The more barrels, the more Boston. The museums and scientific societies and libraries are accidental. They gather around the sands to save carting. The wharf-rats and customhouse officers, and broken-down poets, seeking a fortune amid the barrels." *(Cape Cod)*

Although we grew up, intellectually and emotionally at least, in Cambridge, and once made the big scene there in scores of apartments and houses, V and I now could find only one friendly place to lay our heads and weary bums, and that was Peter Simon's. Everybody who sees his best work agrees that Peter is an extraordinary photographer, mean competition for Cartier-Bresson and Arthur d'Arazien so to speak, and only a kid at twenty-one. We went looking for Peter's head of wild curly red hair, he looks like a freaked-out Howdy Doody really, sure that when we found it there'd be new Beatles and Band music, orange juice in the fridge, place to take your shoes off; and so there was.

We had brought along for the canoe trip the kinds of things that made sense: sleeping bags, tarp, tools, cooking utensils, potatoes and other vegetables we'd grown in the summer, several gallons of honest-to-God Vermont water (safe bacterial content) in the event the waters of the Merrimack should be beyond boiling. We couldn't bake bread on the riverbanks, surely, as we do at home, and sensing that Henry's advice on buying bread from farmers just didn't apply these days, I went to a local sooper-dooper and acquired two loaves of Yah-Yah Bread at 20 cents the loaf, and almost as an afterthought, got a jar of Skippy Peanut Butter for about 40 cents. The Yah-Yah Bread was packed in a psychedoolic magenta plastic with cartoons of hipsters (one boy, one girl) on the outside and Avalon Ballroom lettering, the kind you must twist your head to read, so it did catch my eye. And I have liked Skippy since I discovered (1) peanuts will not grow very well in Vermont; (2) the jar can be used as a measuring cup (but only when it's empty); (3) the Skippy heiress is twenty-two and some kind of pill freak who busts up cocktail parties in New York. I noticed that the Skippy contained no BHA or BHT but that the Yah-Yah Bread did; these chemicals are often called "preservatives," and although I can't responsibly suggest they will kill *you,* they do contain the element which makes most commercial foods taste *dead.* We have found that an astonishingly wide variety of food items contain BHA or BHT or both, so I can only conclude that most of my countrymen subsist on the stuff. They are hooked. The sole advantage of preservatives to the consumer, it seems, is that he can now save money by buying day-old or month-old baked goods and be certain that they will taste like cold putty no matter their birthday. We did spend a goodly part of the harvest season giving away all the fruits and vegetables we couldn't use to city people (old friends and family), who freaked out on what a tomato, or a peach, really is. The middle-aged and elderly ones remembered; the young ones learned. One and all reflected on how sinister & subtle the Dead Food craze came on, how you didn't notice it taking over until it was too late. The old Victory Garden thing may be in for a revival, friends, but I suspect it will reach only a marginal part of the population; the others will be too busy at the shop or office, dump DDT or other chemical killers on their crop, or be afraid to eat an ear of corn that's white, a tomato with a hole in it, a carrot with dirt on it. Tough luck for them what think it's easier to go to the sooper-dooper and get those nice *clean* apples wrapped in cellophane, uniform in size and shining

like mirrors, the kind I have never seen growing on any tree. How about *you?*

We escaped the supermarket, thus, without being tempted by the Meat, Poultry, or Vegetable departments, not to mention the paperbacks and plants. And we then did what everybody does in Cambridge, which amounted to what Bob Dylan called Too Much of Nothing. We waited for the morning to come, the daybreak which would put us on the rivers in our canoe at last; we got stoned and listened to the Beatles; we got bored and went out to spend some money, finally choosing a hip movie house on Massachusetts Avenue and killing some hours in old Orson Welles. We did not get raped, mugged, or robbed as it turned out. We heard the noises and smelled the smells, drank the water and breathed the air. It was altogether quite a risky adventure. Our guides, Plucky Peter and his lady friend Nancy, who is only seventeen, could not have been more hospitable and reassuring; in fact, they agreed to accompany us on parts of the river trip, grateful for some excuse to cut boring college classes, they said. And Nancy even cooked a fine meal out of some farm vegetables, on a stove which produced instant heat from gasoline which comes from under the street!

The canoe arrived after dark, good old Buzzy with it, spinning yarns of rapids and dams, islands to camp on (the name Merrimack meant to the natives "river of many islands"), wild animules, the likelihood of rain. He and Verandah went to sleep early; I stayed up nervously watching commercials on television (including the post-midnight Stoned Voice urging kids not to smoke dope *because it's illegal*), went to sleep on the floor, and dreamed of wild muskrats and other creatures of the past.

MONDAY: CONCORD, MASS.

Monday dawned quietly even in the Hub of the Universe, for Monday this time around was a holiday, the day after Columbus Day. I guessed that those who had gone off on three-day weekends had not yet returned, and the others were all sleeping late; because here it was Monday morning and Central Square was not putrid with humanity, just a few winos hanging around and no policemen for traffic. The canoe advertising OCTOBER 15 was loaded onto Peter's Volvo while I hurry-hid my VW in the neighbor Harry's backyard; Harry was not around anyway, Harry had split to Vermont, but I left Harry a note explaining that since his backyard was full of garbage anyway, it might as well have my VW. Our canoe was eighteen feet long and three feet wide, bright orange, and aluminum. Buzzy had fashioned wheels for it out of a block of wood and two old tricycle wheels, not unlike Thoreau's contraption, I thought. They gave the canoe a faithful if bumpy ride around dams and such.

We took Route 2 past the shopping plazas and biochemical warfare factories out to Concord. There are two sets of signs in Concord, one leading to Walden, the other to the Concord Reformatory. The former is a state park with rules and regulations posted on the trees, the latter a prison for boys with a fancy-pants highway sign in front: "Welcome to Concord, Home of Emerson, Thoreau, and the Alcotts." The Reformatory, a vast gray dungeon, is complemented by a farm where, I am told, the Boys learn vital agricultural skills. And not a few other tricks. Pity the Boy who grows up in Massachusetts, if it has as many gray stone towers to enclose him as it seems.

We stopped for advice, which way to the Concord River please, at a gas station. The man there obliged us, but all the while acting like we were wasting his valuable time. There were no other customers. The spot he led us to proved to be a park, full of monuments and walkways, grass mowed as with a Gillette Techmatic, but a lovely spot notwithstanding. As we readied the canoe for embarkment, a uniformed gent approached us grimly, and I was sure there'd be some Commonwealth law against canoes, but no, he merely wanted to admire the rig and satisfy his curiosity. It is quite legal to launch your boat in Concord still, though they have placed speed-limit signs on the bridges ("River Speed Limit: 10 MPH. ENFORCED"), and so we rolled ours to

what looked like a good place and waited a moment, very like the moment you take before diving off a high covered bridge into a gurgling freshwater pond in July. Peter took funny-face pictures, while a small band of strollers, tourists or townspeople, who can tell the difference, leaf-peepers we called them because they took Kodak Brownie shots of this or that red tree, gathered about to watch and wave. There was no obvious animosity between us this bright morning, for unlike at the gas station, we were together in the beauty of the place and it was a great day for a boat trip. Something in all men smiles on the idea of a cruise up the planet. We knew we'd be heading downstream, or north, to the mouth of the Merrimack, but the river itself had no easily discernible current; rather it looked from the shore like a quiet and friendly scar on the earth, made of such stuff you could put your foot through. Buzzy knew by some mysterious instinct which way was north, but I argued the point for a while. Then, as we were climbing into our silent craft, a noisy crowd of Canadian honkers drifted into view overhead, flying V-formation (V for victory, Vietnam, Verandah, Vermont) due south, and I declare even the tired holiday crowd broke into smiles. Canada geese over Concord; it's enough to make you believe in God.

"The Musketaquid, or Grass-ground River," Henry writes, "though probably as old as the Nile or Euphrates, did not begin to have a place in civilized history until the fame of its grassy meadows and its fish attracted settlers out of England in 1635, when it received the other but kindred name of CONCORD from the first plantation on its banks, which appears to have been commenced in a spirit of peace and harmony. It will be Grass-ground River as long as grass grows and water runs here; it will be Concord River only while men live peaceable lives on its banks. To an extinct race it was grass-ground, where they hunted and fished; and it is still perennial grass-ground to Concord farmers, who own the Great Meadows, and get the hay from year to year." Of course, get the hay! But the Great Meadows are mostly woods now, called the Great Meadows National Wildlife Refuge, according to the brightly painted signs posted here and there on the banks, obviously intended for the information of those who would ride the river in boats. And as we paddled along, we did meet other boats, speedboats mostly with vroom-vroom motors and gaseous fumes. The drivers circled our canoe and laughed as it rocked in the unnatural waves of their passing. One old couple, strictly Monet, paddled a tiny wisp of a canoe. Despite everything, though, the land *did,* goddamn it, open in a great vista, rising up on both sides to support scampering squirrels and the like, and while it lasted the National Wildlife Refuge seemed to me a worthy piece of territory.

Buzzy tired of the paddles before Porche and I did, and over our protests, elected to turn on his pint-sized outboard which went bap-bap rather than vroom-vroom and moved the canoe no faster than the paddles but with less effort on our part of course. I used this respite from work to survey the terrain with the close eye of loving ignorance, and I watched the Wildlife Refuge become plain old Concord and a pastel ranch house come into view. Everything moved so slowly, it was like a super-down drug, and we were spared no details of this modern American prefab architecture—and, beyond it, the rising towers of yon civilization. Fishermen began to appear, at first alone and then in groups; and though we dutifully inquired of each what he had caught that morning, we never found a man with so much as a catfish to show for his efforts. Clearly, I thought, it is Columbus Day (or the day after) and these people are fishing for old times' sake and not in hopes of actually catching something. The last group of fishers were segregated—a half dozen white people on one side of the Concord, and as many black people on the other. The river was narrow and shallow enough at that point to walk across, so I guessed that these people wanted it that way, preferred at least to do their fruitless casting among friends. Soon enough, several hours later, we were in Carlisle, at the Carlisle Bridge, and I'd become concerned that the river still showed no sign of a current. It was just about standing still and we the only

moving things in the landscape. Verandah trailed her fingers through the water from the bow. From my perch in the center, I remarked, "It's pretty, but it's dead."

"Maybe we're all dead" was all she said.

From Carlisle, where we met Peter Simon and enjoyed a Skippy and Yah-Yah lunch, we went on to Billerica with high hopes of making Lowell that day and thus getting over the New Hampshire border the next. For reasons obviously unassociated with fact, I expected the scenery, colors, and water in New Hampshire must be superior to those in Massachusetts, and we reassured ourselves that, bad as the Concord was now becoming, we were at least taking the worst medicine first. The entrance to Billerica by water resembles the old MGM view of distant forts in the Wild West; for the first sign of the approaching town is an American flag flapping in the breeze like somebody's long johns on the line, planted on a hideous red-brick mill with a mammoth black smokestack. No smoke today, though, for it was a holiday, remember (and we do need constant reminders on days like Columbus Day and Washington's Birthday, so difficult has it become for us to *relate* to them), and the only sign of life was a wilted elderly watchman, who sat behind the factory gates merely watching cars go by. The mill, called the North Billerica Company (presumably manufacturers of North Billericas), was built on a dam, which we didn't notice until we very nearly went over it, and seemed to be rooted in the water itself. That is, the sides of the buildings extended below the river line, making the banks absolutely inaccessible except through the mill yard itself, for several hundred yards. And the watchman, clearly, was the old Keeper of the Locks whom Henry had charmed into letting him pass on the Sabbath. Thus did this kind man unchain the gates of the North Billerica Company and lead us through to the safe side of the dam—where, for the first time, we paddled through water actually being used, before our very eyes, as an open sewer. Worse yet, we recognized that the scuz & sludge pouring forth from the mill through six-inch drainpipes would follow us downstream, that it was, in fact, better to navigate on dead but quiet waters than on water teeming with Elimination, at times even belching out gaseous bubbles, and smelling like fresh bait for tsetse flies and vultures. From North Billerica to the end of our journey, we would see only two other craft on these waters, one a crude raft bearing three boys (more or less ten years old) and a smiling dog, straight Huck Finn stuff, but the kids said not a word as we passed them by, and the other a hardware-store rubber bathtub floating two thirteen- or fourteen-year-old boys who were headed for Concord Reformatory, you could just tell. This latter pair were reincarnations of the Bad Boys I'd known back in Lawrence, which is on the Merrimack, boys whom I had joined in some Bad adventures on the river until I finally couldn't make their grade.

Boys will find charm in junk, as every red-blooded small-town scoutmaster knows; boys will hang around burnt-out houses, old railroad yards, town dumps, the backs of breweries, and find there unlimited access to toys for the body and mind. We met these two as our canoe bumped to a stop against huge rocks surrounding a factory which had burned to the ground, only the smokestack erect, nobody else around, as we hauled our gear out of the boat onto broken glass and pieces of brick and charred timbers that fell through when you stepped on them, in this unspeakably North Vietnamese place, Dresden in Billerica, this corner of Massachusetts which could be the scene after World War III. The boys informed us in a heavy local accent—Oh, yah, Oh, yah—that we'd pass "three rapids and a dam" before the Concord emptied into the Merrimack in Lowell, then left us alone again. Buzzy ran the first set of rapids alone while Verandah and I hauled knapsacks and sleeping bags, paddles and outboard through the wreckage to the place where the river deepened. It was then that we began to notice the trees; even the trees in this place were palsied and skinny, their colors muted. An old stump I was using for support caved in on me. And to venture anywhere near the trees or brush meant to be covered with clinging brown dead burrs, pickies I call them, that fall into your

socks and irritate your skin. We were grateful to get back in the canoe and leave that nightmare once-and-past factory behind. It was the worst place I had ever lived, a place where nothing could be salvaged, not even a piece of wire or useful stick on the ground.

A mile or so downstream, just south of Lowell we reckoned, the second set of rapids began, and the canoe quickly became trapped between rocks, which shared the water now with old tires, a refrigerator, a washing machine, wrecked cars and trucks, metal hoops, and bobbing clumps of feces. Verandah had to get out in midstream to lighten our load, and she disappeared into the pickies. A little later, I too got out as the canoe turned sideways, broadstream, and Buzzy warned in a calm and dejected tone, "We are going to capsize very soon; we will capsize if we don't get out of here." Boots tied about my neck and dungarees rolled up over my knees, there's me slipping on rocks slimy with who wants to know what, making for a bank which appears impossible to scale. I lost sight of Buzzy as the canoe bounced and careened downstream, but caught Verandah in my free eye, silently waiting for me at the top of the rise. The current which was imperceptible before was ferocious now, as the shallow water rushed downhill over rocks left there by the Billerica dams; and more than once I felt myself falling over them too, breaking bones, I thought, in my mad rush to the sea. The bank, when I reached it, was knee-deep in garbage of all kinds—metal, paper, and glass. Rolls of toilet paper had been strung like Christmas tinsel on the brittle limbs of the trees, and cardboard containers by the hundreds, flattened by snow and made soggy by rain, had formed layers of mush. I was the creature from the black lagoon, or a soul in purgatory, stretching forth his hand for a lift out of my slime from the mysterious beautiful lady Up There.

When the ascent was made and breaths caught, we discovered ourselves in a railroad yard whose tracks were varnished amber with rust, and freight cars left there, open, to suffer all weather and never move again. Union Pacific, they proudly announced. Nobody was around. I fancied myself a television reporter for some new galaxy, bringing the folks back home a documentary of the continent on Earth that died: "It all began to break down, folks, in fourteen hundred and ninety-two, when Columbus sailed the ocean blue. To an extinct race, it was grass-ground river."

We walked the graveled planet now for maybe a half mile, shouting for Buzzy from time to time. We found him at the end of the third set of rapids with gloom all over his face. The canoe took a bad leap, he said, the outboard was lost somewhere under water too black to reveal it, the Yah-Yah bread soaked to the consistency of liquid BHT, all the bedding and clothing and food dripping wet.

And the sun was setting somehwere but we could not see it.

And the air was turning colder though we couldn't say why.

And the land was impossible to camp on; it would be a bed of broken glass and rusty nails.

Clearly we could only push on to Lowell, where Peter Simon had been waiting hours for us, no doubt, and push we did until we floated into the heart of that town after dark, almost bumping the edge of a vast dam in our blindness, then groping and paddling back and forth across this Concord to find a bank that was neither solid vertical concrete nor sealed off by a high chain link fence, operating by the light of the Lowell *Sun* neon billboard and finally hauling *October 15* from the water behind a taxicab garage and wheeling it through the crowded center of town, wondering where we could safely be alive.

Lowell is a sister city to Lawrence and Haverhill, all three being one-river towns born of the "industrial revolution" and very close in spirit to those almost charming images of factory towns in British literature from Blake to the Beatles. Ethnic neighborhoods remain, and national churches (mostly Catholic) thrive there still—the Greeks are still fiercely chauvinistic, the French Canadians still hard drinkers, the Italians still fond of block parties in honor of the Three Saints. There is a strikingly nineteenth-century downtown area, but despite the energetic promotion of the oldest merchants in town, it is slowly

corroding as it loses ground to the highway shopping plazas. Life there is sooty, and even the young people look hard and wrinkled. Though it is only a stone's throw from cultured, boring Boston, it may as well be a thousand miles away for all the intellectual influence it has absorbed. We didn't know it at the moment we were strolling down Central Street with the canoe between us, but Peter Simon had earlier fled the city, terrified at the fierce looks and obscene catcalls which his long hair had provoked. I was not afraid, though, for I knew that the natives, while resenting our freedom, were yet too pacified and dulled by their daily lives to risk energetic hostility on us. Strangers may securely enough walk the streets of Lowell, Lawrence, or Haverhill, for the locals will kill only each other. Arriving in Lowell was for me a grand homecoming.

Kerouac came back to Lowell after all those years making scenes, and that has scared me crazy since I've known who Kerouac was. "If all else fails," I thought, "we could always go see Kerouac, maybe he'd put us up." Came back to Lowell even though nobody goes anywhere from there, he must have come back to die, that's the only thing makes sense by the gee. Stopped writing he did, just sat there in crummy Lowell with beer and television and the Lowell *Sun* at four in the afternoon, delivered by the local altar boy at Saint Ann's, or Sacred Heart, or Saint Pat's. Was he an altar boy, choirboy, chief Boy Scout, candidate for the priesthood; did he win a Ladies Sodality scholarship, play football, play hooky, play on the big bad river? Kerouac, did you have a paper route and hit all the bars on Christmas Eve? Christ, Kerouac, you're blowing my mind living in Lowell, will you never go back to Big Sur? Kerouac, listen: Frost came from Lawrence too, but he *got out,* man, and he didn't come back. Robert Frost walked our neighborhoods, friend! Kerouac, see: Leonard Bernstein came from here, but *he* got out! Everybody from Lowell & Lawrence had half a break in this world *split.* You stay here, you're as good as dead, baby.

And while I thought these vibrations and rehearsed this conversation with the great author of *On the Road,* indeed at the very moment we were rolling our canoe down Central Street, the man himself *was* dead, though we didn't know it and I still can't say why. He was dead in Florida of too much Lowell, may he rest in peace under that holy graveyard soil on the edge of town. May he not smell the Merrimack River from where he lies. May we, his survivors, escape his fate.

We were befriended by a corpulent Boston *Record American* reporter (Hearst sheet, cheesecake & crime mostly), who put us and the canoe on the back of his truck, which he normally uses for carting secondhand furniture; man's got to make a living. He was also, he said, a member of the Lowell police force and found out about us from the police radio's moment-by-moment broadcast report of our progress through the city. He called the cops on a side-street phone and arranged for us to sleep on the Boulevard riverbank, past all the dams and fetid canals of Lowell, and there we took our rest at last. The Boulevard traffic passed several yards from our heads at 60 and 70 miles per hour, and some local teen-agers drove their jalopy up to our encampment with bright-lights on at 2 or 3 A.M., and the bank was littered with broken beer bottles, but I slept soundly nonetheless. We had no food now, so I got up in the night and walked up the Boulevard to where I knew an all-night pizza stand existed, and in the process, bumped into a parked car with two kids fucking noisily in the back seat. Of course, I thought, Lowell is the last place on the planet where kids still ball in Dad's car because there is no place to go, there are no private apartments for kids or independent kid-societies. Walking back with coffeecake and hamburgers, I noticed dozens of parked cars just off the road, a road without sidewalks, where nobody but me had walked for a long time. And just before I got back to our encampment, I met an old man with whiskey on his breath who looked me straight in the eye and said, "Going to Lawrence?"

Around midnight, a group of married couples had arrived with Dunkin' Donuts for us to eat; they had heard of the legendary canoe, it was all over town, they wanted to see if it was really so. One man used to fish for salmon in the Merrimack, but he "wouldn't piss in it now." His wife blamed the rich people who own the mills; they are the ones, she said, who have destroyed the water. All who came to talk with us that night said how many years had passed since they last saw a real boat seriously navigating up the Merrimack River. "Are you sure," one woman asked in a harsh voice, "nobody's makin' ya do it?"

TUESDAY: LOWELL, MASS.

Culture-hero Steve McQueen has said, "I would rather wake up in the middle of nowhere than in any city on earth." Naturally, I second that. Morning in Lowell cannot properly be called "sunrise," for it is the General Electric plant and not the burning star which first appears on the horizon. Our *Record American* reporter friend returned to take pictures of us for his newspaper, but we waited around a long time hoping for Peter Simon to arrive in the magic Volvo, which could both fetch new groceries and go searching for the lost outboard. We would be paddling upstream now, and in the face of a stiff wind, so the motor might have proved useful in a pinch. But there was no Peter, no coffee, no breakfast, and no hope, so we shoved off at 9 A.M. with only the Boston *Record American* for witness. We had camped, it turned out, next to a row of garbage cans on which somebody in Lowell (maybe someday she'll come, come, come along) had painted peace signs and slogans like "Smile on your brother" and "Let's clean up Big Muddy." It was a noble but pathetic gesture, this youthful assumption that the Dirt in the Merrimack was nothing worse than Mud, and that it could be cleaned up if only each of us smiled more. As the rows of factories proved beyond doubt, and there is something hard and undeniable in this, Lowell would cease to be Lowell if it did not pollute the Merrimack River. Lowell and its sister cities create shoes, textiles, and paper for you and me — who, as literate people, do not live on the Merrimack River anyway. The industries in Lowell pay their employees very poorly indeed, yet their profits cannot be what they used to be, for the shops are slowly and one-by-one closing down. We paddled furiously against the wind to get the hell out, aiming ourselves toward Tyngsboro by noon and Nashua, New Hampshire, by nightfall.

The Merrimack is substantially wider and deeper than the Concord, a real river and not just a stream, so for the first time I felt that flush of anxiety which comes after knowing you are too far out to swim back in the event of trouble. It was backaching work, but we could manage about two miles per hour, which seemed to me fast enough for any sensible voyage. I set myself little targets, such as the big drive-in movie screen on Route 113, and overtook each one in my stride. I enjoy slow progress and gradual change in my own life as much as I deplore it in social trends; but I am sufficiently tuned-in to the century to realize that we men never really get *anywhere.* It's always more of the same, so to speak — birth, life, death, walking abroad in a shower of your days, how soon having Time the subtle thief of youth stealing on his wing your three-and-twentieth year, etc. etc. Life does move exquisitely slow, all the crap in newspapers about "revolutionary developments" aside, and we do tend to end up where we started. The absurdity of our situation, too, lay in the fact that we could have gotten from Lowell to Tyngsboro in three minutes rather than three hours, but there was no reason to go to Tyngsboro *anyway* as none of us believed it would be the idyllic spot Henry described; thus we never felt we were *wasting time.*

Two or three miles up from Lowell, as we paddled through water absolutely white with swirling pools of some awful chemical substance, we heard Peter Simon's voice calling us from afar. He and Nancy were on the opposite bank, trapped in the Volvo by a pack of ravenous house dogs, yet overjoyed to have found us again. We paddled over to them and mutually decided on a spot just up a piece to disembark and confer. Verandah and Nancy stayed behind to cook a breakfast of oatmeal and eggs, while we menfolk took off in the car to look for that outboard, got a flat on the

Boulevard, got soaking wet, got in trouble with an elderly French-Canadian lady who objected to Buzzy's using her backyard as an approach to the river until I calmed her in the best Lawrence-Lowell half-Canuck accent I could muster from memories of my grandmother. In all, got nothing accomplished and returned to the breakfast site close to noon, Peter swearing it was gonna rain and Buzzy just swearing. The outboard had cost B his last $60, and was purchased especially for this trip; moreover, he was beginning to feel sick in the stomach, and wondered just what poisons we might be picking up from the fair Merrimack.

I wanted Pierre to join us at that point, abandon his car and get on the boat. Fancying myself Kesey and all of us Merry Pranksters, I said, "Peter, you must be On the Boat or Off the Boat." But Tuesday was a Mets day, Peter said, and though he would follow us upstream and generally watch out, he must stay close to the car radio to keep tabs on Tom Seaver and so-and-so's stealing third. It meant nothing to me, but since Peter thought it was important, who was I to belittle it? Some people get their energy off Kesey & Kerouac & Thoreau, others off Seaver and Swoboda; stocks and bonds, movies and periodicals, movements and rallies, rivers and oceans, balls and strikes; you name it, somebody lives on it. Friends of mine have been addicted to such dangerous drugs as television, bourbon, and the New York *Times,* daily *and* Sunday. I myself have been addicted to Pall Mall cigarettes for years, and have more than once gone hungry to support my habit; I am also a Black Coffee freak, and have been known to drink fifteen to twenty cups in a day. Everything in me which responds to reason prays for the imminent day when mass-produced and commercially distributed goods will simply stop coming, all the bright red Pall Mall trucks will break down in North Carolina and all the Colombian coffee boats rot in their harbors. Then we, poor weaklings, will have at least a chance to aspire to that personal independence which we all so desperately need. We will be addicted to making do for ourselves; each of us will be President of the

United States and responsible for the social welfare of the whole world; we will rise to our godheads at the same moment we stoop to gather scrap wood for the fire. We will be able to afford, then, to offer and accept a little help from our friends.

So Peter was hooked on the Mets, and there seemed no solution but to plan the rest of the trip *around* this handicap. Peter had to break camp early, drive to towns for newspaper reports of the previous day's game, leave the canoe to its own progress while he sought out television stores where the American Series would be coming across display color sets, return to us radiant with news of the latest victories. The Mets were *winners* at least, that's more than I could say for Pall Malls — which I consumed, though moderately, throughout the journey.

These pathetic addictions came together in Tyngsboro in an odd fashion. When we arrived at the bridge there, Peter was nowhere to be found, off watching the Mets; and we three were out of cigarettes and of course carrying no money. Buzzy, to the rescue, found a selection of old two-cent and nickel soda pop bottles embedded in the silt bank, and cashed them in for a pack of smokes at the variety store conveniently located on top of the bank. All else we found there was a single half-rotted sunfish, five inches or so, washed ashore.

We were always looking for "a nice little island" on which to camp. The only one we found that day was King's Island, which is now a golf course with buildings, garages, a bar, and a bridge to the highway. Three lady golfers, the kind with jewel-encrusted sunglasses roped to their necks on aluminum chains, spied us from the ninth hole, and one chirped, "Well, isn't that *adorable*." A painted sign on the bank read "Watch out for golf balls," and the river around the island had obviously become a God-made water trap for the wives of the Lowell-Nashua managerial class. It became evident near here, too, that many of the houses along the banks had eliminated the need for septic tanks by flushing directly into the river through underground pipes.

Both Buzzy and Verandah being now sick at their centers, and the prospect of

sleeping in industrial Nashua too bleak to consider, we elected after much procrastination to drive around that city altogether, and thus ended up resuming the trip and camping out in Bow Junction, New Hampshire, birthplace of Mary Baker Eddy. Peter parked the Volvo on what we assumed to be a lonely access road, and we paddled to what looked like a stretch of serious forest, arriving there just in time to spread out a few tarps and start a fire before dark fell. Stumbling about in the night in search of a place to Eliminate, I discovered that the woods were only 30 to 40 feet wide, bordered by the river on one side and a real, if dirt, road on the other; and they were only a quarter mile long, bordered by immense machines of one kind or other on either end. The access road was studded with houses suburban-style, whose lights shone brightly at us and were reflected in the water, and the traffic on it sounded high-speed. We had been once more cruelly tricked. Sirens filled the air and our heads. Brakes screeched and a metallic thud bounced off our ears. The quiet but persistent rumble of technology charged the atmosphere, never letting up; it was the trembling of the earth which you, friend, can hear tonight if you but focus your attention on it. The earth is crying; what can I do to help it? Give it a Demerol?

WEDNESDAY: BOW JUNCTION, N.H.

I love mankind but I hate the institutions of the dead unkind. Men execute nothing so faithfully as the wills of the dead, to the last codicil and letter. They rule this world, and the living are but their executors.
Thoreau
A Week on the Concord and Merrimack Rivers

When we were babes in college and thought ourselves the only people in America smart enough to be unilaterally opposed to the United State's presence in Vietnam, we'd sit around the Protestant house at BU, though we were none of us Protestants, and say, "This war won't end until every mother who loses a son, every wife who loses a husband, knows that their men died *in vain*." As long as the families of the 42,000 dead in fruitless combat could congratulate themselves on giving a boy to the good cause, more deaths would be unavoidable, we analyzed. It seemed the very will of the dead that America continue its genocidal assault on the East, the voices of those Southside Bad Boys crying out, "Get him back, Emile!" to the runty kid from Sacré Coeur Parish. I'm not sure when this attitude began to corrode, sometimes I flatter myself with the thought that I did my part to bring it about (though a fat lot of good it has done over *there*); but I see with my own eyes that the wife of a dead Marine in Manchester, New Hampshire, on the Merrimack, refuses to have her husband's coffin draped in the Stars and Stripes. There is great mourning in New Hampshire over a group of six men who came back in boxes; five are buried with all attendant military honors, the sixth with Bob Dylan and angry rhetoric. In Manchester, New Hampshire, the most reactionary town in all of New England. So the will of the dead is *now* that we take revenge on the government, on Lyndon Johnson (remember that stinker?) and Richard Nixon and Lew Hershey, McNamara, Rusk, Rostow, Clifford, Laird, Westmoreland, Abrams, as if these men together and alone caused it to happen, and not the entire lot of us. The American people, in taking revenge on the gooks, have all but destroyed the paradisal terrain and refined culture of Vietnam; now they will turn on themselves and do the same at home. What is ambiguously called "the system" will crumble and fall, it is all too clear. The economy, military effectiveness, control and discipline of the young, none of these is looking too good for "the system." What will replace it? Does it matter?

After Marshal Bloom's suicide last week,* I was exhorted by some old friends to come back to Washington, where my personal adventure with Bloom began, and rip up a

* Marshall Irving Bloom was the founder of the Amherst Lecture Series at Amherst College in Massachusetts, editor of the student newspaper there, one of the founders of the *Southern Courier* newspaper in Alabama, leader of the London School of Economics student uprising in 1966, executive director of the United States Student Press Association, and founder of a farm-commune in Montague, Massachusetts. With Ray Mungo, he began Liberation News Service in Washington, D.C., in 1967. He took his own life on November 1, 1969, in Montague, Massachusetts.

cloud in the streets; have a reunion with my former allies in the movement. I declined. Just as I have avoided Chicago, Berkeley, New York City, even Woodstock, where all the heavy scenes have been going down, I shall absent myself from Washington on November 15. For I am choosing to refuse to execute the wills of the dead. Marshall had asked me, in his note, to be an executor of sorts, distributing his personal things from a second-floor closet at the farm to his friends around the country & on the farms; but I can't even do that, at least I haven't been able to yet.

The New York *Times* seized on Marshall's death to print a five-column headline, "Suicide Puzzles Friends of Founder of Radical News Service," and an article which mocked his conviction that activists will move to rural areas because "the city burns people out." The *Times* suggested that the last laugh was on Marshall & his friends, for while the citified branch of our Liberation News Service was still churning out propaganda from Claremont Avenue in New York, *we* were running vacuum-cleaner hoses from exhaust pipes into vent windows and expiring of despair. And it is true winter is here, Michael's toe was broken by a cow, Richard is in the county hospital with an esoteric fever, John's VW was turned over up on Route 91, Peter's father died last week in Pennsylvania, Pepper is in Rochester waiting for hers to go, the freezer broke down and much of the harvest moved to another house until we can fix it, no storm windows for lack of money and howling winds outside. But it has nothing to do with the city versus the country, it has only to do with the strange twists in our lives which yet excite the attention of the newspapers who display our photographs and write our biographies as professional hippies and postrevolutionaries; and it has to do with Marshall himself, and there will never be another.

Marshall's death was the logical extension of the Concord and Merrimack rivers trip; indeed, it followed hard on the heels of the boating. Sensitive as he was, he no doubt saw the opportunity to embellish the awfullest October in history and couldn't pass it up; get all the bad shit out of the way, he must have thought, before the new decade begins. What bad angel, thus, has elected to sit over our chimney? When your crop don't fail and your house don't burn down, your best friend will leave you stranded and helpless. Winter will come and snow you in, yet you can't move back to the city despite it because any natural hardship is better than an unnatural life. Every winter the hospitals in Vermont declare dead those old men who one evening simply neglected to light their stoves.

And here I had the chicken house one-quarter shingled too when it happened, and after that Saturday it rained day and night for six days. Everybody stared at each other, each was broken down in his unique way. Nothing got accomplished, and yet there was nowhere to go.

Death generates death, then, though we know in our remaining animal instincts that organic material makes carrots grow. It will be a long winter with ghosts behind the walls, and what wise man could be certain that we will make it to the spring? Spring, or life, is always a surprise and a gift, not something we have earned any firm right to.

It will be long ere the marshes resume,
It will be long ere the earliest bird,
So close all the windows and not hear the
wind,
But see all wind-stirred.

Robert Frost

So the army of corpses, some freshly laid in the ground and others now grown cold and bony, led the people of my country to create a Moratorium, which was nothing more or less than a Memorial Day of the new regime. Didn't Ho Chi Minh have generals? Thus will the Provisional Revolutionary Government have its holidays, and the time of Vietnam will be marked in history books in Skokie, Illinois, as an era of great plague and disaster in the nation. And monuments raised to the great men who "gave their lives" in the service of destroying the old. Marshall wasn't like that, he searched for the life in things, but found it unsatisfactory in the end. He was always taking us down with him, demanding a group involvement in

his pain, and he has done it again; and all in the course of living like crazy and kicking up, as John said, a lot of shit for twenty-five years old.

Was he serious about it or is this just Super-Burn? Will he show up in the cucumber patch next July, and will we say, "Marshall, you son of a *bitch"?* Or will this empty numb halfheartedness go on forever, and will we always be sailing the River Styx in our canoe, surveying the damage? Spring is right around the coroner.

From Bow Junction all the way to Plymouth, further north than Thoreau ever managed to get, we jumped from canoe to Volvo as sections of the river gave out underneath us, became too foul to navigate, turned into a bed of high, sharp rocks, and trickled weakly through dams and obstructions thrown up by cities like Concord and Manchester, the latter being, as one and all recognize, the worst city on the planet. We drove to Plymouth at last, determined to find some water worth paddling through, and believing that the Pemigewasset, which runs through that town and becomes the Merrimack just north of Manchester, would still be relatively unspoiled. But in the course of the afternoon's rowing from there down to Ashland, we encountered more rapids alongside a sandbar which, when we sank into it, proved to be quicksand mixed with putrefaction impossible to describe. And we passed a yellow machine engaged in pushing trees into the water and despoiling the air with vast clouds of exhaust, so that even the atmosphere was no longer enjoyable and the sky invisible.

We also discovered that Route 93, which runs from Boston up through Lawrence and north, follows the course of the Merrimack exactly, so that no camping spot or island left on the river can be free from the vroom-vroom noises of hell-for-leather diesel trucks and all-night passenger cars tooling up and down the planet bringing people their Pall Malls and Kentucky Bourbon, DDT and mass-produced foam rubber parlor chairs, and a million other things. And these monsters unkindly refused to declare Moratorium since they are not people anyway and thus insensitive to the needs of the living and the demands of the dead. Peter left his car, though, at a place in Ashland or Bridgewater where two bridges crossed the Pemigewasset, one for the railroad and the other for traffic, and we found ourselves all together as night fell on a forest glen in which all the trees were marked with surveyor's identifying paint, signifying that they were scheduled to be bulldozed in the near future. We made the last wood fire that place will know.

The stars were out despite everything, and I gave them my thorough uneducated scrutiny (I have never been able to find the Big Dipper, though I can immediately recognize the Northern Lights when they come around in March) as I thought and thought about the war. For the first time I could remember, I felt not the slightest indignity at being punished for an evil I did not create or support. "You get what you pay for," as the fat Texans say. We lived off the destructive energy in Vietnam *even though we were opposed to it,* and now our efforts to find and encourage life are of doubtful promise at best. But we're still alive and trying, and I suppose you are too. Do you suppose it is too late?

Shall we go out and rebuild this thing together? That was on my mind. Will we be able to start anew without nature, with only mankind, to support us? Dresden in ashes was yet potentially a prosperous center for the manufacture of Volkswagens; what will come out of an Atlantic Ocean which casts death and waste on the beaches as well as foam and salt? For lack of anything more overwhelming to tackle, I am willing to try to prevent it. At least most of the time. Do you have the strength to join?

THURSDAY: ASHLAND, N.H.

Breakfast was hearty and the coffee was strong, so this kid was raring once again to go, though by now with no illusions of having a pleasant or honestly working experience. He longed for his dog, Barf Barf, and thanked whatever stars put him in Vermont for the fact that Mr. B didn't have to drink *this* water. He wondered what the point was in further subjecting his body and soul to such a diseased and hopeless piece of the earth, but pushed these reservations

aside to climb into the stern for more of Buzzy's dead-serious lessons in steering. He was not prepared to discover, a full mile from the camping place, that Peter Simon had lost his wallet somewhere among those doomed trees, with money, driver's license, and BankAmericard; and to eat up a large part of the day in searching the banks for the exact spot in Ashland where we'd camped, and then finding the missing papers. God forbid that we should wander the rivers and forests of the planet without our papers in order! Why, friends of mine have been incarcerated for weeks simply for lacking the right papers while passing through Cheyenne, Wyoming. As much as we might philosophically contend that we are free creatures on God's earth, we do not question when a brother says, "Turn around, bow-man, for my driver's license and BankAmericard."

Great confusion now ensued as we considered which way to go: north to the White Mountain National Forest, south to the Concord again, east to Portsmouth, west to Vermont? It hardly made any difference, we'd so badly botched up Thoreau's itinerary by then, and so much of the original waters were now inaccessible to living creatures. The question was resolved by paddling back to where we had left Peter's car so he could drive to Plymouth and watch the Mets win their Series. Somebody hit a homer and somebody else got hit by a pitch. I imagined our party in a Camel ad (we'd paddle a mile, etc.) and loudly said, "You other guys, *start walkin'*." We fooled around in Bridgewater, Ashland, and Holderness until we found a small tributary which led us to a stand of virgin pine holding out majestically in full view of an abandoned homestead and a railroad trestle. Buzzy guessed that the pine was on too great a pitch to be of use to 1930 American lumbering equipment, but in this nuclear age, we knew, it would not long go on rising. I hugged one of the trees and could hardly stretch my arms around it.

With all the time lost in wallets and such, darkness seemed to fall inordinately early, but of course we were approaching the solstice with every day and might have expected as much. While I was in the cities,

I lived by night and slept all day, for the streets of town were always more bearable under thin cover of gray; their lights made it easy to walk, and all the enclosed spaces were brightly lit with fraudulent sunshine, so I had the *impression* that I was alive. In the woods, though, nightfall is literally the end of the day. The degree to which you may perform outdoor chores depends on variables like the temperature, the moon, and the stars. You *must* make your hay while the sun shines. It terrifies me at times, so ill adjusted am I to progress, to think that these very terms (names for the planets and stars) are just about obsolete in the day-to-day language of working people in Manchester and Lowell, professional people in L..A. and Paris, even greenhouse farmers in Pennsylvania.

The waning hours of afternoon also brought rain: and, disgusted, we set out in the car for—somewhere. The conversation in the back seat was in the quiet tones you can imagine defeated football players using after the big game. Buzzy spoke of real rivers he had sailed, most of them outside the United States; and I protested mildly that Vermont was still OK, then wondered how long it would take for my words to be ready-to-eat. The general talk rested on the subject of expatriation, the hows and wheres of it. I mean, I imagined a family in Greenland taking in Verandah and me as "refugees from America"; it would not be an extraordinary scene in history. National boundaries mean nothing in the New Age, of course, and all we know of American history would make us anxious to leave, were the genuine natives not so thoroughly destroyed and the prospect of finding an untarnished culture and geography so dismal. Besides, our leaving would be the same as our staying, just the shifting of bodies from one spot to another on the checkerboard, and the land never noticing.

And that's where the story ends, I suppose, with the land, though the trip ended in Dr. Gus Dodge's house in Portsmouth, Peter getting injected with gamma globulin as protection against Merrimack Hepatitis. (As a Merrimack native, I am immune.) The land, at this writing, is alive and well, if soaked with rain. It stretches out as far as my eyes can see, forming exquisite perspectives on all sides and limited only by the open sky, which protects it. It generates new life at a furious pace, such that our main problem is keeping the forest from reclaiming itself; trees, saplings, grass, hay, vegetables, spices, flowers, and weeds crop up in riotous confusion, making oxygen and protein for deer, muskrats, coons, owls, porcupines, skunks, bobcats, snakes, goats, cows, horses, honeybees, rabbits, mice, cats, dogs, and people, and a million other fine fellows and gals great and small. "Live off the land," our fathers said, and so we do. They didn't tell us to live in groups, they preferred the lonely family circle, so we have rejected that part. They didn't care enough about living off the rivers, oceans, and skies. We'll burn no oil or gases in our houses, or in our cars. We'll bury our organic waste as deep as we can. We'll try to stay alive, for what else can we do? Friend, we are barking up the right trees.